Science

Toucan

Harcourt
SCHOOL PUBLISHERS

Orlando   Austin   New York   San Diego   Toronto   London

Visit *The Learning Site!*
www.harcourtschool.com

T 54263

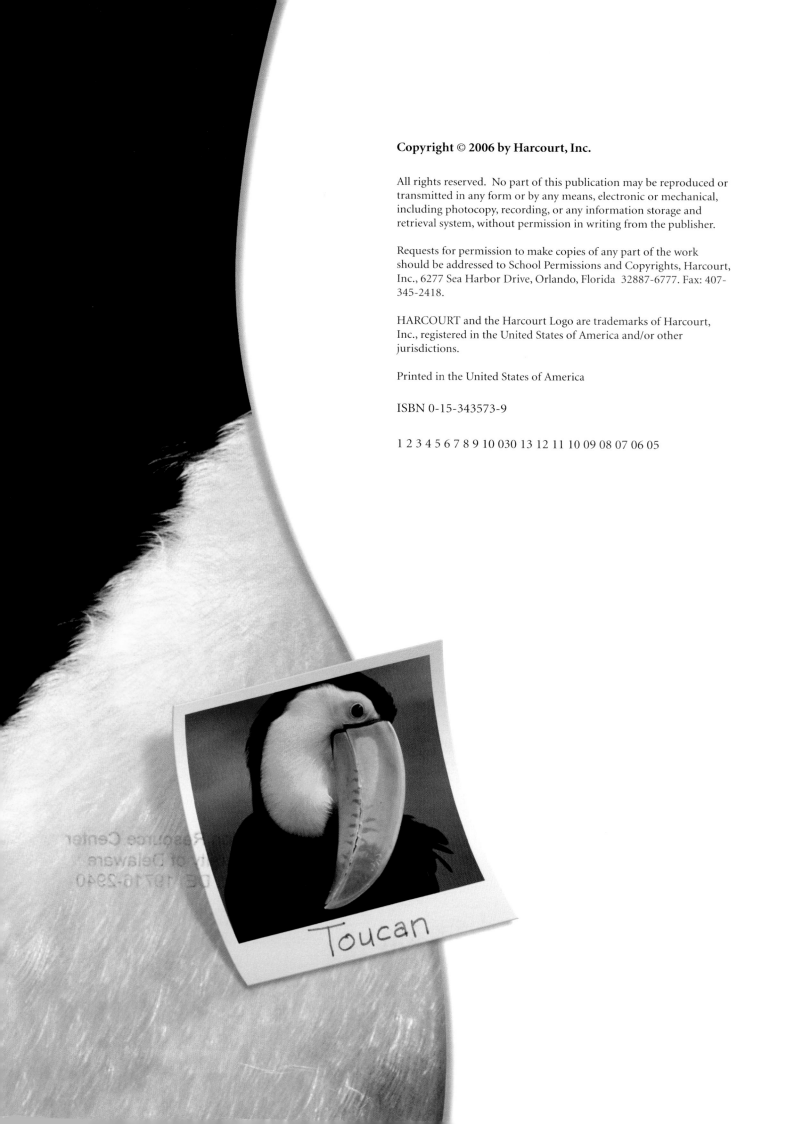

ISBN 0-15-343573-9

1 2 3 4 5 6 7 8 9 10 030 13 12 11 10 09 08 07 06 05

Toucan

Science

TEACHER EDITION CONTENTS

About the Program

Units and Chapters

References and Resources

Correlations

Consulting Authors

Michael J. Bell

Assistant Professor of Early Childhood Education
College of Education
West Chester University of Pennsylvania

Gerald H. Krockover

Professor of Earth and Atmospheric Science Education
Purdue University
West Lafayette, Indiana

Michael A. DiSpezio

Curriculum Architect
JASON Academy
Cape Cod, Massachusetts

Joyce C. McLeod

Adjunct Professor
Rollins College
Winter Park, Florida

Marjorie Frank

Former Adjunct Professor, Science Education
Hunter College
New York, New York

Barbara ten Brink

Science Specialist
Austin Independent School District
Austin, Texas

Carol J. Valenta

Senior Vice President
St. Louis Science Center
St. Louis, Missouri

Barry A. Van Deman

President and CEO
Museum of Life and Science
Durham, North Carolina

Senior Editorial Advisors

Napoleon Adebola Bryant, Jr.
Professor Emeritus of Education
Xavier University
Cincinnati, Ohio

Robert M. Jones
Professor of Educational Foundations
University of Houston–Clear Lake
Houston, Texas

Mozell P. Lang
Former Science Consultant
Michigan Department of Education
Science Consultant, Highland Park Schools
Highland Park, Michigan

Dear Educator,

The call for improvements in science education has never been greater. A successful future for our children will be highly dependent upon the scientific and technological skills they attain. Thus, national and state standards have set high expectations for students in science achievement.

Science, **by Harcourt School Publishers,** was developed to help administrators, teachers, and students meet those high expectations. The program is based on the following principles of scientific literacy:

- All children can investigate and learn science concepts and can experience success in science.

- Children must develop knowledge of and the ability to use the tools, skills, and methods of scientific inquiry.

- While engaged in the study of science, children should have the opportunity to build success in other curricular areas.

- Children's competence in the concepts and processes of science should be assessed through a variety of tools that are consistent, authentic, and fair.

- Children experience success in science when they develop age-appropriate knowledge and understanding of the life, earth, and physical sciences and when they learn about the history and nature of science.

- Science instruction should be differentiated so that all learners can experience success through instruction that is appropriate to their needs.

Science gives you the resources to promote scientific literacy by nurturing in your students a lifelong fascination with the natural world.

Sincerely,

The Authors

Advisors and Content Reviewers

Paul D. Asimow
Assistant Professor of Geology and Geochemistry
California Institute of Technology
Pasadena, California

John Brockhaus
Department of Geography and Environmental Engineering
United States Military Academy
West Point, New York

Mapi Cuevas
Professor of Chemistry
Santa Fe Community College
Gainesville, Florida

Robert Fronk
Vice Provost
Florida Institute of Technology
Melbourne, Florida

Linda K. Gaul
Epidemiologist
Texas Department of State Health Services
Austin, Texas

William Guggino
Professor of Physiology and Pediatrics
Johns Hopkins University, School of Medicine
Baltimore, Maryland

John L. Hubisz
North Carolina State University
Raleigh, North Carolina

Steven A. Jennings
Associate Professor in Geography
University of Colorado at Colorado Springs
Colorado Springs, Colorado

Joseph McClure
Associate Professor Emeritus
Department of Physics
Georgetown University
Washington, D.C.

Dork Sahagian
Professor of Earth and Environmental Science
Lehigh University
Bethlehem, Pennsylvania

Classroom Reviewers and Contributors

Janet M. Acerra
Forest Lakes Elementary School
Oldsmar, Florida

Carol P. Anderson
Mandarin Oaks Elementary School
Jacksonville, Florida

Colleen Barsin
MILA Elementary School
Merritt Island, Florida

Linda Bierkortte
Parkmoor Urban Academy
Columbus, Ohio

Andrea Blake-Garrett
Science Supervisor
Jersey City Board of Education
Jersey City, New Jersey

Marie Blum
Principal
York Central Elementary School
Retsof, New York

Linda S. Brown
DeSoto Trail Elementary School
Tallahassee, Florida

Maria R. Cannizzaro
Science Supervisor
Livingston Public Schools
Livingston, New Jersey

Michael Chan
Director of Science
Rochester City School District
Rochester, New York

Gary Corbin
Math/Science Coordinator
University School District
University City, Missouri

Michael L. Corney
Fink Elementary School
Middletown, Pennsylvania

Lori Crandall
Peter Vetal Elementary School
Detroit, Michigan

Susan D'Angelo
Taylor Ranch Elementary School
Venice, Florida

Maria De Christofano
West Melbourne School for Science
West Melbourne, Florida

Phyllis Deese
Hutchinson Beach Elementary School
Panama City Beach, Florida

Martha Downing
Alta Vista Elementary School
Sarasota, Florida

Brenda Dudley
MILA Elementary School
Merritt Island, Florida

Steve Elgersma
Waupaca Learning Center
Waupaca, Wisconsin

Andaiye N. Foluke
Chancellor Avenue Elementary School
Irvington, New Jersey

Linda M. Fonner
New Martinsville Elementary School
New Martinsville, West Virginia

Erin French
Science Curriculum Coordinator K–5
Boston Renaissance Charter School
Boston, Massachusetts

Laurie Enia Godfrey
Director of Curriculum Development
Lorain City Schools
Lorain, Ohio

Stephanie Gould-Olson
Pine View School
Osprey, Florida

Arlene Grant
Tropical Elementary School
Miami, Florida

Pamela Grifka
Wilkerson Elementary School
Warren, Michigan

Christine Hamilton
Curriculum Specialist
Toledo Public Schools
Toledo, Ohio

Missy Hansen
Doctors Inlet Elementary School
Middleburg, Florida

Melissa Hartery
Rowlette Magnet School
Bradenton, Florida

Gretchen Hibbs
White Hall Elementary School
Fairmont, West Virginia

Chantelle Holt
Brookshire Elementary School
Winter Park, Florida

Sharon E. Hough
Lincoln Elementary School
Janesville, Wisconsin

Alison Hubbard
Mildred Helms Elementary School
Largo, Florida

Dolores Hudson
Frontier Elementary School
Clearwater, Florida

Martha Hudson
Loxahatchee Grove Elementary
   School
Loxahatchee, Florida

Pat Jones
Mildred Helms Elementary School
Largo, Florida

Clarann K. Josef
Director of Science
Buffalo Public Schools
Buffalo, New York

Patricia Kissell
Jupiter Farms Elementary School
Jupiter, Florida

Linda L. Klungle
Dieck Elementary School
Swartz Creek, Michigan

Patricia Kosis
Science Coordinator
Alexander Hamilton Elementary
   School
Tonawanda, New York

Ruthrae Koth
Bear Creek Elementary School
St. Petersburg, Florida

Amy Krohn
Tombaugh Elementary School
Las Cruces, New Mexico

Mary Ann Lamb
Sunrise Elementary School
Ocala, Florida

Nancy Latzoni
District Science Supervisor K-8
Elementary School #3
Clifton, New Jersey

Sharlene Lutz
Hidden Lake Elementary School
Dothan, Alabama

Marilyn Majer
Kings Highway Elementary School
Clearwater, Florida

Barbara Mammen
Supervisor of Science and
   Technology
Manalapan-Englishtown Regional
   Schools
Englishtown, New Jersey

Jeanne Matt
Manatee Elementary School
Lake Worth, Florida

Cindy Maytrott
Roosevelt Elementary School
Cocoa Beach, Florida

Jerome Mescher
Science/Math Coordinator
Hilliard City Schools
Hilliard, Ohio

Kristy Monson
Smith Elementary School
Plymouth, Michigan

David Morgan
Assistant Superintendent for
   Curriculum and Instruction
Great Valley School District
Malvern, Pennsylvania

Jennifer L. Murray
Southern Oak Elementary School
Largo, Florida

Karen Nelson
Sunflower Elementary School
Paola, Kansas

Karen Newman
Pine Ridge Elementary School
Clermont, Florida

Sondra Pair
Johnson Elementary School
Pinson, Alabama

Brenda Payton
Wedgwood Elementary
Florissant, Missouri

Ruthann B. Perkins
Robert C. Hill School
Romeoville, Illinois

Cheryl Pilatowski
Science Support Teacher/
   Coordinator
Toledo Public Schools
Toledo, Ohio

Beth Rice
Loxahatchee Grove Elementary
Loxahatchee, Florida

Catherine L. Rogers
Jayenne Elementary School
Fairmont, West Virginia

Florence L. Russell
Tanglewood Riverside Elementary
   School
Fort Myers, Florida

Lisa Seiberling
Elementary Science Coordinator
Columbus Public Schools
Columbus, Ohio

Dorothy Smith
Indian Pines Elementary School
Lake Worth, Florida

Leslie Sparks
South Daytona Elementary School
South Daytona, Florida

Kathleen G. Sparrow
Science Learning Specialist, K–12
Akron Public Schools
Akron, Ohio

Cheryl Surrett
Audubon Elementary School
Merritt Island, Florida

Matthew Alan Teare
Science Resource Teacher
Miles Park Elementary School
Cleveland, Ohio

Connie Tiehen
Belvidere Elementary School
Grandview, Missouri

Judy Timms
Ocean City Elementary School
Fort Walton Beach, Florida

Sidonia Todd
Tanglewood Riverside Elementary
   School
Fort Myers, Florida

Cathy J. Trent
North Fort Myers Academy
North Fort Myers, Florida

Penny Turner
Fleming Island Elementary School
Orange Park, Florida

Colleen Vannoy
Kanawah County Schools
Charleston, West Virginia

Sandy Wall
Ridgecrest Elementary School
Largo, Florida

Shirley Welshans
Parkmoor Urban Academy
Columbus, Ohio

Cindy Zylstra
John R. Tibbott School
Bolingbrook, Illinois

Resources for Inquiry

Science provides many opportunities for students to develop and maintain the essential skills that form the basis for scientific inquiry.

Inquiry Skills

Inquiry skills are important tools and are essential for investigating the natural world. Opportunities for developing inquiry skills are embedded throughout *Science*.

Inquiry Skill	Description
Observe	use one or more of the senses to perceive properties of objects and events; can be done directly with the senses or indirectly through the use of simple or complex instruments
Compare	identify common and distinguishing characteristics among objects or events
Classify/Order	group or organize objects or events into categories based on specific criteria
Gather, Record, Display, or Interpret Data	make observations of objects or events to make inferences or predictions; write down the observations on paper as notes or display the data in charts, tables, or graphs; make predictions, inferences, and hypotheses from a set of data
Use Numbers	estimate or quantify data
Communicate	transmit observable data or ideas visually, orally, or electronically
Plan and Conduct Simple Investigations	use one or more of the inquiry skills to find the answer to a question or the solution to a problem
Measure	make quantitative observations using both nonstandard and standard measures
Predict	anticipate outcomes of future events, based on patterns or experience
Infer	use logical reasoning to make conclusions based on observations
Draw Conclusions	interpret data to make conclusions; the final step of an investigation
Use Time/Space Relationships	estimate the relationships of moving and of nonmoving objects to one another; includes sequencing
Hypothesize	pose a testable explanation for observations or events and state it as the expected outcome of an experiment
Formulate or Use Models	make a mental or physical representation of a process or structure, or use a model that someone else has provided
Identify and Control Variables	state or control factors that affect the outcome of an experiment
Experiment	design procedures for gathering data to test hypotheses under conditions in which variables are controlled or manipulated

Program Resources

A variety of instructional tools provide many opportunities for developing inquiry skills.

Daily Practice

Daily Inquiry Transparencies can be used to provide individuals or small groups with self-contained experiences that reinforce the nature of science and the use of inquiry tools and skills. These activities can be done at any time and are not necessarily related to chapter content. They are designed for use in learning centers, as sponge activities, or with students who are early finishers. Many of the Daily Inquiry activities have students practice using essential science tools.

An Inquiry Tool Kit, available from Harcourt School Publishers, provides the following basic tools:

- Hand lens
- Magnifying box
- Thermometer
- Forceps
- Tape measure
- Ruler
- Dropper
- Measuring cup
- Spring scale (for intermediate grades only)

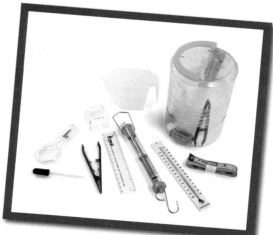

Structured and Guided Inquiry

Insta-Labs are short-term, quick activities that reinforce chapter concepts by using easy-to-find classroom materials. Every lesson in *Science* includes one Insta-Lab.

Investigates begin each lesson and form the basis for concept development. Within each Investigate, direct instruction is provided for Inquiry Skills. The Teacher Edition provides tips for guided inquiry, and the Investigate Log in the Lab Manual provides even more support for Inquiry Skills.

Inquiry Skills Mini-Lessons in the Teacher Edition provide focused instruction on inquiry skills. A transparency helps guide the instruction.

Independent Inquiry

The Experiments can be used in a variety of ways to promote many levels of inquiry. Students can use each prompt as a springboard for writing essential questions and designing their own experiment. Students who need more structure and guidance for experimenting can use formats that are provided in the Lab Manual and on the Teaching Transparencies. For more information, see any of the Experiments provided at the beginning of each unit.

Science Projects for Home or School also provide opportunities for students to design their own experiments or to prepare projects for a science fair. These pages are provided at the end of every chapter in *Science*.

Science Fair Project Ideas are provided in the back of the Lab Manual. Information about setting up school science fairs can be found in Teaching Resources.

Reading Support

Reading underlies everything students do in school, and many of the skills taught in reading programs can be reinforced during science instruction.

(Focus Skill) Reading Focus Skills

A Reading Focus Skill is identified at the beginning of each lesson in *Science*. The content in that lesson is organized to provide signal words and text structure consistent with the reading skill. Throughout the lesson, the Focus Skill logo alerts the student to each opportunity for practicing and applying the skill. The six reading skills are:

Identify Main Idea and Details

Compare and Contrast

Cause and Effect

Sequence

Draw Conclusions

Summarize

Reading is also reinforced in *Science* in the following ways:

- A reading comprehension question appears after every "chunk" of text in the Student Edition. The question helps students check their comprehension of the text and also reinforces the Focus Skills.
- In the Teacher Edition, Reading Skill Mini-Lessons can be used to provide focused instruction on each skill. The Mini-Lessons address a wide range of skills appropriate to the particular grade level.
- In Reading Support and Homework, each Lesson Quick Study helps students review the lesson vocabulary, Focus Skill, and key concepts.
  - The Graphic Organizer at the end of each lesson provides an opportunity for students to summarize what they have learned. The Graphic Organizers are also provided on Teaching Transparencies in both print and electronic format.
    - The Reading in Science Handbook in the back of each Student Edition provides detailed, student-friendly information about each skill.
      - Leveled Readers provide many opportunities for additional content-area reading experiences. The readers reinforce chapter reading skills and vocabulary and enrich and extend chapter concepts.

Toucan

Weekly Reader

Harcourt School Publishers has partnered with *Weekly Reader* to help students get the "spin" on science. *Weekly Reader,* a leader in classroom publishing for more than 100 years, has provided a series of Science Spin features specifically for *Science.* At the end of each chapter are two Science Spin articles—one focusing on technology, the other a profile of a prominent scientist or student who is experiencing science firsthand. The articles also introduce students to careers in science.

The *Weekly Reader* Science Spin features

- provide high-interest, real-world content.
- expand learning and add depth to chapter concepts.
- emphasize the nature of science and make connections among science, technology, and society.
- provide students with opportunities to read science magazine articles and content in a variety of formats.
- inspire students to explore science on their own.

WEEKLY WR READER

For more than 100 years, *Weekly Reader* products have brought the world into the nation's classrooms. Whether it was the development of the polio vaccine, the space race, or a wonderful machine called the computer, *Weekly Reader* has a long tradition of covering science stories for students. To find out more about *Weekly Reader,* log onto www.weeklyreader.com or call 1-800-446-3355.

Reaching All Learners

Science offers an array of components, strategies, and activities to ensure that all students can experience science success.

 ESL / ESOL Support

Throughout this Teacher Edition, point-of-use strategies provide activities and ideas for addressing language needs in three critical areas:
- Comprehensible Input
- Language and Vocabulary
- Background and Experience

The strategies are provided for students at varied levels of proficiency: Beginning, Intermediate, and Advanced.

A separate component, ESL Support, provides modified instruction for every lesson in the program. Scaffolding structures are built into each lesson, and a variety of language experiences are offered. A reproducible student worksheet is also included for each lesson.

 Below-Level/Intervention

Intervention and reteaching strategies are provided at point-of-use throughout this Teacher Edition. Suggestions for reteaching include hands-on activities designed to help students who have difficulty grasping key chapter concepts.

The Intervention Readers are recommended for students who have difficulty understanding chapter concepts because of low reading ability. The readers present the chapter content and vocabulary at a below-grade reading level. They use a visual glossary, simplified language, and comprehension aids designed especially for struggling readers.

The Intervention Reader Teacher Guide provides instructional strategies and reproducible student worksheets for reviewing vocabulary, building fluency, and checking comprehension.

 On-Level/Enrichment

Strategies for on-level learners are also provided at point-of-use in this Teacher Edition. The On-Level Readers promote success on state science tests by reinforcing tested content objectives, chapter vocabulary, and reading skills.

Curriculum connections, Science Projects for Home or School, Investigate Further activities, and technology products such as the Science Up Close activities provide enrichment for all learners.

 Advanced/Challenge

Advanced learners will benefit from many features built into the *Science* Student Edition and Teacher Edition. Unit experiments and Investigate Further options will challenge students who are ready for independent inquiry. Challenge suggestions at point-of-use in this Teacher Edition can be used with above-level students as well. The Above-Level Readers also provide a variety of interesting nonfiction reading to enrich and extend chapter concepts.

Three leveled Readers are provided for each chapter.

More Components for Reaching All Learners

Audio Text

Audio CDs can be used with all learners. The CDs provide readings of all the chapters and are especially helpful for use with struggling readers or students who need auditory reinforcement.

Science eBook

Each chapter in *Science* is also available online and has provisions for students with special needs. Adjustable text size and audio text can be used with students who have vision impairments or learning difficulties.

The *Science eBook* also provides extension and enrichment for all learners. For more information, visit **www.hspscience.com**.

The Learning Site

Harcourt's award-winning website, **The Learning Site**, provides an array of online activities and experiences for all learners. Students can visit the site, found at **www.hspscience.com** any time for interactive learning games and activities. A multimedia Science Glossary is also provided.

Science Up Close

ONLINE EXPERIENCE
For animations and activities, visit **www.hspscience.com**

Assessment Program

The chart below shows the options offered by the assessment program in Science. The various options reveal the multidimensional aspect of the program.

ASSESSMENT OPTIONS

1 ▶ Formal Assessment
- Chapter Review and Test Preparation *SE*
- Chapter Test *AG*
- Unit Test *AG*

2 ▶ Standardized Test Preparation
- Reading Review and Test Prep *SE*

3 ▶ Harcourt School Publishers Online Assessment
- Online chapter and unit test with automatic scoring
- Item bank from which to build tests

4 ▶ Ongoing Assessment
- Assess Prior Knowledge— Chapter Opener *TE*
- Daily Inquiry Transparencies
- Teacher Edition questions *throughout TE*
- Focus Skill questions *throughout SE*
- Reaching All Learners *throughout TE*
- Reading Review *SE*
- Observation Checklist *AG*

5 ▶ Performance Assessment
- Long Option *AG*
- Short Option *TE*

6 ▶ Student Self-Assessment
- Investigate Self-Assessment *Lab Manual*
- Self-Assessment *AG*

7 ▶ Portfolio Assessment
- Using Portfolio Assessment *AG*
- Suggested work samples *TE*

1 ▶ Formal Assessment

To help you reinforce and assess mastery of chapter objectives, Science includes both reviews and tests. You will find the Chapter Review and Test Preparation in the Student Edition and the Chapter Test and Unit Test in the Assessment Guide. Answers to all assessments, including sample responses to constructed-response items, are provided.

2 ▶ Standardized Test Preparation

Large-scale assessment of science literacy has been mandated by the No Child Left Behind Act (NCLB), the 2001 reauthorization of the Elementary and Secondary Education Act. To help prepare students for district- or state-mandated assessments, *Science* includes items that reflect the format of standardized tests. These items can be found in the Reading Review that follows each lesson and in the Chapter Review and Test Preparation in the Student Edition.

3 ▶ Online Assessment

The ability to deliver tests online provides the teacher with increased flexibility in managing classroom assessment. The Chapter Tests and Unit Tests that appear in the Assessment Guide can be delivered online. In addition, *Harcourt School Publishers Online Assessment* allows you to assemble custom tests from a bank of multiple-choice, short-response, and extended-response items. Multiple-choice items are scored automatically, and a user-friendly interface allows teachers to enter scores for short- and extended-response items. You can also build tests according to your state's standards. For more information, visit www.hspscience.com.

4 ▶ Ongoing Assessment

Within each lesson in the Student Edition, Focus Skill questions appear at the end of each section to help you assess students' immediate recall of information. At the end of each lesson is a Reading Review to help you evaluate how well students grasped the concepts taught. The Teacher Edition offers a number of informal assessment tools. By using the Assess Prior Knowledge that accompanies each chapter opener, you can gauge students' foundational knowledge. Daily Inquiry Transparencies are designed to reinforce and evaluate students' use of inquiry skills. Questions that address a variety of dimensions—including critical thinking skills, inquiry skills, and use of reading strategies—are strategically placed throughout each lesson. Additional material for reviewing the lesson is provided in Reading Support and Homework. The Observation Checklist (p. AGxv) can be used to record noteworthy classroom observations.

5 ▶ Performance Assessment

Performance tasks provide evidence of students' ability to use science inquiry skills and critical thinking skills to complete an authentic task. A brief performance task is included as part of the information in the Teacher Edition that accompanies each chapter review. A more comprehensive performance task follows each Chapter Test in the Assessment Guide. Each includes teacher directions and a scoring rubric. Also in the Assessment Guide, you will find the Experiment/Project Evaluation Checklist (p. AGxviii) for evaluating unit experiments and projects.

6 ▶ Student Self-Assessment

Students should be challenged to reflect on their work and to monitor and control their own learning. Various checklists are provided for this purpose. An Investigate Self-Assessment accompanies each Investigate in the Lab Manual. Two checklists are located in the Assessment Guide. One is the Self-Assessment—Reading in Science (p. AGxvii), which helps students reflect on instruction in a particular lesson or chapter. The other is the Experiment/Project Summary Sheet (p. AGxix), on which students describe and evaluate their own science projects and experiments.

7 ▶ Portfolio Assessment

In *Science,* students may create their own portfolios. The portfolio contains self-selected work samples that the student feels represent increased science literacy. The portfolio may also contain a few required or teacher-selected papers. Support materials are included in the Assessment Guide (pp. AGxx–AGxxiv) to assist you and your students in developing portfolios.

Scope and Sequence

	Grade K	UNIT	Grade 1	Grade 2
Life Science	**Animals and Plants** 7 Animals A to Z 8 Plants All Around	**A**	**Plants and Animals All Around** 1 All About Animals 2 All About Plants	**A World of Living Things** 1 Living and Nonliving Things 2 Animals 3 Plants
	Habitats 9 Places to Live and Grow	**B**	**Living Together** 3 Environments for Living Things 4 Places to Live	**Homes for Living Things** 4 Living Things in Their Environments
Earth Science	**Earth and Its Weather** 4 Our Earth 5 Weather and the Seasons	**C**	**About Our Earth** 5 Our Earth 6 Natural Resources	**Our Earth** 5 Exploring Earth's Surface 6 Natural Resources
	Earth and Space 6 Up in the Sky	**D**	**Weather, Seasons, and the Sky** 7 Measuring Weather 8 Seasons 9 Objects in the Sky	**Weather and Space** 7 Weather 8 The Solar System
Physical Science	**Matter and Energy** 1 The World Around Us 2 About Energy	**E**	**Investigating Matter** 10 All About Matter	**Exploring Matter** 9 Observing and Classifying Matter 10 Changes in Matter
	Force and Motion 3 On the Move	**F**	**Energy in Our World** 11 Heat, Light, and Sound 12 Motion	**Energy in Motion** 11 Light and Heat 12 Sound 13 Motion

LIFE SCIENCE

UNIT A: Living Things in Our World

Science Spin
Weekly Reader

Technology
Planting Trees in
Africa, **46**
People
Amazing Shark
Skin, **48**

Science Spin
Weekly Reader

Technology
All Wrapped Up, **78**
People
Hunting the
Moonseed, **80**

Science Spin
Weekly Reader

Technology
The Secret of
Silk, **114**
People
Girl Protects Police
Dogs, **116**

iv

UNIT B: Living Things Interact

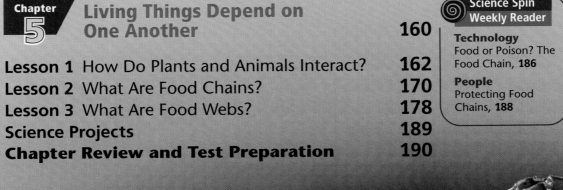

v

EARTH SCIENCE

UNIT C: Earth's Land

UNIT D: Weather and Space

vii

PHYSICAL SCIENCE
UNIT E: Investigating Matter and Energy

UNIT F: Exploring Forces and Motion

ix

Program Components

Program Components	1	2	3	4	5	6
Student Editions	•	•	•	•	•	•
Student Editions on CD-ROM	•	•	•	•	•	•
Student eBook	•	•	•	•	•	•
Unit Big Books	•	•				
Unit Student Editions			•	•	•	•
Teacher Editions	•	•	•	•	•	•
Online ePlanner	•	•	•	•	•	•
Lab Manuals	•	•	•	•	•	•
Lab Manuals, Teacher Editions	•	•	•	•	•	•
Reading Support and Homework	•	•	•	•	•	•
Reading Support and Homework, Teacher Edition	•	•	•	•	•	•
Assessment Guides	•	•	•	•	•	•
Online Assessment	•	•	•	•	•	•
Teaching Resources	•	•	•	•	•	•
ESL Support	•	•	•	•	•	•
Teaching Transparencies	•	•	•	•	•	•
Electronic Teaching Transparencies	•	•	•	•	•	•
Below-Level/Intervention Readers	•	•	•	•	•	•
Below-Level/Intervention Readers, Teacher Guides	•	•	•	•	•	•
On-Level/Enrichment Readers	•	•	•	•	•	•
Above-Level/Challenge Readers	•	•	•	•	•	•
Picture Cards	•	•	•			
Teaching Resources	•	•	•	•	•	•
Audio Text CDs	•	•	•	•	•	•
Science Up Close and Enrichment Activities	•	•	•	•	•	•
Activity Videos/DVD	•	•	•	•	•	•
Inquiry Tool Kits	•	•	•	•	•	•
Materials Kits	•	•	•	•	•	•
The Learning Site Activities	•	•	•	•	•	•

For Kindergarten

- Big Book
- Teacher Edition
- ePlanner
- Activity Book
- Teaching Resources and Assessment
- Science Readers
- Big Book of Science Readers
- Big Book of Science Songs and Rhymes
- Teaching Transparencies
- Picture Cards
- Science Songs CD
- Inquiry Tool Kit
- Materials Kits
- Learning Site Activities and Resources

For more resources and component updates, visit **www.hspscience.com.**

Unit E

Investigating Matter and Energy

UNIT Ⓔ
Exploring Matter

UNIT OVERVIEW

Unit Theme

Matter has predictable physical and chemical properties that determine the ways in which it can change. Energy is the ability to cause change. Heat, light, and sound are types of energy.

Curriculum Integration

Use these topics to integrate science into your daily planning.

 Reading
Main Idea and Details–pp. 374, 392, 416, 422, 436, 448, 462
Use Context Clues–pp. 374, 474
Compare and Contrast–pp. 384, 408, 442
Use Typographic Clues–p. 392
Use Reference Sources–p 416
Distinguish Fact From Opinion–pp. 422, 436
Use Word Structure: Compound Words–p. 448
Use Signal Words–p. 462
Sequence–p. 468
Cause and Effect–pp. 474, 482
Use Paragraph Structure–p. 482
Reading in Science Handbook–pp. R16–R27

 Math
Number Sense–p. 378
Interpret Data–pp. 388, 418
Solve a Problem–pp. 397, 439
Make a Graph–p. 425
Graph Favorite Colors–p. 479
Math in Science Handbook–pp. R28–R35

 Writing
Writing Expository–pp. 381, 397, 413, 419, 445, 479, 485
Narrative Writing–p. 389, 465, 471
Persuasive Writing–p. 425, 451
Expository—How-To–p. 439
Describe What Magnets Do–p. 449

 Art and Music
Music Physical Properties
Symphony–p. 381
Uses for Magnets–p. 445
Mixing Colors–p. 478
Make Your Own Musical Instrument–p. 485

 Social Studies
California Gold Rush–p. 394
Inventing the Generator–p. 451
Using Shadows to Tell Time–p. 471

 Health and Physical Education
Using Energy–p. 413
Putting Out a Fire–p. 465
Health Handbook, pp. R1–R15

 Literature
See pages 370C and 404C for Chapter Readers and trade book suggestions.

Technology Resources

Use a variety of technology resources for interactive tools and experiences. www.hspscience.com

For the Teacher

ePlanner
This online resource allows you to:
▶ Customize planning and pacing,
▶ Select resources for daily instruction,
▶ Reorder content to meet your state, district, or local needs.

Activity Video/DVD
This DVD provides previews of the activities, offers classroom-management techniques, and presents expected results.

Harcourt School Publishers Online Assessment
This online program provides:
▶ Online chapter and unit test taking and automatic scoring,
▶ Banks of items from which to build tests.

Teacher Resources CD-ROM
Electronic versions of all your teaching tools and resources.

Electronic Transparencies
Can be used to display transparencies with an LCD projector or monitor.

For the Student

eBook
An online version of the student edition, plus interactive explorations and investigations. Accessible for those with special needs.

Science Up Close CD-ROM
Activities that enhance and expand key chapter concepts through simulations and investigations.

For the Family

The Harcourt Learning Site

Family members can visit the Science section of The Learning Site for a variety of interactive learning experiences.

www.hspscience.com

UNIT E Materials List

Quantities are indicated for a class of 30 students working individually or in groups of 5, depending on the nature of the activity. Where shared equipment is suggested, a smaller number of items is specified. Quantities are also listed for those materials included in the Materials Kit.

Nonconsumable Materials

Materials	Class Quantity	Kit Quantity	Activity Page
balance	6	1	369A
beaker, plastic	6	6	383
bowl (20 oz)	6	6	447
brush, small	6		369A
button, metal	6	pkg/6	461
clock	1		407
comb, plastic	6	6	435
cup, measuring (metric)	6	6	369A, 373, 383, 391
flashlight	6	6	467
goggles, safety	30		461
hand lens	6	pkg/6	391
magnet, bar	6	6	441, 447
magnet, horseshoe	6	6	441
penny	6		461
prism	6	6	473
ruler	6	6	421
scissors	6 pairs		369A, 421
spoon, measuring	6 sets	6	391
stapler	1		481
stopwatch	6	6	447
thermometer (plastic, dual scale)	6	pkg/6	383, 407, 415
truck, toy (matchbox-type)	6	6	467

Consumable Materials

Materials	Class Quantity	Kit Quantity	Activity Page
battery, D-cell	12	12	467
bead, plastic	bag	pkg/144	447
cloth, wool (12" x 24")	1	1	435, 461
container, clear plastic (large)	1		373
container, plastic (8 oz)	6	6	373
crayons	6 boxes		473
cup, clear plastic (300 ml)	18	pkg/50	373, 415
cup, foam	18		461
jar, plastic, wide-mouth (16 oz)	6		391
jar, tall, plastic (12 oz)	6		373
label	6		369A
milk carton, empty	18		369A
paper	12 sheets		421
paper clip, steel	1 box	1 box	441, 447
paper, red	6 sheets		473
paper, white	24 sheets		421, 435, 461, 473
paper, tissue	6		435
pencil with eraser	6		421
poster board	6 sheets		467
pushpin	1 box	1 box	421
rice (1 lb)	1 bag	1 bag	481
salt, non-iodized (737 g)	1	1	391
sand, fine (2.5 kg)	1 bag	1 bag	369A, 391
seeds, pinto	1 bag	1 bag	481
spoon, plastic	12	pkg/24	383, 391, 461
tape, masking	1 roll		373, 481
tube, cardboard (large)	6	6	481

A complete grade-level materials list and lists for all life, earth, or physical science chapters are provided on page R67.

Unit E

Inspire Inquiry

Invite students to read and discuss the e-mail messages. Have them share any experiences they might have had with similar events or visits to other landmarks. Lead students in generating a list of questions they may have about the phenomena described in the e-mail messages or any other unit topics.

Ask students to suggest ways that they might begin to answer the questions they have asked. List out the steps. Encourage interested students to explore more and to develop ways to answer their questions through research and experimentation.

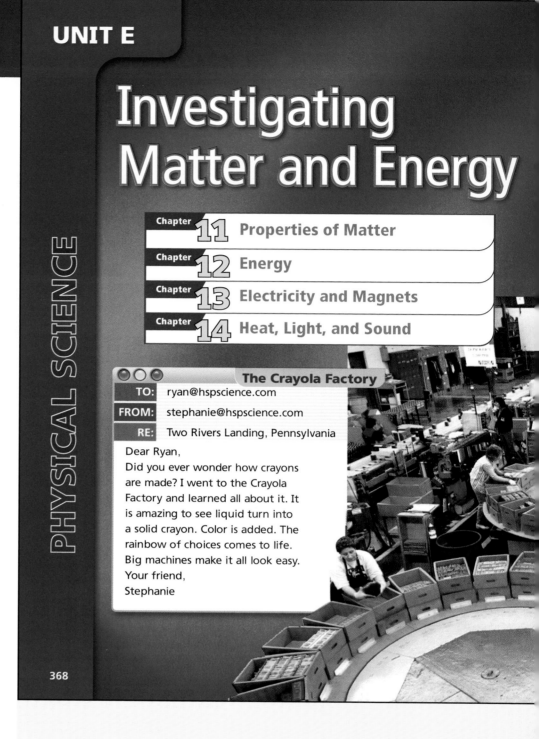

Investigating Matter and Energy

PHYSICAL SCIENCE

The Crayola Factory

TO: ryan@hspscience.com
FROM: stephanie@hspscience.com
RE: Two Rivers Landing, Pennsylvania

Dear Ryan,
Did you ever wonder how crayons are made? I went to the Crayola Factory and learned all about it. It is amazing to see liquid turn into a solid crayon. Color is added. The rainbow of choices comes to life. Big machines make it all look easy.
Your friend,
Stephanie

368

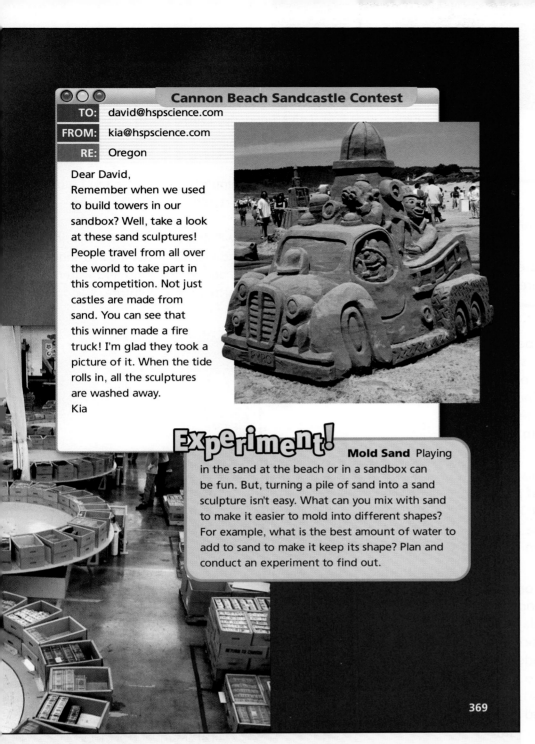

Cannon Beach Sandcastle Contest

TO: david@hspscience.com
FROM: kia@hspscience.com
RE: Oregon

Dear David,
Remember when we used to build towers in our sandbox? Well, take a look at these sand sculptures! People travel from all over the world to take part in this competition. Not just castles are made from sand. You can see that this winner made a fire truck! I'm glad they took a picture of it. When the tide rolls in, all the sculptures are washed away.
Kia

Experiment!

Mold Sand Playing in the sand at the beach or in a sandbox can be fun. But, turning a pile of sand into a sand sculpture isn't easy. What can you mix with sand to make it easier to mold into different shapes? For example, what is the best amount of water to add to sand to make it keep its shape? Plan and conduct an experiment to find out.

369

More About the Crayola Factory The Crayola Factory at Two Rivers Landing is a popular tourist destination where children can explore and discover their own creativity. Visitors will learn about the Crayola brand, as well as its history. Children get a better understanding of how crayons are made at the Crayola Factory.

More About the Cannon Beach Sandcastle Contest The Cannon Beach Sandcastle Contest began back in 1964 when a bridge was washed out by a tsunami, leaving residents stranded. Making lemonade out of lemons, the residents decided to have a community sandcastle contest. Each year, the contest brings many spectators, as it is one of the largest contests of its kind on the west coast. Teams are each given a plot of sand to use, and no sand can be added or removed from that plot. Other materials that teams can use are limited to natural materials, such as seaweed, sticks, shells, or rocks. At the end of the day, the tide rolls in and washes away all of the beautiful creations.

Writing Link

Have students generate their own e-mail message describing a personal experience or observation about an event or phenomena related to the unit topics.

A unit writing prompt and prewriting activity is provided in *Reading Support and Homework*, p. RS 79.

Experiment!

Turn the page to see options for helping students complete the experiment.

Unit E

Mold Sand

Objectives

- Promote scientific inquiry.
- Use a scientific method to plan and conduct a long-term investigation.
- Design an experiment to determine what mixture of sand and water will make the best sand sculptures.

OPTIONS FOR INQUIRY

Option 1: Independent Inquiry Assign the experiment for students to complete independently. Students should use the prompt as a springboard for writing their own questions and designing their own experiment. They can write a hypothesis, design a procedure, select materials, and conduct the experiment. Students can refer to pages 131–134 in the **Lab Manual** for guidance.

Option 2: Guided Inquiry Suggest that students use the prompt and the experiment log (**Lab Manual** pages LM 131–134) to help them plan their experiment The Experiment Log pages shown below appear in the **Lab Manual**, but without answers. Use the lesson plan to guide students as they design the experiment.

Option 3: Structured Inquiry Have students complete the experiment by testing the hypothesis and using the procedure that has been provided for them. Display the overhead transparencies shown (or provide photocopies from the transparency package), and have students copy the hypothesis, variables, and procedure into the Experiment Log (**Lab Manual** pages LM 131–134). Students then should conduct the experiment and gather and record their data. Use the Lesson Plan to guide students as they complete the experiment.

Science Background

Sand and Water When a sand sculptor mixes sand and water, there is not a chemical reaction. The sand and the water are not changed, they are simply mixed together. This is called a mixture because the original ingredients can easily be separated out. A sand sculpture does not require adding glue or any other adhesive. Water acts like glue when mixed with sand.

Webliography
Keyword exploring space
www.hspscience.com

Experiment! LESSON PLAN

Resources

Experiment Log, *Lab Manual* pp. LM 131–134

Experiment Transparencies, Unit E

Time 30 minutes to prepare the molds and measure and mix the sand and water; 30 minutes to make the sand sculptures, obtain data, and record results

Expected Results Students will find that the sand will not stick together if it is too dry and will not make a good sand sculpture. If too much water is added, the sand and water mixture will be too runny to form a sand sculpture.

Suggested Materials

- ▶ sand
- ▶ water
- ▶ scissors
- ▶ used milk cartons
- ▶ measuring cup
- ▶ balance
- ▶ small brush

Preparation The tops of the milk cartons can be cut off before the experiment. Sand must be purchased before the experiment and must be dry before being used. For best results, purchase sand with small-sized grains. Tables can be dressed with old newspapers to make clean-up easy.

Transparency EX 131

Lab Manual p. LM 131

Mold Sand

1. **Observe and Ask Questions**

   Building a large sand sculpture is not always easy. What can you add to sand to make a sand sculpture better? Make a list of questions you have about the sand in a good sand sculpture. Then circle a question you want to investigate. Does adding water to sand make it easier to build a sand sculpture?

2. **Form a Hypothesis**

   Write a hypothesis. A hypothesis is a suggested answer to the question you are testing. Sand with a moderate amount of water will make a better sand sculpture than sand with no water or sand with too much water.

3. **Plan an Experiment**

   Identify and Control Variables

   To plan your experiment, you must first identify the important variables. Complete the statements below.

   The variable I will change is
   the amount of water added to the sand

   The variables I will observe or measure are
   how much sand crumbles from the sand sculpture I make

   The variables I will keep the same, or *control*, are the amount of sand in each sculpture and the shape of each sculpture

❶ Observe and Ask Questions

Have students discuss the prompt and then brainstorm a list of other questions they may have about the topic. Students can record their questions in the Experiment Log, and then circle the question they are going to test.

Find Out More A first step in answering questions in science is to find out what is already known. Suggest that students use their textbooks and media resources to find out more about sand sculpting. The research may lead them to investigate other questions or to vary their experiments as a result of any interesting facts they may uncover.

❷ Form a Hypothesis

Guided Inquiry Guide students in forming a testable hypothesis.

- **Look at the question you have chosen to investigate.** What can you add to sand to make a good sand sculpture? **What do you predict will be an answer to this question?** Possible answer: You can add water to sand to help it stick together and make a good sand sculpture.

- **Use your answer to form a statement. Your statement should include all the things you are testing. This statement will be your hypothesis.** Possible hypothesis: Sand sculptures made with too much or too little water will have more sand crumble after being removed from the mold.

❸ Plan an Experiment

Identify and Control Variables Remind students that an experiment is a fair test of a hypothesis. Identifying and controlling the variables will ensure that the test is conducted fairly. Have students complete the statements in the Experiment Log.

Develop a Procedure and Gather Materials Have students write a detailed procedure or have them use the procedure that appears on the transparency.

❹ Conduct the Experiment

Gather and Record Data Students can record their data in the Experiment Log.

Common Error Alert When collecting data, record the volume of sand that falls off of the sculpture. Recording the mass of sand would skew the data because a different amount of water was added to each sculpture.

Interpret Data Data can be displayed on a bar graph. Students should use the graph to determine the optimal amount of water to mix with sand to form a sand sculpture. Discuss trends or patterns seen as the data is analyzed.

❺ Draw Conclusions and Communicate Results

Have students answer the questions in the Experiment Log.

Using Inquiry Skills Emphasize that there is no "right" answer for an experiment. Hypotheses may not be supported by the data. If so, the hypothesis needs to be changed, not the data. Consider experimental results honestly and objectively.

Independent Inquiry Encourage students to build upon this experiment to develop further investigations.

Transparency EX 132
Lab Manual p. LM 132

Develop a Procedure and Gather Materials Write the steps you will follow to set up an experiment and collect data.

1. Make a mold for the sand from old milk cartons.
2. Measure out piles of sand that have the same volume.
3. Measure out and add a different amount of water to each pile of sand.
4. Attempt to turn each pile of sand into a square sand sculpture using the milk carton mold.
5. Sweep up and measure the amount of sand that falls off of each sand sculpture.

Use extra sheets of blank paper if you need to write down more steps.

Materials List Look carefully at all the steps of your procedure, and list all the materials you will use. Be sure that your teacher approves your plan and your materials list before you begin.

Sand

Water

Used Milk Cartons

Scissors

Measuring Cup

Balance

Small Brush

Transparency EX 133
Lab Manual p. LM 133

4. Conduct the Experiment

Gather and Record Data Follow your plan and collect data. Use the table below or a table you design to record your data. **Observe** carefully. **Record** your observations and be sure to note anything unusual or unexpected.

Amount of sand in each sculpture: _____ g

Sand pile number	Amount of water added to sand pile (mL)	Amount of sand that fell off of sand sculpture (g)
1		
2		
3		
4		
5		
6		
7		
8		

Transparency EX 134
Lab Manual p. LM 134

Interpret Data Make a graph of the data you have collected. Plot the data on a sheet of graph paper or use a software program.

5. Draw Conclusions and Communicate Results

Compare the hypothesis with the data and the graph. Then answer these questions.

1. Given the results of the experiment, do you think the hypothesis was correct? Explain.

_____

_____

2. How would you revise the hypothesis? Explain.

_____

_____

3. What else did you observe during the experiment?

_____

_____

Prepare a presentation for your classmates to communicate what you have learned. Display your data tables and graphs.

Investigate Further

Write another hypothesis that you might investigate.

_____

CHAPTER 11 LESSON PLANNER

Lesson	Pacing	Vocabulary	Objectives & Reading Focus	Resources & Technology
1 What Is Matter? pp. 372–381	2 days	matter physical property volume mass density	■ Measure the volume of a liquid ■ Describe physical properties of matter. ■ Explain why some objects float and others sink. **MAIN IDEA AND DETAILS** Find out about the properties of matter. Main Idea detail · detail · detail	■ Lab Manual pp. LM 135–137 Transparencies DI35, IS35, RS35, GO 35 Electronic Transparencies ■ Activity Video/DVD 3000 ESL Support pp. 148–151 ■ Reading Support and Homework pp. RS81–82
2 What Are States of Matter? pp. 382–389	2 days	solid liquid gas evaporation condensation	■ Observe a change of state. ■ Identify properties of solids, liquids, and gases. ■ Describe evaporation and condensation. **COMPARE AND CONTRAST** Find out how the states of matter are *alike* and *different*. alike — different	■ Lab Manual pp. LM138–140 Transparencies DI36, IS36, RS36, GO 36 Electronic Transparencies ■ Activity Video/DVD 3001 ESL Support pp. 152–155 ■ Reading Support and Homework pp. RS83–84
3 How Does Matter Change? pp. 390–397	2 days	mixture solution	■ Make a mixture and a solution. ■ Describe several types of physical changes. ■ Explain how a chemical change differs from a physical change. **MAIN IDEA AND DETAILS** Find out how physical and chemical changes happen. Main Idea detail · detail · detail	■ Lab Manual pp. LM 141–143 Transparencies DI37, IS37, RS37, GO 37 Electronic Transparencies ■ Activity Video/DVD 3002 ESL Support pp. 156–159 ■ Reading Support and Homework pp. RS85–86
pp. 398–403	2 days		■ Evaluate relationships of science, technology, and society ■ Review chapter concepts	■ Intervention, On-Level, and Above-Level Readers ■ Assessment Guide pp. AG85–90

Plan Ahead for Activities

Investigate

Measuring Volume p. 373

Materials: metric measuring cup, water, 3 clear containers of different shapes, masking tape

Time: 15–20 minutes

(Inquiry Focus: Predict)

Prep Tip: You may wish to have students repeat the measurements several times. Discuss how this improves the accuracy of data.

Temperature and Matter p. 383

Materials: metric measuring cup, hot water, plastic jar or beaker, thermometer, 3 ice cubes, plastic spoon

Time: 20–30 minutes

(Inquiry Focus: Communicate)

Prep Tip: Have students stir in each ice cube until it melts and then immediately take the temperature of the water.

Will It Mix? p. 391

Materials: water, metric measuring cup, 2 clear plastic jars, measuring spoon (1/4 teaspoon), sand, plastic spoon, hand lens, salt

Time: 20–30 minutes

(Inquiry Focus: Communicate)

Prep Tip: Cover students' work surfaces with paper towels for quick clean up. Depending on the water temperature, students should be able to dissolve about 3–4 teaspoons of salt in the water.

Insta-Lab

Densities
p. 379

 5 minutes

Materials: two sealable plastic bags, marbles, cotton balls

Tip: Be sure to use durable plastic bags capable of supporting the weight of the marbles without tearing.

Is It Solid?
p. 485

 5 minutes

Materials: butter, bright light

Tip: Warn students not to touch the hot bulb. Make sure the butter is at room temperature when starting the Investigate. Butter that is cold will take longer than 5 minutes to melt.

Chemical Change
p. 396

 5 minutes

Materials: vinegar, jar, teaspoon, baking soda

Tip: Remind students not to ingest any of the materials and not to rub their mouths and eyes before washing their hands.

Reading Support

Page R61 provides additional information

Below-Level/Intervention

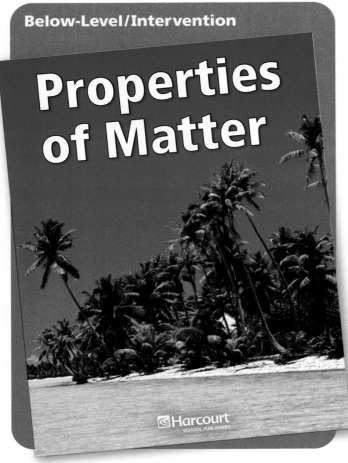

Properties of Matter

When used along with the hands-on experiences from the **Student Edition**, the Intervention Reader promotes science success for all students.
Reading Level 1.5–2.0

The Intervention Reader presents identical chapter content and vocabulary at a below-grade reading level. The reader uses a visual glossary, simplified language, and comprehension aids especially designed for struggling readers. The **Intervention Readers Teacher Guide** provides additional strategies and support.

On-Level/Enrichment

Matter Is Everything!

This reader promotes success on state science tests by reinforcing test content objectives, chapter vocabulary, and reading skills.
Reading Level 2.5–3.5

Advanced/Challenge

What's Heavy?

This interesting nonfiction reader enriches and extends chapter concepts.
Reading Level 4.0–5.5

Trade Books for Students

These books provide in-depth information on chapter content. For more information about each selection, see the Bibliography beginning on page R48.

Easy
Temperature by Rebecca Olien, Capstone, 2005

Average
Make It Change by David Evans and Claudette Williams, Dorling Kindersley, 1992

Challenge
Water, Water Everywhere by Mark J. Rauzon and Cynthia Overbeck Bix, Sierra Club Books, 1994

Alternative Teaching Strategies

ESL/ESOL Support

ESL Support

This guide provides additional support for the strategies and activities that appear throughout this chapter.

Intervention and Reteaching

Strategies for reteaching key lesson concepts provide options for addressing a variety of learning styles.

Intervention Reader p. 375

Are Air and Light Matter? p. 376

How Does Matter Change State? p. 386

Evaporation and Condensation p. 388

Using the E-Book

This chapter is also available online and has provisions for children with special needs. Adjustable text size and audio text can be used with children who have vision impairments or learning difficulties.

www.hspscience.com

Science Concepts Across the Grades

Grade 2	Grade 3	Grade 4
Related Chapters		
Chapter 9 Observing and Classifying Matter **Lesson 1** What Is Matter? **Lesson 2** What Are Solids? **Lesson 3** What Are Gases? **Chapter 10 Changes in Matter** **Lesson 1** How Can Matter Change? **Lesson 2** How Can Water Change? **Lesson 3** What Are Other Changes to Matter?	**Chapter 11 Properties of Matter** **Lesson 1** What Is Matter? **Lesson 2** What Are States of Matter? **Lesson 3** How Does Matter Change?	**Chapter 10 Matter and Its Properties** **Lesson 1** How Can Physical Properties Be Used to Identify Matter? **Lesson 2** How Does Matter Change States? **Lesson 3** What Are Mixtures and Solutions? **Chapter 11 Changes in Matter** **Lesson 1** What Is Matter Made Of? **Lesson 2** What Are Physical Changes in Matter? **Lesson 3** How Does Matter React Chemically ?
Learning Goals		
▶ Identify solids, liquids, and gases, and use tools to measure them. ▶ Observe how matter can change and that not all matter responds to change in the same way; Know that water can be a solid, a liquid, or a gas.	▶ Describe the physical properties of matter. ▶ Identify properties of solids, liquids, and gases. ▶ Explain the difference between physical and chemical changes.	▶ Know how physical properties identify matter; Know how temperature changes the states of matter and that matter isn't lost or gained. ▶ Describe states of matter and changes of state; Understand physical and chemical changes.

RESOURCES FOR INQUIRY

Daily Practice

Daily Inquiry pp. 372, 382, 390
Teaching Transparencies **DI 35–37**
Electronic Transparencies **DI 3000–3002**

Inquiry Tool Kit

Harcourt Investigations

Harcourt School Publishers offers an alternative program that provides more opportunities for inquiry-based science experiences. The program provides a series of investigations that promote guided, structured, and independent inquiry using student journals, lab manuals, science readers and other materials.

Visit **www.hspscience.com** for more information.

Guided Inquiry

Investigate pp. 373, 383, 391;
Lab Manual **pp. LM 135–137, 138–140, 141–143**

Inquiry Skill Mini Lesson pp. 373, 383, 391; *Teaching Transparencies* **IS 35–37;** *Electronic Transparencies* **IS 3000–3002**

Insta-Lab pp. 379, 485, 396

Unit Experiment pp. 369A–B; *Lab Manual* **pp. LM 131–134**

Independent Inquiry

Investigate Further *Lab Manual* **pp. LM 374, 384, 392**

Lab Manual

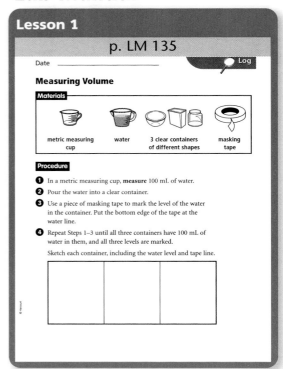

Use with **Student Edition** p. 373.

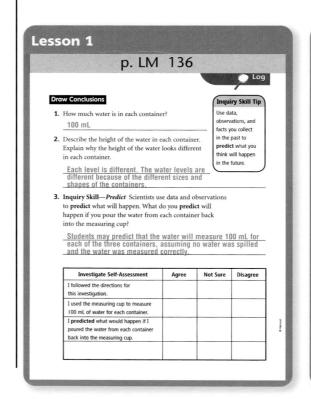

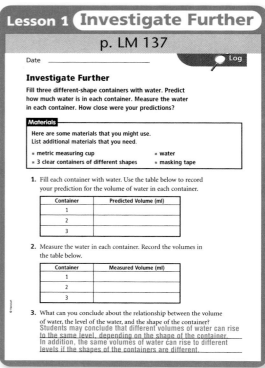

Independent Inquiry (continued)

Science Projects for Home or School
  p. 401 *Teaching Resources* **p. TR 21**

Unit Experiment pp. 369A–B; Lab Manual pp. LM 9–11 and Science Fair Projects *Lab Manual* **LM 196–201**

Lab Manual (cont.)

Lesson 2

p. LM 138

Date _____   ● Log

Temperature and Matter

Materials

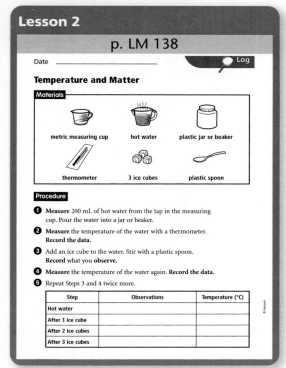

metric measuring cup   hot water   plastic jar or beaker

thermometer   3 ice cubes   plastic spoon

Procedure

❶ **Measure** 200 mL of hot water from the tap in the measuring cup. Pour the water into a jar or beaker.

❷ **Measure** the temperature of the water with a thermometer. **Record the data.**

❸ Add an ice cube to the water. Stir with a plastic spoon. **Record** what you **observe.**

❹ **Measure** the temperature of the water again. **Record the data.**

❺ Repeat Steps 3 and 4 twice more.

Step	Observations	Temperature (°C)
Hot water		
After 1 ice cube		
After 2 ice cubes		
After 3 ice cubes		

Use with **Student Edition** p. 383.

Lesson 2

p. LM 139

● Log

Draw Conclusions

1. What happened to the ice cubes in the water? They got smaller or melted. They changed from solid to liquid.

2. What happened to the temperature of the water each time you added an ice cube? It decreased.

3. Is the temperature of ice higher or lower than the temperature of water? How do you know? Ice is colder than water. The temperature dropped.

4. **Inquiry Skill—Communicate** One way scientists communicate data is in a bar graph. Make a bar graph to **communicate** what happened to the temperature in this activity.

> Bar graphs should have "Number of Ice Cubes"(0–3) on the *x*-axis and "Temperature" on the *y*-axis. The bars get shorter with the addition of each ice cube. Students may say that ice lowers the temperature of the water. In truth, melting the ice removes heat energy from the water.

Inquiry Skill Tip

You can also use tables, charts, drawings, line graphs, or circle graphs to **communicate** what happened in an investigation. When deciding which method to use, consider the message that you want to communicate. For example, in this Investigate, you use a bar graph because you need to compare temperatures for different numbers of ice cubes.

Investigate Self-Assessment	Agree	Not Sure	Disagree
I followed the directions for this investigation.			
I used the thermometer to measure the temperature of the water.			
I **communicated** my data by making a bar graph.			

Lesson 2 (Investigate Further)

p. LM 140

Date _____   ● Log

Investigate Further

Put 100 mL of water in a freezer. Take it out every 10 minutes and measure its temperature. Communicate the data in a bar graph and interpret data.

Materials

Here are some materials that you might use. List additional materials that you need.

▪ metric measuring cup	▪ water	▪ thermometer
▪ plastic jar or beaker	▪ freezer	▪ timer or clock

1. What will this investigation test? The investigation will test how the temperature of water changes as it freezes.

2. Record your measurements in the data table below. Make a bar graph to communicate the results.

Time (min)	Temperature (°C)
0	
10	
20	
30	
40	
50	
60	

3. Interpret the data in the graph. What can you conclude about the temperatures of the water and the freezer? Students should explain that the freezer was colder than the water because the temperature of the water dropped inside the freezer. Students may explain that freezing takes heat away from the water.

Lesson 3

p. LM 141

Date _____   ● Log

Will It Mix?

Materials

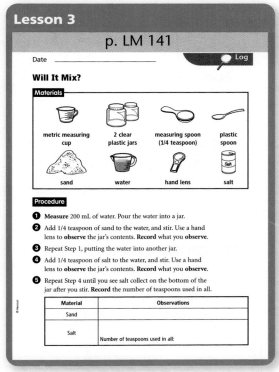

metric measuring cup   2 clear plastic jars   measuring spoon (1/4 teaspoon)   plastic spoon

sand   water   hand lens   salt

Procedure

❶ **Measure** 200 mL of water. Pour the water into a jar.

❷ Add 1/4 teaspoon of sand to the water, and stir. Use a hand lens to **observe** the jar's contents. **Record** what you **observe.**

❸ Repeat Step 1, putting the water into another jar.

❹ Add 1/4 teaspoon of salt to the water, and stir. Use a hand lens to **observe** the jar's contents. **Record** what you **observe.**

❺ Repeat Step 4 until you see salt collect on the bottom of the jar after you stir. **Record** the number of teaspoons used in all.

Material	Observations
Sand	
Salt	Number of teaspoons used in all:

Use with **Student Edition** p. 391.

Lesson 3

p. LM 142

● Log

Draw Conclusions

1. What did you **observe** when you stirred sand in water? The sand and water did not mix at all. They stayed separate.

2. What did you **observe** when you stirred salt in water? Possible answer: At first, the salt seemed to disappear in the water when I stirred it. After several teaspoons, I observed that the salt did not mix with the water and settled to the bottom of the jar.

3. **Inquiry Skill—Communicate** Scientists sometimes use drawings to **communicate.** Make a drawing to **communicate** what happened to sand in water. Make another drawing to **communicate** what happened to salt in water.

Inquiry Skill Tip

If you use drawings to **communicate,** make the drawings clear and simple. Be sure they show the details you want to communicate. If necessary, use labels to explain the drawing.

Sand	Salt
Students' drawings should show sand undissolved in water and salt dissolved in water.	

Investigate Self-Assessment	Agree	Not Sure	Disagree
I observed what happened when I mixed sand into water and salt into water.			
I used the measuring spoon to measure the amount of salt I added to the water.			
I **communicated** my observations by making drawings.			

Lesson 3 (Investigate Further)

p. LM 143

Date _____   ● Log

Investigate Further

What do you predict will happen if you leave the jar with salt water in a warm place? Try it.

Materials

Here are some materials that you might use. List additional materials that you need.

▪ jar with salt water

1. What do you think will happen if you leave the jar with salt water in a warm place? Students may correctly predict that the water will evaporate, leaving the salt in the bottom of the jar.

2. Leave the jar in a warm place for a week. Make a drawing to communicate the results.

3. Did the results agree with your prediction? Explain. Students should describe their results and note whether their predictions were correct.

READING SUPPORT AND HOMEWORK

 **Pages available online.**
www.hspscience.com

Reading Support and Homework also includes Vocabulary Power, and Vocabulary Cards and Activities.

Lesson 1

p. RS 81

Lesson Quick Study

Name _____
Date _____

Lesson 1 - What Is Matter?

1. **Inquiry Skill Practice–Predict**

Imagine you have the 7 pieces of wood shown to the right. Predict what will happen to the mass and volume of the pieces of wood if you put them together without cutting them to make a birdhouse. Explain. Possible answer: The pieces of wood will not be changed, just put together; therefore, the mass will remain the same. The volume will increase since the pieces of wood put together to make a birdhouse take up more space than the same pieces of wood laying flat.

2. **Use Vocabulary**

Complete each sentence with the correct term from the box.

_____Matter_____ is anything that takes up space.

_____Volume_____ is the amount of space something takes up.

| matter mass volume |

The amount of matter in something is its _____mass_____.

3. **Reading Skill Practice–Main Idea and Details**

Read the selection. Underline the main idea. List at least three details about the main idea.

Julio wants to buy a special kind of flower for his mom. He walks into a flower shop. As Julio looks around the store, he notices the bright yellow color of large sunflowers. Julio touches their silky petals. He smells their soft smell. The sunflowers will make his mom smile.

Possible answers: Sunflowers are bright yellow and large. They have silky petals. Sunflowers have a soft smell.

Use with *Student Edition* pp. 372–381.

Lesson 1

p. RS 82

Name _____

4. **Main Idea and Details**

Use this space to complete the graphic organizer shown in the Reading Review of the Student Edition.

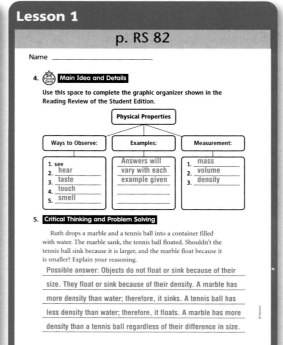

Physical Properties

Ways to Observe:
1. see
2. hear
3. taste
4. touch
5. smell

Examples:
Answers will vary with each example given

Measurement:
1. mass
2. volume
3. density

5. **Critical Thinking and Problem Solving**

Ruth drops a marble and a tennis ball into a container filled with water. The marble sank, the tennis ball floated. Shouldn't the tennis ball sink because it is larger, and the marble float because it is smaller? Explain your reasoning.

Possible answer: Objects do not float or sink because of their size. They float or sink because of their density. A marble has more density than water; therefore, it sinks. A tennis ball has less density than water; therefore, it floats. A marble has more density than a tennis ball regardless of their difference in size.

Lesson 2

p. RS 83

Lesson Quick Study

Name _____
Date _____

Lesson 2 - What Are States of Matter?

1. **Inquiry Skill Practice–Communicate**

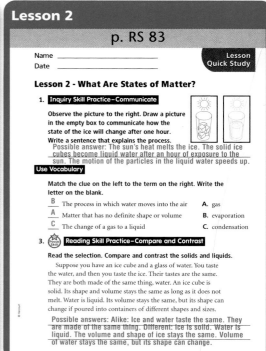

Observe the picture to the right. Draw a picture in the empty box to communicate how the state of the ice will change after one hour. Write a sentence that explains the process.
Possible answer: The sun's heat melts the ice. The solid ice cubes become liquid water after an hour of exposure to the sun. The motion of the particles in the liquid water speeds up.

Use Vocabulary

Match the clue on the left to the term on the right. Write the letter on the blank.

__B__ The process in which water moves into the air   A. gas

__A__ Matter that has no definite shape or volume   B. evaporation

__C__ The change of a gas to a liquid   C. condensation

3. **Reading Skill Practice–Compare and Contrast**

Read the selection. Compare and contrast the solids and liquids.

Suppose you have an ice cube and a glass of water. You taste the water, and then you taste the ice. Their tastes are the same. They are both made of the same thing, water. An ice cube is solid. Its shape and volume stays the same as long as it does not melt. Water is liquid. Its volume stays the same, but its shape can change if poured into containers of different shapes and sizes.

Possible answers: Alike: Ice and water taste the same. They are made of the same thing. Different: Ice is solid. Water is liquid. The volume and shape of ice stays the same. Volume of water stays the same, but its shape can change.

Use with *Student Edition* pp. 382–389.

Lesson 2

p. RS 84

Name _____

4. **Compare and Contrast**

Use this space to complete the graphic organizer shown in the Reading Review of the Student Edition.

State of Matter	Shape	Volume
Solid	has a definite shape (shape stays the same)	has a definite volume (volume stays the same)
Liquid	takes shape of container that it's in	has a definite volume (volume stays the same)
Gas	spreads out to fill the shape of container that it's in	its volume fills the container it's in

5. **Critical Thinking and Problem Solving**

Suppose you are playing in your backyard. All of a sudden, it starts to rain. What happened to cause a dry day to turn into a wet one? Explain your reasoning.

Possible answer: There was water in the air in the form of gas. The gas cooled and it turned into liquid, rain. This is called condensation.

Lesson 3

p. RS 85

Lesson Quick Study

Name _____
Date _____

Lesson 3 - How Does Matter Change?

1. **Inquiry Skill Practice–Communicate**

An artist takes a large marble block and starts to carve it. After a few hours, the artist has a horse carved out of the marble. Write a sentence to communicate what kind of change the marble went through. Possible answer: The marble went through a physical change. The marble continues to be marble even if now it is in the form of a horse.

2. **Use Vocabulary**

Write a complete sentence that uses the terms *mixture* and *solution* correctly.

Check students' sentences.

3. **Reading Skill Practice–Main Idea and Details**

Read the selection. Underline the main idea. List at least two details about the main idea.

Matter can go through both physical and chemical changes. Suppose you want to build a play house with wood. After some time of hard work, the pile of wood you started out with is a play house. The change you observed, from wood planks to a play house, is a physical change. A terrible disaster happens. Lightning hits your play house, and a flame of fire destroys it. Your play house is now ashes. This change in the wood is a chemical change.

Possible answers: Wood goes through a physical change when the wood planks take a new shape as a play house. Wood goes through a chemical change when the wood is burnt and becomes ashes.

Use with *Student Edition* pp. 390–397

Lesson 3

p. RS 86

Name _____

4. **Main Idea and Details**

Use this space to complete the graphic organizer shown in the Reading Review of the Student Edition.

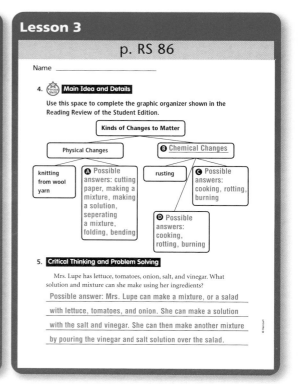

Kinds of Changes to Matter

Physical Changes
- knitting from wool yarn
- **A** Possible answers: cutting paper, making a mixture, making a solution, seperating a mixture, folding, bending

B Chemical Changes
- rusting
- **C** Possible answers: cooking, rotting, burning
- **D** Possible answers: cooking, rotting, burning

5. **Critical Thinking and Problem Solving**

Mrs. Lupe has lettuce, tomatoes, onion, salt, and vinegar. What solution and mixture can she make using her ingredients?

Possible answer: Mrs. Lupe can make a mixture, or a salad with lettuce, tomatoes, and onion. She can make a solution with the salt and vinegar. She can then make another mixture by pouring the vinegar and salt solution over the salad.

ASSESSMENT OPTIONS

5 1 3 7 3 4 6 9

Formal Assessment
- Chapter Review and Test Preparation SE pp. 402–403
- Chapter Test AG pp. 85–88

Standardized Test Preparation
- Reading Review and Test Preparation SE pp. 381, 389, 397

Harcourt School Publishers Online Assessment
- Chapter test taking and automatic scoring
- Banks of items from which to build tests

Ongoing Assessment
- Assess Prior Knowledge
- Daily Inquiry Transparencies
- Teacher Edition questions throughout
- ✪ Focus Skill questions throughout SE
- Reaching All Learners throughout TE
- Reading Review SE 381, 389, 397
- Observation Checklist AG

Performance Assessment
- Long-Option AG 89–90
- Short-Option TE p. 403

Student Self–Assessment
- Investigate Self-Assessment Lab Manual
- Self-Assessment AG

Portfolio Assessment
- Using Portfolio Assessment AG
- Suggested work samples TE p. 402

Chapter Test

AG 85

Name _____
Date _____

Chapter Assessment

Properties of Matter

Vocabulary 4 points each

Match each term in Column B with its meaning in Column A.

	Column A	Column B
E	1. The amount of matter in something	A. density
D	2. Matter with a volume and shape that stay the same	B. gas
A	3. The mass of matter compared to its volume	C. matter
G	4. A mixture in which different kinds of matter mix evenly	D. solid
B	5. Matter with no definite shape or volume	E. mass
C	6. Anything that takes up space	F. liquid
H	7. The amount of space matter takes up	G. solution
F	8. Matter with a volume that stays the same but a shape that changes	H. volume

Science Concepts 4 points each

Write the letter of the best choice.

A 9. Which of the following is matter that you cannot see?
- A. air
- B. clouds
- C. ice
- D. water

AG 86

Name _____

F 10. Kevin needs to measure the mass of an apple. What tool can he use?
- F. a balance
- G. a barometer
- H. a ruler
- J. a thermometer

C 11. Which group of words names physical properties of matter?
- A. mirror, wool, cotton
- B. salt, candy, sugar
- C. sour, green, hot
- D. tall, building, glass

H 12. Which of the following groups names three states of matter?
- F. gas, oil, water
- G. liquid, water, ice
- H. solid, liquid, gas
- J. solid, penny, liquid

D 13. Which of the following has the greatest density?

A. cotton balls

C. jelly beans

B. feathers

D. rocks

H 14. Mica makes a salad of oranges, apples, and bananas. What is the bowl of fruit salad an example of?
- F. condensation
- G. evaporation
- H. a mixture
- J. a solution

A 15. Which is a chemical change?
- A. burning wood
- B. cutting cloth
- C. folding paper
- D. mixing salt and water

AG 87

Name _____

J 16. Which of these is a solution?
- F. cereal and milk
- G. ice cream and nuts
- H. orange and apple slices
- J. sugar and water

Inquiry Skills 8 points each

17. Janet knows the mass of some peanuts and the mass of some pretzels. She mixes them together to make trail mix. How can she determine the mass of the trail mix if she doesn't have a tool to **measure** it? Explain.

Possible answer: She can add the mass of the peanuts and the mass of the pretzels to find the mass of the trail mix. The mass of two or more things together is the sum of their separate masses.

18. Charlie is testing whether things sink or float. He puts a plastic-foam board in the water. **Predict** whether the board will sink or float. Explain your reasoning.

The plastic-foam board will float, because plastic-foam is not very dense. An object that is less dense than water will float.

AG 88

Name _____

Critical Thinking 10 points each

19. Tyrell had a large bowl of ice cubes. He left the bowl out in the hot sun for a couple of hours. What happened to the ice cubes? Explain.

The heat from the sun melted the solid ice cubes, causing them to change to liquid water.

20. Teresa popped some popcorn and cooked some rice. She measured a cup of each as shown in the pictures.

Compare the volumes of the popcorn and the rice. Then determine which is denser, the popcorn or the rice. Explain.

The volumes are the same, because volume is the amount of space that matter takes up. Both volumes fill one cup. A cup of rice has a greater mass than a cup of popped popcorn, which is mostly air. The rice is denser, because density is the mass of matter compared to its volume.

Performance Task

AG 89

Name _____
Date _____

Performance Assessment

Student Task

Sink or Float?

Materials

measuring cup   water   several small objects

Procedure

1. Fill the measuring cup three-quarters full with water.
2. Place an object in the water. Does it sink, or does it float? Record your observations in the data table below.
3. Remove the first object from the water. Repeat Step 2 for the other objects. Refill the cup with water if necessary.
4. Review the data you recorded in the table. Which objects are more dense than water? Which objects are less dense? Tell how you know.

Object	Sinks	Floats	Denser Than Water	Less Dense Than Water

Rubric

AG 90

Sink or Float?

Performance Assessment

Teacher's Directions

Materials Performance Task sheet, measuring cup, water, several small objects

Time 30 minutes

Suggested Grouping individuals or pairs

Inquiry Skills observe, compare, draw conclusions, communicate

Preparation Hints Gather small objects—some that float and some that sink—for example, marbles, paper clips, coins, leaves, corks, and plastic bottle caps.

Introduce the Task Tell students that they will determine whether some common objects sink or float in water. From this, they will conclude which objects are more dense than water and which are less dense than water.

Promote Discussion When students finish, ask them to share their observations about the objects that sank and those that floated. Were their observations similar? Then review the definition of *density*. Ask students to explain density in terms of the mass of matter in a given volume and to relate this to the objects that sank or floated.

Scoring Rubric

Performance Indicators

_____ Determines whether each object sinks or floats.
_____ Records observations accurately.
_____ Concludes that objects sink or float because they are more dense or less dense than water, respectively.
_____ Understands that density is a relationship between mass and volume.

Observations and Rubric Score

3	2	1	0

Assess Prior Knowledge

Use the photograph to get students interested in the chapter topic. Invite volunteers to suggest different types of matter they observe in the picture. Write their suggestions on the board. Ask students if they can group any of the listed types into a larger group (for example, trees, sand, and rock into solids)

Have students discuss their ideas about the question: **Is there any matter you can't see?** Note their answers as a key to prior knowledge and misconceptions. (See also the Science Background.) Students may talk about matter hidden behind the trees or under the water but may not mention the air.

Later, as students read in Lesson 1 about matter, they will have an opportunity to reevaluate the photo. They should then note that air and some other gases are matter that is invisible to the eye.

Generate Science Questions

In this chapter, students will learn about what matter is, the states of matter, and how matter changes. Have students write a list of questions they have about matter and how it changes from one form to another. Have them exchange lists with a partner.

To prepare for effective instruction, you may wish to consult these resources:

  The **Activity Video/DVD** provides previews of the activities, offers classroom-management techniques, and presents expected results.

  The **Science eBook** provides chapter content online, with greater depth via additional content and activities.

  The **Science Background** features throughout this Teacher Edition provide content support.

Visit **www.hspscience.com** for additional Professional Development resources.

Chapter 11 Properties of Matter

Lesson 1 **What Is Matter?**

Lesson 2 **What Are States of Matter?**

Lesson 3 **How Does Matter Change?**

Vocabulary

matter
physical property
mass
volume
density
solid
liquid
gas
evaporation
condensation
mixture
solution

370

 Science Background **To Address Misconceptions**

Is air matter?

Assess Prior Knowledge *Ask:* Is air a form of matter?

Students May Think that air, oxygen, and other gases are not matter because they can't be seen.

Scientists Explain that gases are matter, but the particles are spread out and are too small to be seen individually. Water changes to a gas when it is heated. The water particles are spread out, but gas is still matter.

What You Can Do Tie an inflated balloon at each end of a meterstick. Tie a string at or near the middle of the stick, and hang the stick so that the balloons are balanced. *Ask:* What will happen if I break one balloon? Pop one balloon with a pin. Ask students why the meterstick became unbalanced. Point out that the air in the balloon had mass.

What do **YOU** wonder?

Matter is anything that takes up space. What matter can you see in this picture? Is there any matter you can't see?

Vocabulary

Opportunities for developing chapter vocabulary include:

- Develop Science Vocabulary strategies at point-of-use in the teaching plan

- Vocabulary questions in each Reading Review and the Chapter Review and Test

- Vocabulary sections on the Quick Study pages in *Reading Support and Homework*

- Vocabulary Cards and activities and Vocabulary Power worksheet in *Reading Support and Homework*

Students can use the **Vocabulary Power** Worksheet below to preview and explore more about the chapter vocabulary.

Reading Support and Homework

p. RS 80

Properties of Matter

A. **Words with Multiple Meanings**

Read each sentence and the definitions of the underlined word. Circle the letter that shows which way the word has been used.

1. Scientists proved that the black hole contained underline{matter}.
   (A) anything that takes up space
   B an issue or problem

2. The scale measured the underline{mass} of the pebbles.
   (A) the amount of matter in something
   B a religious ceremony

3. The orange juice comes in two different underline{volumes}, a half-gallon and a whole gallon container.
   A the loudness of a sound
   (B) the amount of space that matter takes up

4. Trees produce an important underline{gas} called oxygen as they grow.
   (A) matter that has no definite shape or volume
   B the fuel used to run a car

B. **Explore Word Meanings**

Think about the meaning of the underlined words. Answer each question.

5. When a gas cools, it changes into a underline{liquid}. What does *liquid* mean?
   Possible answer: a state of matter that has a volume that stays the same, but it has a shape that can change

6. The boys hiked with a underline{mixture} of peanuts, raisins, and chocolate chips. What is a *mixture*? Possible answer: a substance with two or more kinds of matter

Reading Focus Skills

The content of each lesson is organized to focus on a key reading skill. The skill is reinforced by questions that appear at the end of each section and the graphic organizer at the end of the lesson. Additional practice is also provided in *Reading Support and Homework*.

The Reading Focus Skills for this chapter are:	
Lesson 1	Main Idea and Details
Lesson 2	Compare and Contrast
Lesson 3	Main Idea and Details
All Lessons	Draw Conclusions and Summarize

Strategies for other reading skills also appear in the Reading Mini-Lessons throughout the chapter.

ESL/ESOL Support

Spanish-speaking students may already be familiar with English words such as these cognates:

chemical changes/cambios químicos

density/densidad

gas/gas

liquid/líquido

mass/masa

matter/materia

physical changes/cambios físicos

physical property/propriedad físico

Objectives

- Measure the volume of a liquid.
- Describe physical properties of matter.
- Explain why some objects float and others sink.

Transparency DI 35

Daily Inquiry

Floaters and Sinkers

 forceps

Other Materials: cup of water, light objects

Review Skill Experiment, Predict

What to Do

- Do you think you could float an object on top of the water? Make a list of five light objects to test, such as a paper clip or tiny piece of paper. Record the names of the objects on a chart and tell whether you think each will sink or float.
- Use forceps to gently place each object on top of the water. Does it sink or float? Record your results on the chart.
- Why do some objects sink while others float?

1 Introduce

Build on Prior Knowledge

Use the Fast Fact for a discussion starter about the lesson topic.

How can a cow drink so much more water than a human?

Does an adult or a child need more water? Why?

When *Minutes* Count . . .

If time is short, consider these options.

Conduct the Investigate as a **whole class demonstration**.

Use the Activity Video/DVD to model . After previewing, conduct the Investigate.

What Is Matter?

Fast Fact

A Lot of Water An adult human needs about 10 cups of water each day. That sounds like a lot, but it isn't much for a cow. A cow needs at least 400 cups of water each day! In the Investigate, you will measure the volume of water.

372

Science Background

Customary and SI Units Most students are familiar with customary units for volume, such as cups, ounces, or gallons. Provide students with measuring cups and spoons marked with both SI and customary units. Challenge them to measure and think in SI units.

When introducing students to mass, point out that grams and kilograms do not convert to ounces and pounds because they don't measure the same thing. Tell students that kilograms measure the amount of matter in an object, while pounds measure weight. That is why mass is measured by comparing the unknown object with a known mass on a balance.

Webliography
Keyword measuring matter
www.hspscience.com

Measuring Volume

Materials
- metric measuring cup
- water
- metric ruler
- 3 clear containers of different shapes
- masking tape

Procedure

1. Measure 100 mL of water.

2. Pour the water into a clear container.

3. Use a piece of masking tape to mark the level of the water in the container. Put the bottom edge of the tape at the water line.

4. Repeat Steps 1–3 until all three containers have 100 mL of water in them, and all three levels are marked.

Step 2

Step 3

Draw Conclusions

1. How much water is in each container?

2. Describe the height of the water in each container. Explain why the height of the water looks different in each container.

3. **Inquiry Skill** Scientists use data and observations to predict what will happen. What do you predict will happen if you pour the water from each container back into the measuring cup?

Investigate Further

Fill three containers of different shapes with water. **Predict** how much water you will find in each container. **Measure** the water in each container. How close were your predictions?

373

Inquiry Skill Mini-Lesson

Predict Tell students that they can use what they observe to predict what will happen. Display the transparency. Point out that the three glasses each contain 100 mL of water. Have students answer the questions on the transparency.

Inquiry Skill practice is provided in *Reading Support and Homework*.

Transparency IS 35

Electronic Transparency IS 3000

Predict

Each of the glasses holds 100 mL of water.
1. **Predict** what the volume and shape of the water will be if you pour the contents of each glass into 3 identical measuring cups.
   The volume and shape should be the same in each measuring cup.

2. **Predict** if there would be a difference in volume or shape if you poured 100 mL of milk instead of water into the 3 identical measuring cups.
   There would be no difference in volume or shape.

3. **Predict** what would happen if you poured the water from one glass into a flat, shallow pan? Would the volume change? Possible answer: the water would cover the bottom of the pan, but the volume wouldn't change.

4. What statement can you make about the volume and shape of a liquid when you pour the liquid from one container to another?
   Possible answer: the volume of the liquid stays the same, but that the liquid takes the shape of whatever container it is in.

Science   © Harcourt

---

2 Teach

Video Segment 3000

Time 15–20 minutes

Grouping groups of 4

Alternative Materials

▶ Have students use a washable glass marker instead of tape.

Lab Manual pages can be used to record results. Inquiry Skill Tips and Self-Assessment are also provided.

Tips and Guided Inquiry

You may want to have students repeat the measurements several times. Discuss how this improves the accuracy of data.

Would the results change if you used a different liquid, such as lemonade? no **Why does the water change shape, but a solid, such as the glass, doesn't?** Possible answer: Water flows, so it can't hold a shape.

Expected Results

Students should find that water changes shape to fit the container it is in, but this does not affect the volume.

Draw Conclusions

1. 100 mL

2. Each level is different. The water levels are different because of the different sizes and shapes of the containers.

3. The water will measure 100 mL for each of the three containers, assuming no water is spilled and the water is measured correctly.

Investigate Further

Students can use this page in the *Lab Manual* for **Independent Inquiry**.

Lab Manual

p. LM 137

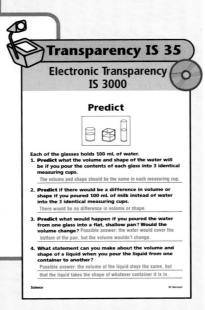

Date _____   ● Log

Investigate Further
Fill three different-shape containers with water. Predict how much water is in each container. Measure the water in each container. How close were your predictions?

Materials
Here are some materials that you might use.
List additional materials that you need.
- metric measuring cup   • water
- 3 clear containers of different shapes • masking tape

1. Fill each container with water. Use the table below to record your prediction for the volume of water in each container.

Container	Predicted Volume (ml)
1	
2	
3	

2. Measure the water in each container. Record the volumes in the table below.

Container	Measured Volume (ml)
1	
2	
3	

3. What can you conclude about the relationship between the volume of water, the level of the water, and the shape of the container? Students may conclude that different volumes of water can rise to the same level, depending on the shape of the container. In addition, the same volumes of water can rise to different levels if the shapes of the containers are different.

2 Teach
continued

VOCABULARY For Vocabulary Cards and activities, see ***Reading Support and Homework***.

SCIENCE CONCEPTS Have students turn each statement into a question and then use their prior knowledge to suggest responses. List the responses on the board. Have students review and revise their responses as they discuss the lesson.

 READING FOCUS SKILL

MAIN IDEA AND DETAILS Tell students that the information in this lesson is organized to help them recognize a main idea and the details that support it.

1 Develop Science Vocabulary

matter Remind students that the word *matter* has a number of meanings, such as when someone asks, "What's the matter?" meaning "What's the problem?" or "What's wrong?" In science, the word *matter* means anything that takes up space. Tell students to use context to determine or confirm word meanings to be sure they have the correct meaning. (See the Reading Skill Mini-Lesson.)

2 Key Science Concepts

What are some examples of matter?
Possible answers: ice, water, clouds, air, people

VOCABULARY	SCIENCE CONCEPTS	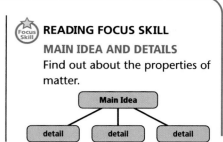 READING FOCUS SKILL
matter p. 374	▶ what matter is	**MAIN IDEA AND DETAILS**
physical property p. 376	▶ how to measure some physical properties of matter	Find out about the properties of matter.
mass p. 378		
volume p. 379		
density p. 379		

Matter

Ice-skating can be fun. Skaters glide over the ice. They feel the breeze against their cheeks.

Everything that the skaters see and feel is **matter**. Matter is anything that takes up space. Ice, water, and clouds are matter. The air the skaters breathe is matter. Skaters are matter, too.

What examples of matter do you see in this picture? ▼

374

Reading Skill Mini-Lesson

USE CONTEXT CLUES

Tell students that clues to the boldfaced vocabulary words often are found by reading the words and sentences before and after them. Display the Transparency. Have students read the section entitled *Matter* to complete the table together.

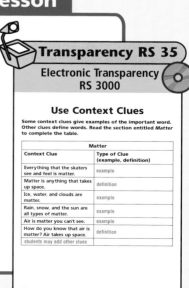

Transparency RS 35

Electronic Transparency RS 3000

Use Context Clues

Some context clues give examples of the important word. Other clues define words. Read the section entitled *Matter* to complete the table.

Matter	
Context Clue	**Type of Clue (example, definition)**
Everything that the skaters see and feel is matter.	example
Matter is anything that takes up space.	definition
Ice, water, and clouds are matter.	example
Rain, snow, and the sun are all types of matter.	example
Air is matter you can't see.	example
How do you know that air is matter? Air takes up space.	definition
students may add other clues	

Science

▲ Is there any matter in this picture that you can't see?

Look around you. What matter can you see? Your desk, books, and other objects in the classroom are matter. Your teacher and your classmates are matter. You know they are matter because they take up space.

Now, look outside. Is it raining? Is it sunny? Is it snowing? Rain, snow, and the sun are all types of matter. Is the wind blowing? Air is matter that you can't see. How do you know that air is matter? Air takes up space. You can see air move leaves on trees. You can feel air on your skin.

MAIN IDEA AND DETAILS What is matter?

375

How many different examples of matter can you identify in the pictures on this page? Possible answers: people, water, clothes, trees, rope, air, clouds

4 ▶ **Critical Thinking**

Is light matter? no

Students may think that light is matter because it seems to "fill" the space in the room. See the Reaching All Learners activity to correct this misconception.

5 ▶ **Main Idea and Details** (Focus Skill)

Answer: Matter is anything that takes up space.

What do YOU wonder?

Have students look back at the picture on the chapter opener and think about what they've learned about matter. **Are there any forms of matter in the picture that you didn't notice before?** Students may notice clouds, or perhaps name air as a form of matter.

Reaching All Learners

Below / On-Level / Advanced / ESL **Intervention** **Reteach**

Intervention Reader

Target: Struggling readers

Intervention Strategy: The Intervention Reader presents the essential lesson content at the reading level 1.5–2.0. A visual glossary and other text-style and comprehension aids increase student understanding of the content.

Assess: Use the strategies in the *Intervention Reader Teacher Guide* to assess learning, along with the guided questions in the reader.

Types of Living Things

Harcourt

6 Develop Science Vocabulary

physical property Point out the difference between an object, such as a book, and the substance out of which the book is made—paper. Help students focus first on the properties of an object and then on the properties of the matter from which the object is made. Point out that observing doesn't simply mean seeing. Students should practice using all their senses to identify properties. Explain that even if something has no smell or taste, those are also properties.

7 Critical Thinking

Pose the following situation to the class:

Two plates on the table are the same size and shape. One is made of glass, and the other of smooth, hard plastic. How can you tell which is which without lifting them or taking off your blindfold? Possible answer: Tap them with a pencil or your fingernail. The glass should ring and the plastic should make a sound like a dull thud.

8 Inquiry Skills

Compare Pose the following situation to the class:

Molly says that a substance is pretty, large, cold, and smells bad. Dolly says that the same substance is a yellow liquid with a volume of 3 L. It has a temperature of 6 degrees Celsius and smells like rotten eggs. Whose description of the substance might best help you identify it? Why? Dolly's; it gives detailed information about properties and measurements. Point out to students that descriptions such as *pretty*, *large*, *cold*, and *bad-smelling* are opinions, not directly observable properties. What one person thinks is *pretty* or *large* may not be the same as what another thinks is *pretty* or *large*.

Physical Properties of Matter

6 Anything you can observe about matter by using one or more of your senses is a **physical property**. Here are some things you observe with your senses.

Sight—Young ducks are small and yellow. You observe their size and color.

Hearing—Bells ring. Rain pings on a metal roof. Wind rustles leaves. Sound is a physical property of some matter.

7 Touch—Ice feels cold and hard. Blankets feel soft. Sandpaper feels rough.

Smell: Baking bread smells delicious. Rotting garbage doesn't.

Taste: A physical property of a food is its flavor. Flavors can be sweet, salty, sour, or bitter.

▲ This pineapple feels rough on the outside. The inside tastes sweet.

Your sense of touch tells you that the cat is fluffy. ▼

Your sense of smell tells you that there is popcorn in the container. ▼

376

Reaching All Learners **Intervention** **Reteach**

Are Air and Light Matter?

Target: Students having trouble understanding air is matter but light is not
Intervention Strategy: Hands-On Activity
Provide students with a balloon and a miniflashlight. Have students blow up the balloon. *Ask:* **How do you know the air in the balloon is matter?** It takes up space. Have students stretch the mouth of the balloon over the head of the flashlight and turn on the light. *Ask:* **How do you know that light isn't matter?** It doesn't change the shape of the balloon. Therefore, it doesn't take up space.

Assess: *Ask:* **If you push an "empty" glass upside down into a pan of water, what will happen?** The water won't go into the glass because it's already "full" of air, which takes up space because it is matter.

Color, size, shape, and texture are physical properties matter can have. Some matter, such as rubber, can bounce and stretch. Other matter, such as salt, mix with water. Some metals bend easily. Others, such as steel, do not. These are just a few examples of the many physical properties of matter. Think of the different physical properties of matter that you can find in your classroom.

MAIN IDEA AND DETAILS For each of your five senses, name a physical property you can observe.

Sound is a physical property of some matter. What sense lets us observe it? ▼

Color is a property you observe with your eyes. What are other physical properties of this glass? ▼

377

9 ▶ Interpret Visuals

What are other physical properties of this glass? Students may mention that the glass feels smooth, hard, and cool.

Which sense lets people observe banging cymbals? sound

10 ▶ Critical Thinking

Explain to students that some physical properties of matter, such as length, mass, temperature, and volume, can't be precisely observed by sight. Tools can extend the senses and make observations more precise.

What are some tools you can use to more precisely observe length, mass, temperature, and volume? Possible answers: ruler for length; thermometer for temperature; measuring cup or spoon for volume; balance for mass

11 ▶ Main Idea and Details

Answer: Students should include all five senses, such as color, the sound an object makes, how the object feels, and whether it has a smell or taste or is odorless and tasteless. Remind students to consider all the senses in their answers.

PROFESSIONAL DEVELOPMENT   **Science Background**   **To Address Misconceptions**

What is a physical property?

Assess Prior Knowledge *Ask:* What are some physical properties of objects in this room?

Students May Think that the uses of objects are physical properties, such as paper is to write on, or a carrot is something to eat.

Scientists Explain that the most useful physical properties are things you can observe about the substance from which an object is made.

What You Can Do Write a list of properties on the board, mixed with uses for the same object. For example, to describe a plastic glass, you might write *clear, drink out of, breakable, melts in heat*. Help students differentiate between the properties of the glass and the uses of the glass.

12 Develop Science Vocabulary

mass Tell students that when scientists talk about mass, they are talking about a property of an object that does not change. Use a balance to find the mass of two books, one of which has about half the mass of the other. Let students handle the two objects. Tell them that the object with the greater mass has more matter in it.

If you took these books to the moon, would their mass change? Explain.
No; the amount of matter doesn't change.

Point out that weight is not the same as mass. Weight measures how hard gravity pulls on an object. For example, the moon has only about 1/6 the gravity of Earth. The weight of the books on the moon would be less, but their mass would be the same as on Earth.

Science Up Close

ONLINE EXPERIENCE
For animations and activities, visit
www.hspscience.com

13 Inquiry Skills

Use Numbers You have a 2-kg bag of flour. You measure out 1 cup of flour and find that it has a mass of 200 g. How could you estimate how many more cups of flour are left in the bag?
Possible answer: 1 kg = 1000 g, so 2 kg = 2000 g. Add 200 g 10 times to get 2000 g, so there are 9 more cups of flour in the bag.

14 Develop Science Vocabulary

volume The scientific meaning of the word *volume* is the amount of space an object takes up. Liquid volume is measured in liters and milliliters. The volume of a regular solid, such as a cube, can be found by measuring the length, width, and height of the cube and multiplying them together. The answer is given in units cubed.

density Tell students that the density of a substance depends on how closely packed the matter is. Help students understand that you can't say one substance is denser than another unless you compare the same volume of each substance. Also point out that you don't find the density of objects, but of the substances out of which the objects are made. This is an important distinction.

Measuring Matter

12 ▶ Another property of matter is mass. **Mass** is the amount of matter in something. You can measure mass by using a balance. Mass is often measured in grams (g) or kilograms (kg). One kilogram equals 1,000 grams.

Suppose you have some apple slices. You know their mass. You also have some orange slices. You know their mass, too. You mix them together to make a fruit salad. How can you find the mass of the salad
13 ▶ without using a balance? If you said, "Add the two known masses," you were right! The mass of two or more things together is the sum of their masses.

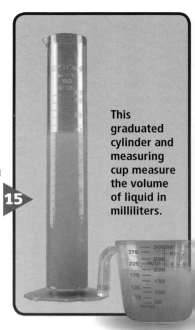

15 ▶ This graduated cylinder and measuring cup measure the volume of liquid in milliliters.

Science Up Close

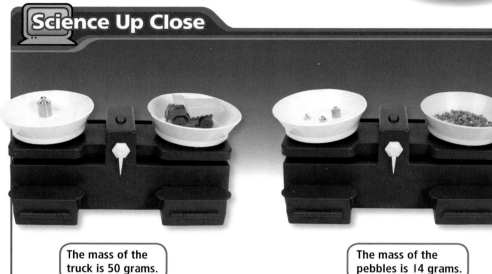

The mass of the truck is 50 grams.

The mass of the pebbles is 14 grams.

378

9÷3 Math Link

Number Sense

Have students answer these questions to make sure they understand that breaking matter apart or putting it together does not change the total mass.

- What happens to the mass of a loaf of bread if you slice it into 20 pieces? Nothing. The mass stays the same.
- Suppose you know the mass of one slice of bread and the number of slices in a loaf of bread. How could you figure out the mass of the loaf of bread? by adding the masses of all the slices

Another physical property of matter is volume. **Volume** is the amount of space matter takes up. In the Investigate, you measured 100 mL of water. The volume of the water was 100 mL.

Density is another property of matter. **Density** is the mass of matter compared to its volume. Think about two identical boxes. You fill one box with feathers. You fill the other box with rocks. The boxes have the same volume, but the box of rocks has much more mass. Rocks have greater density than feathers.

 MAIN IDEA AND DETAILS What is density?

Compare Densities
Fill one sandwich bag with marbles. Fill another with cotton balls. Seal the bags. Measure the mass of each bag. How do their volumes compare? How do their densities compare? Which matter is denser—cotton or marbles?

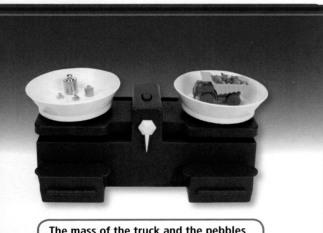

The mass of the truck and the pebbles is 64 grams. That is the sum of the two masses added together.

379

15 ▶ **Interpreting Visuals**

Which cylinder can hold a larger volume? How do you know? Students should realize that though the containers are shaped differently, they will hold similar volumes.

16 ▶ **Main Idea and Details** (Focus Skill)

Answer: the mass of certain volume of a substance

 5 minutes

Compare Densities

Materials: two resealable plastic bags, marbles, cotton balls

Be sure students fill each of the bags and then seal them. The volume of the two bags is the same. The bag of marbles has more mass. Therefore, marbles must be denser than cotton balls. You may want to discuss the idea that the matter in glass is more closely packed than the matter in cotton.

17 Key Science Concepts

Students of this age usually believe that objects with more mass sink and objects with less mass float. Help them understand that mass is not the determining factor but density—the relationship of mass to volume. Point out that an oceangoing ship has a mass of many thousands of tons, but it floats because of its huge volume.

18 Interpret Visuals

Students should identify the balls that are floating as less dense than water and the balls that sank as denser than water.

19 Main Idea and Details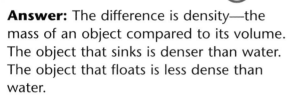

Answer: The difference is density—the mass of an object compared to its volume. The object that sinks is denser than water. The object that floats is less dense than water.

Sink and Float

How well an object floats is a physical property, too. Steel bars sink. Steel boats float. Why?

Density is the reason. Matter that is less dense than water floats. Matter that is denser than water sinks.

17 How could you make a steel bar float? You would have to change its shape to increase its volume. Changing a steel bar into a boat shape changes the volume of the steel. The same steel in a boat's shape takes up more space. Yet its mass doesn't change. The same mass that has a greater volume is less dense. If the volume of the steel boat is great enough, the boat floats.

19 **MAIN IDEA AND DETAILS** What is the difference between an object that sinks and one that floats?

Which balls in this picture are less dense than water? Which are denser? How do you know? ▼

380

1. MAIN IDEA AND DETAILS Draw and complete this graphic organizer.

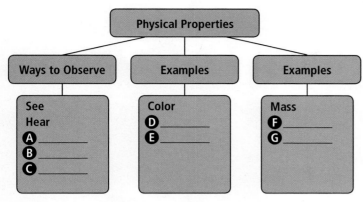

2. SUMMARIZE Use the completed graphic organizer to write a lesson summary.

3. DRAW CONCLUSIONS You have two equal masses of feathers and rocks. Which has more volume?

4. VOCABULARY How is volume different from mass?

Test Prep

5. A boat loaded with too much cargo sank. Why?

  A. It became less dense than water.

  B. Its volume became too great.

  C. Its density increased.

  D. All heavy things sink.

Links

Writing

Expository
Gather five classroom objects. Write a **description** of each object's physical properties. Then ask a classmate to identify the objects by using only the properties you described.

Music

Physical Properties Symphony
Use the sounds that different kinds of matter make to perform an original physical properties symphony. Perform your symphony for the class.

 For more links and activities, go to www.hspscience.com

381

Lesson Quick Study

The Lesson Quick Study in **Reading Support and Homework** provides the opportunity for students to practice inquiry skills, review lesson vocabulary, apply reading skills, and use critical thinking and problem solving. Students can use the second page of the Lesson Quick Study to complete the graphic organizer from the Reading Review. The graphic organizer is also available on overhead and electronic transparencies.

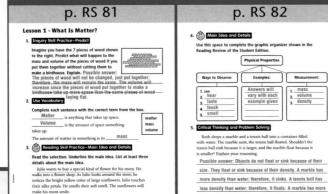

Reading Support and Homework

p. RS 81   p. RS 82

---

3 Assess and Extend

Graphic Organizer

Transparency GO 35
Electronic Transparency GO 3000

1. **A** taste; **B** touch; **C** smell; **D** texture; **E** odor; **F** volume; **G** density;

2. Possible answer: You can observe physical properties, such as sound, color, texture, odors, and sweetness by using your senses. Some physical properties, such as mass, volume, and density can be measured.

3. the feathers

4. Volume is the space matter takes up. Mass is the amount of matter in something.

5. C, Its density increased.

Links

Writing Suggest to students that they use tools, such as a balance, a ruler, and a hand lens, to help them describe such physical properties as mass, length, and texture in addition to the more obvious properties.

 Students can consult *Writing Models* in **Teaching Resources** as they complete the link. Rubrics are also provided.

Music Encourage students to consider typically nonmusical sounds, such as knocks on wood, footsteps, and claps, in their symphony in addition to the more musical sounds made by striking metals or drumheads.

Objectives

- Observe a change of state.
- Identify properties of solids, liquids, and gases.
- Describe evaporation and condensation.

Transparency DI 36

Electronic Transparency DI 300 I

Daily Inquiry

Filling Up with Cotton

 forceps, measuring cup

Other Materials: cotton, water

Review Skill Infer, Observe

What to Do

- How many dry cotton balls will fill the measuring cup? Using forceps, pick up one cotton ball at a time and place it in the measuring cup. Continue until the cup is full. How many dry cotton balls were needed to fill the cup?
- Repeat the activity, using wet cotton balls. First, predict how many wet cotton balls will fill the cup.
- Why did it take more wet cotton balls than dry cotton balls to fill the cup?

1 Introduce

Build on Prior Knowledge

Use the Fast Fact for a discussion starter about the lesson topic.

Is it possible for some of the water in this picture to change states?

What could cause this to happen?

When *Minutes* Count . . .

Conduct the Investigate as a **whole-class demonstration**.

Use the Activity Video/DVD to model the Investigate. After previewing, students can conduct the Investigate in small groups.

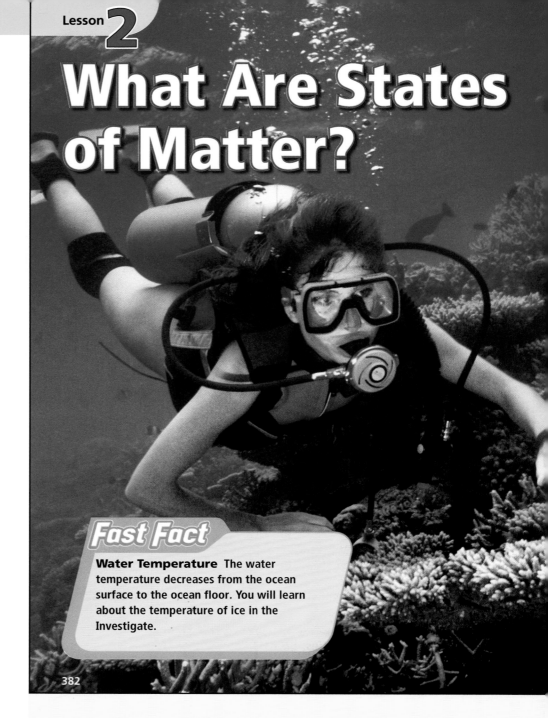

Lesson 2

What Are States of Matter?

Fast Fact

Water Temperature The water temperature decreases from the ocean surface to the ocean floor. You will learn about the temperature of ice in the Investigate.

382

PROFESSIONAL DEVELOPMENT   **Science Background**

Changes of States The distinction between *objects* and the pure substances (elements or compounds) out of which they are made is important when discussing changes of states. Elements, such as iron, and compounds, such as water or carbon dioxide, have a single melting point and boiling point. Mixtures, such as air, soil, or wood, do not. Many objects are mixtures, not pure substances. Most pure substances can exist in all three states but usually don't under the normal temperature ranges on Earth. Metals, with the exception of mercury, generally require temperatures in the hundreds or thousands of degrees to melt or vaporize. Gases, such as carbon dioxide, can exist briefly as solids ("dry ice").

Webliography
Keyword states of matter
www.hspscience.com

Temperature and Matter

Materials • metric measuring cup • hot water • plastic jar or beaker
• thermometer • 3 ice cubes • plastic spoon

Procedure

1. **Measure** 200 mL of hot water from the tap in the measuring cup. Pour the water into the jar or beaker.

2. **Measure** the temperature of the water with the thermometer. **Record** the data.

3. Add an ice cube to the water. Stir with the plastic spoon. **Record** what you **observe**.

4. **Measure** the temperature of the water again. **Record** the data.

5. Repeat Steps 3 and 4 twice.

Step 2

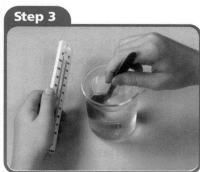

Step 3

Draw Conclusions

1. What happened to the ice cubes in the water?

2. What happened to the temperature of the water each time you added an ice cube?

3. **Inquiry Skill** One way scientists can **communicate data** is in a bar graph. Make a bar graph to **communicate** what happened to temperature in this activity.

Investigate Further

Put 100 mL of water in a freezer. **Measure** its temperature every 10 minutes. **Communicate** the data in a bar graph. **Interpret** the data.

383

Inquiry Skill Mini-Lesson

Communicate Tell students that information can be communicated in many ways, including tables, graphs, pictures, or words. Display the transparency. Have students study the graph and answer the questions.

Inquiry Skill practice is provided in **Reading Support and Homework**.

Transparency IS 36

Electronic Transparency IS 3001

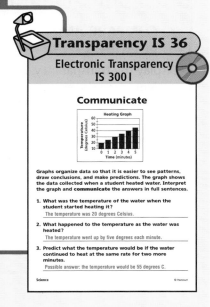

Communicate

Heating Graph

Graphs organize data so that it is easier to see patterns, draw conclusions, and make predictions. The graph shows the data collected when a student heated water. Interpret the graph and **communicate** the answers in full sentences.

1. What was the temperature of the water when the student started heating it?
   The temperature was 20 degrees Celsius.

2. What happened to the temperature as the water was heated?
   The temperature went up by five degrees each minute.

3. Predict what the temperature would be if the water continued to heat at the same rate for two more minutes.
   Possible answer: the temperature would be 55 degrees C.

Science   © Harcourt

---

2 Teach

Video Segment 3001

Time 20–30 minutes

Grouping pairs

Lab Manual pages can be used to record results. Inquiry Skill Tips and Self-Assessment are also provided.

Tips and Guided Inquiry

Have students stir each ice cube until it melts and then immediately take its temperature.

What would happen if you continued to add ice cubes? Students may suggest that the water would continue to get colder. The temperature would eventually become nearly as cold as the ice.

Expected Results

Students will find that each ice cube lowers the temperature more.

Draw Conclusions

1. They got smaller or melted. They changed from solid to liquid.

2. It went down (decreased).

3. Ice is colder than water. The temperature dropped.

4. Have students make a bar graph with Number of Ice Cubes *0-3* on the *x*-axis and *Temperature* on the *y*-axis. The bars will get shorter with the addition of each ice cube. Students may say that ice lowers the temperature of the water, but explain that heat moves from the water into the ice.

Investigate Further

Students can use this page in the *Lab Manual* for **Independent Inquiry**.

Lab Manual

p. LM 140

Date

Investigate Further
Put 100 mL of water in a freezer. Take it out every 10 minutes and measure its temperature. Communicate the data in a bar graph and interpret data.

Materials
Here are some materials that you might use. List additional materials that you need.

• metric measuring cup   • water   • thermometer
• plastic jar or beaker   • freezer   • timer or clock

1. What will this investigation test?
   The investigation will test how the temperature of water changes as it freezes.

2. Record your measurements in the data table below. Make a bar graph to communicate the results.

Time (min)	Temperature (°C)
0	
10	
20	
30	
40	
50	
60	

3. Interpret the data in the graph. What can you conclude about the temperatures of the water and the freezer?
   Students should explain that the freezer was colder than the water because the temperature of the water dropped inside the freezer. Students may explain that freezing takes heat away from the water.

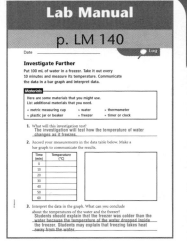

2 Teach
continued

VOCABULARY For Vocabulary Cards and activities, see **Reading Support and Homework**.

SCIENCE CONCEPTS Have students turn the concepts into questions. Ask volunteers to suggest answers to the questions. Write the questions and students' ideas on the board. Have students skim the chapter to see where the answers might be found.

 READING FOCUS SKILL

COMPARE AND CONTRAST Tell students that the information in this lesson is organized to help them compare and contrast science facts and ideas. Use the Reading Skill Mini-Lesson below to discuss a strategy that students can use to compare and contrast.

1 Key Science Concepts

How many states of matter are there? three

What are the states of matter? solid, liquid, and gas

2 Interpret Visuals

What are some solids and liquids in this picture? solids: the airplane, the land, the trees, the snow; liquids: water

What are some gases in this picture? Students will probably say that air is a gas.

3 Compare and Contrast

Answer: They are both matter and can both change states.

VOCABULARY	SCIENCE CONCEPTS	READING FOCUS SKILL
solid p. 385 liquid p. 386 gas p. 387 evaporation p. 388 condensation p. 388	▶ what the three states of matter are ▶ how temperature affects states of matter	**COMPARE AND CONTRAST** Find out how the states of matter are alike and different. alike — different

States of Matter

You have read that matter takes up space. Matter also has different forms called states.

In the Investigate, you watched an ice cube change states. If you had boiled the water, it would also have changed to another state.

The wax of a candle can also change states. To make a candle, wax is melted and poured into a mold. When the wax has cooled and 1 hardened, it has changed states. Three states of matter are solid, liquid, and gas.

3 **COMPARE AND CONTRAST** How are ice and the wax of a candle alike?

What are some solids and liquids in this picture? ▶

2

384

Reading Skill Mini-Lesson

 COMPARE AND CONTRAST

Display the transparency. As students read the sections on solids, liquids, and gases, have them complete the table and then answer the question.

Transparency RS 36

Electronic Transparency RS 3001

Compare and Contrast

Use what you have learned about solids, liquids, and gases to compare and contrast their shape and volume.

States of Matter		
State	**Shape**	**Volume**
Solid	Definite shape (shape stays the same)	Definite volume (volume stays the same)
Liquid	Shape changes with container	Volume stays the same
Gas	Shapes changes with container	Volume changes with container

Substance A takes the shape of whatever container it is in. Its volume also changes with whatever container it is in. What state of matter is Substance A?

It is a gas.

Science   © Harcourt

Name the solids you see in these pictures.

Solids

Think about what an ice cube is like. An ice cube is a solid. A **solid** is matter with a volume and a shape that stay the same.

Solids stay solids unless something, such as heat, changes them. When ice is heated, it melts and becomes a liquid. When you heat matter, the motion of its small particles, or pieces, speeds up.

The opposite happens, too. If you remove enough heat from water, it freezes. When matter cools, the motion of its small particles slows down.

 COMPARE AND CONTRAST How are all solids alike?

Insta-Lab

Is It Solid?

Take a frozen pat of butter and place it on a dish. Record your observations about the butter. Then place the dish and butter under a lamp. Turn the lamp on and record what happens to the butter every minute. Write description of how the butter changed.

385

Reaching All Learners

Enrichment

On-Level Reader

Target: Students who need reinforcement and enrichment of science concepts and vocabulary

Enrichment Strategy: The On-Level Reader reinforces and enriches lesson content and vocabulary by using different visuals and examples. The reader also reinforces the Reading Focus Skills in each lesson.

Assess: Use strategies in the back of the reader to assess student understanding.

Matter Is Everything!

Harcourt
SCHOOL PUBLISHERS

4 ▶ Develop Science Vocabulary

solid Tell students that they can decide whether matter is a solid, liquid, or gas by observing what happens when the matter is moved from one container to another. A solid keeps both its original shape and volume as it moves around. Some students may think that matter must be hard to be a solid. Point out that a marshmallow, although soft, keeps its shape and volume when moved to another container, and so it is a solid.

5 ▶ Key Science Concepts

What happens to the particles in a solid when you heat the solid? They speed up.

How can a liquid become a solid? by removing heat from it and slowing down the particles

6 ▶ Critical Thinking

Water changes from a solid to a liquid at 0°C and from a liquid to a gas at 100°C. The mean temperature on Venus is 464°C. **Would you expect to find any ice or water on Venus? Why or why not?** No; it would all change to a gas at 100°C.

7 ▶ Compare and Contrast

Answer: All solids keep their shape and volume unless something such as heat changes them.

Insta-Lab

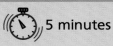 5 minutes

Is It Solid?

Materials: butter, bright light

Make sure to place butter on a heat-resistant plate or dish for easy clean-up. remind students to check the progress of the butter often and note its consistency change from solid to liquid.

8 ▶ Develop Science Vocabulary

liquid Begin with a measured amount of water in a measuring cup. Have a volunteer read the volume. Pour the water into a different container, making every effort to get all the drops transferred. Ask students what they think the volume is in the new container. To find out or to verify, pour the water back into the original measuring cup, and invite a volunteer to read the volume once more.

9 ▶ Key Science Concepts

Demonstrate the concepts of the second paragraph by pouring a measured volume of water from a tall, slim container into a shallow, wide one. Discuss that the volume of the water did not change at all, just the shape of the container.

10 ▶ Interpret Visuals

Which property of liquid allows it to be pushed through the pump of the soap dispenser? It can change its shape.

11 ▶ Compare and Contrast

A liquid takes the shape of its container. Solids don't change shape.

Liquids

Think about a glass of water. The water in the glass is a liquid. A **liquid** is matter that has a

8 ▶ volume that stays the same but a shape that can change.

9 ▶ Like a solid, a liquid has a volume that doesn't change. However, a liquid's shape can change.

10 ▶ A liquid takes the shape of whatever container holds it. The volume of water can look large in a tall, slim container. In a short, wide container, it can look small.

You know that water is a liquid. Paint, juice, and shampoo are liquids, too. What are some liquids you see or use every day?

11 ▶ COMPARE AND CONTRAST How are liquids and solids different?

▲ This soap is a liquid.

Vinegar and oil are liquids that make salads tasty.

Water changes shape as it falls.

386

Fizzy drinks have carbon dioxide gas in them. The bubbles you see are bubbles of gas.

Gases

The helium inside this balloon is a gas. A **gas** has no definite shape or volume. A gas takes up all the space in a container. If you blow up a balloon, you can see that the air spreads out to fill the space inside the balloon.

The air that you breathe is a mixture of gases. Some stoves cook with natural gas. You can't see natural gas, but when it burns, you can see a blue flame.

A gas called helium fills this balloon.

 **COMPARE AND CONTRAST** How are gases different from solids and liquids?

387

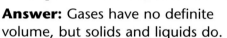
12 ▶ Develop Science Vocabulary

gas Students may confuse the term *gas*, meaning "a state of matter," with the shortened name for the gasoline used in cars. Point out that gasoline is a particular liquid that is burned in cars to produce energy. *Gas* is a term that refers to any matter that has no definite shape or volume.

13 ▶ Inquiry Skills

Draw Conclusions When you walk through water, you push hard with your legs to move forward. You don't have to push very hard to walk through air. What conclusion can you draw about the density of water as compared to the density of air? Water has a greater density than air.

14 ▶ Compare and Contrast (Focus Skill)

Answer: Gases have no definite volume, but solids and liquids do.

Reaching All Learners

 ESL / ESOL Support

Comprehensible Input

Write the words *solid, liquid,* and *gas* on the board.

Beginning Provide students with a variety of pictures from magazines, including solids, liquids, and gases. Point to one of the words on the board, and have students point to an example in one of the pictures.

Intermediate Have students draw pictures of examples of a solid, a liquid, and a gas.

Advanced Have students create a graphic organizer to help them distinguish among solids, liquids, and gases.

For strategies and lesson support, see *ESL Support* pp. 152-155.

15 ▸ Develop Science Vocabulary

evaporation Point out that evaporation takes place when heat is added to a liquid. The energy makes the particles move faster, and individual particles have enough energy to escape from the container. When all the particles have sufficient energy, the liquid boils. At room temperature, the particles of water have enough energy to escape. This accounts for the slow evaporation of water left standing at room temperature.

condensation Tell students that condensation is the reverse of evaporation. When heat is removed from a gas, the particles slow down. When they are moving slowly enough, they attract one another and form a liquid.

16 ▸ Critical Thinking

When you leave a glass of ice water standing on the counter, water forms on the outside of the glass. Where does this water come from? The water is condensation from the air. Some students have the misconception that the water somehow leaks through the glass. Point out that there is always water vapor in the air. The cold glass cools the water vapor in the air around the glass, causing it to condense on the glass.

17 ▸ Interpret Data

Freezing point is 0°C. Boiling point is 100°C. At any temperature greater than 0°C and less than 100°C, water is a liquid.

18 ▸ Compare and Contrast

Answer: Both involve a change of states, but in evaporation, a liquid becomes a gas, while in condensation, a gas becomes a liquid.

Changes of State

In the Investigate, heat changed solid ice to liquid water. Heat can also change a liquid to a gas. If you leave a cup of water in a warm place, after a day or **16** ▸ two, the cup will be empty. The liquid changes into a gas, but it's still water. Water moves into the air in **15** ▸ the process of **evaporation**. Boiling also makes water evaporate, but it happens more quickly.

When a gas cools, it changes back to a liquid. The change of a gas to a liquid is **condensation**. You have seen this happen. When the water in air, a gas, changes to a liquid, it rains.

18 ▸ **COMPARE AND CONTRAST** How are evaporation and condensation the same? How are they different?

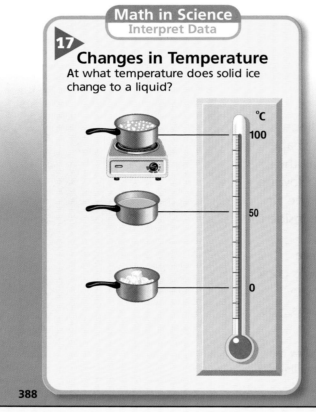

Math in Science
Interpret Data

17

Changes in Temperature
At what temperature does solid ice change to a liquid?

°C
100
50
0

388

Reaching All Learners — Below / On-Level / Advanced / ELL — **Intervention** **Reteach**

Evaporation and Condensation

Target: Students who confuse evaporation and condensation

Intervention Strategy: Hands-On Demonstration

■ Half-fill two identical glasses with room-temperature water. Mark the level of water with tape or a marker. Place a piece of plastic wrap tightly over one glass and leave the other uncovered. Place the two glasses side by side in the sun or in a warm place in the room.

■ Later in the day, have students observe the water level in the two glasses. They should also observe water droplets on the underside of the plastic wrap. Use what they observe to review evaporation and condensation.

Assess: *Ask:* If you leave a glass of water on the counter, what would you expect to see the next day? less water in the glass

1. COMPARE AND CONTRAST Copy and complete this graphic organizer.

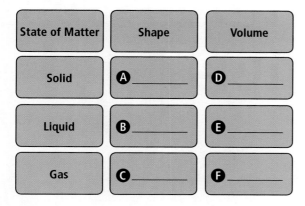

State of Matter	Shape	Volume
Solid	Ⓐ _____	Ⓓ _____
Liquid	Ⓑ _____	Ⓔ _____
Gas	Ⓒ _____	Ⓕ _____

2. SUMMARIZE Use the completed graphic organizer to write a lesson summary.

3. DRAW CONCLUSIONS If matter has a definite volume but no definite shape, in what state is it?

4. VOCABULARY Write a sentence to explain how evaporation relates to a change of state.

Test Prep

5. Critical Thinking A solid object melts to become a liquid. Was heat added or removed to cause the change? Explain.

Links

Writing

Narrative
Write a **story** about an ice cube as temperature changes cause it to change into the different states of matter.

Math 9÷3

Solve a Problem
Maria took a frozen pop out of the freezer at 3:23 and placed it in a dish. At 3:35, the pop was a puddle of liquid. How long did it take the frozen pop to melt?

For more links and activities, go to
www.hspscience.com

389

Lesson Quick Study

The Lesson Quick Study in **Reading Support and Homework** provides the opportunity for students to practice inquiry skills, review lesson vocabulary, apply reading skills, and use critical thinking and problem solving. Students can use the second page of the Lesson Quick Study to complete the graphic organizer from the graphic Reading Review. The graphic organizer is also available on overhead and electronic transparencies.

Reading Support and Homework

p. RS 83

Lesson 2 - What Are States of Matter?

1. Inquiry Skill Practice–Communicate

Observe the picture to the right. Draw a picture in the empty box to communicate how the state of the ice will change after one hour. Write a sentence that explains the process.
Possible answer: The sun's heat melts the ice. The solid ice cubes become liquid water after an hour of exposure to the sun. The motion of the particles in the liquid water speeds up.

Use Vocabulary

Match the clue on the left to the term on the right. Write the letter on the blank.

B. The process in which water moves into the air   A. gas
A. Matter that has no definite shape or volume   B. evaporation
C. The change of a gas to a liquid   C. condensation

3. Reading Skill Practice–Compare and Contrast

Read the selection. Compare and contrast the solids and liquids.

Suppose you have an ice cube and a glass of water. You taste the water, and then you taste the ice. Their tastes are the same. They are both made of the same thing, water. An ice cube is solid. Its shape and volume stays the same as long as it does not melt. Water is liquid. Its volume stays the same, but its shape can change if poured into containers of different shapes and sizes.

Possible answers: Alike: Ice and water taste the same. They are made of the same thing. Different: Ice is solid. Water is liquid. The volume and shape of ice stays the same. Volume of water stays the same, but its shape can change.

p. RS 84

4. Compare and Contrast

Use this space to complete the graphic organizer shown in the Reading Review of the Student Edition.

State of Matter	Shape	Volume
Solid	has a definite shape (shape stays the same)	has a definite volume (volume stays the same)
Liquid	takes shape of container that it's in	has a definite volume (volume stays the same)
Gas	spreads out to fill the shape of container that it's in	its volume fills the container it's in

5. Critical Thinking and Problem Solving

Suppose you are playing in your backyard. All of a sudden, it starts to rain. What happened to cause a dry day to turn into a wet one? Explain your reasoning.

Possible answer: There was water in the air in the form of gas. The gas cooled and it turned into liquid, rain. This is called condensation.

---

3 Assess and Extend

Graphic Organizer

Transparency GO 36

Electronic Transparency GO 3001

1. Ⓐ has a definite shape; Ⓓ has a definite volume; Ⓑ takes the shape of a container that it's in; Ⓔ has a definite volume; Ⓒ takes the shape of container that it's in; Ⓕ expands to fill the container it's in;

2. Possible answer: Matter has three states—solid, liquid, and gas. A solid has a shape and volume that stay the same. A liquid has a definite volume, but its shape is the same as the container that holds it. A gas has no definite shape or volume.

3. liquid

4. Evaporation is a change in states from liquid to gas.

5. Since particles in a liquid have greater motion than the particles in a solid, heat was added to cause the change.

Links

Writing Stories should accurately describe what happens to the particles of ice as the ice cube changes states.

 Students can consult *Writing Models* in **Teaching Resources** as they complete the link. Rubrics are also provided.

Math 12 minutes

Objectives

■ Make a mixture and a solution.

■ Describe several types of physical changes.

■ Explain how a chemical change differs from a physical change.

Transparency DI 37

Electronic Transparency DI 3002

Daily Inquiry

Measure Again

 ruler

Other Materials: classroom objects from inside your desk

Review Skill Measure, Predict

What to Do

■ Choose five objects from inside your desk. Measure the length of each object in centimeters. Record the measurements.

■ Show the five objects to a partner. Have the partner guess which measurement matches each object. Have your partner measure again to check his or her answers.

■ Were your measurements the same as your partner's?

1 Introduce

Build on Prior Knowledge

Use the Fast Fact for a discussion starter about the lesson topic.

Why do you think the water makes the sand stick together? What happens when the sand dries out?

When *Minutes* Count . . .

If time is short, consider these options.

Conduct the Investigate as a **whole-class investigate**.

Use the Activity Video/DVD to model. After previewing, conduct the Investigate.

Lesson **3**

How Does Matter Change?

How Big Can It Get? One of the world's largest sand castles stood more than 20 meters (66 ft) high. Its builders spent three weeks making it, packing the sand into place with water. In the Investigate, you will work with sand and water.

390

Science Background

Physical and Chemical Changes Although scientists find distinguishing between physical and chemical changes easy, the differences are not always obvious to students. The idea of "a new substance" being formed can be confusing. Students may not see why the bubbles produced when water boils are different from the bubbles produced when vinegar and baking soda combine. Boiling an egg may appear to be less of a change than dissolving sugar in water. Reversibility is not an absolute test for a physical change. For example, it would be more difficult to separate the ingredients for a cake once they were mixed than it would be to separate water into hydrogen and oxygen.

Webliography
Keyword changes in matter
www.hspscience.com

Will It Mix?

Materials • water • metric measuring cup • 2 clear plastic jars • measuring spoon ($\frac{1}{4}$ teaspoon) • sand • plastic spoon • hand lens • salt

Procedure

1. **Measure** 200 mL of water. Pour the water into one of the jars.

2. Add $\frac{1}{4}$ teaspoon of sand to the water, and stir. Use a hand lens to **observe** the jar's contents. **Record** what you **observe**.

3. Repeat Step 1, using the other jar.

4. Add $\frac{1}{4}$ teaspoon of salt to the water, and stir. Use a hand lens to observe the jar's contents. **Record** what you **observe**.

5. Repeat Step 4 until you see salt collect on the bottom of the jar after you stir. **Record** the number of teaspoons of salt you used in all.

Step 2

Step 4

Draw Conclusions

1. What did you **observe** when you stirred in the sand? The salt?

2. **Inquiry Skill** Scientists sometimes use drawings to **communicate**. Make two drawings that will **communicate** what happened to the sand and the salt in when they were stirred into the water.

Investigate Further

What do you **predict** will happen if you leave the jar of salt water in a warm place? Try it. Was your **prediction** correct?

391

Inquiry Skill Mini-Lesson

Communicate Tell students that the drawings they made for this Investigate are only one way to communicate information. Graphs, tables, and words are other ways. Display the transparency. Help students interpret both the table and graph by working through several examples. Then have students answer the questions.

Inquiry Skill practice is provided in *Reading Support and Homework.*

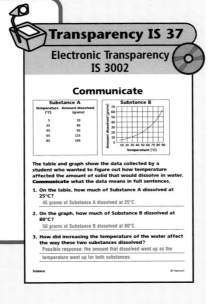

Transparency IS 37

Electronic Transparency IS 3002

Communicate

Substance A	
Temperature (°C)	Amount dissolved (grams)
5	10
25	45
45	95
65	125
85	195

Substance B

The table and graph show the data collected by a student who wanted to figure out how temperature affected the amount of solid that would dissolve in water. **Communicate** what the data means in full sentences.

1. On the table, how much of Substance A dissolved at 25°C?
   45 grams of Substance A dissolved at 25°C.

2. On the graph, how much of Substance B dissolved at 80°C?
   50 grams of Substance B dissolved at 80°C.

3. How did increasing the temperature of the water affect the way these two substances dissolved?
   Possible response: the amount that dissolved went up as the temperature went up for both substances.

Science

© Harcourt

---

2 Teach

Video Segment 3002

Time 20–30 minutes

Grouping pairs

Lab Manual pages can be used to record results. Inquiry Skill Tips and Self-Assessment are also provided.

Tips and Guided Inquiry

Depending on the water temperature, students should be able to dissolve about 3 to 4 teaspoons of salt in the water. **If you had used sugar instead of salt, how might the results have changed?** Students may realize that sugar dissolves easily in water and that more of it would have dissolved than the salt. **Where do you think the salt went when you could not see it?** Use answers to this question to check for misconceptions that can be addressed later in the lesson.

Expected Results

Students will observe that the sand did not dissolve and that some salt dissolves.

Draw Conclusions

1. The sand and water didn't mix at all. They stayed separate.

2. The salt seemed to disappear in the water when I stirred it. After about 3 teaspoons, the salt didn't mix with the water and settled to the jar bottom.

3. Students' drawings should show sand not dissolved in water and salt dissolved in water.

Investigate Further

Students can use this page in the *Lab Manual* for **Independent Inquiry.**

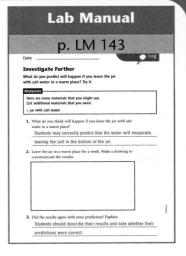

Lab Manual

p. LM 143

Date _____

Investigate Further
What do you predict will happen if you leave the jar with salt water in a warm place? Try it.

Materials
Here are some materials that you might use. List additional materials that you need.
• jar with salt water

1. What do you think will happen if you leave the jar with salt water in a warm place?
   Students may correctly predict that the water will evaporate, leaving the salt in the bottom of the jar.

2. Leave the jar in a warm place for a week. Make a drawing to communicate the results.

3. Did the results agree with your prediction? Explain.
   Students should describe their results and note whether their predictions were correct.

LESSON 3 ▪ 391

2 Teach
continued

VOCABULARY For Vocabulary Cards and activities, see *Reading Support and Homework.*

SCIENCE CONCEPTS Have students work in pairs to turn the concepts into questions and suggest ways to answer those questions. Students can write the questions and answers in their notebooks and revisit them as they complete the lesson.

 READING FOCUS SKILL

MAIN IDEA AND DETAILS Tell students that the information in this lesson is organized to help them recognize a main idea and the details that support it.

▶1 Inquiry Skills

Draw Conclusions Is breaking glass a physical change? Why or why not? Yes, because the matter—glass—doesn't change. It just breaks into smaller pieces.

▶2 Critical Thinking

Is a change of states, such as ice melting, a physical change? Explain your answer. Yes, it is a physical change. Even though the ice doesn't look like the water, it is the same kind of matter. If students say that it isn't a physical change, help them understand that it isn't the appearance, but whether the kind of matter changed that is the test of a physical change.

VOCABULARY	SCIENCE CONCEPTS	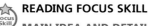 **READING FOCUS SKILL**
mixture p. 394 solution p. 395	▶ what physical and chemical changes are ▶ what mixtures and solutions are	**MAIN IDEA AND DETAILS** Find out how physical and chemical changes happen.

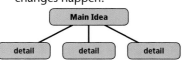

Physical Changes

What can change and still be the same? The answer is matter. Changes in matter that don't form new kinds of matter are **1**▶physical changes.

An example of a physical change is cutting. Cutting makes a piece of paper smaller, but the paper is still paper. Its size changes, but the paper pieces are **2**▶still the same kind of matter.

Sheep grow a thick coat of wool.

Yarn is packaged to be sold.

▲ A machine spins sheep's wool into yarn.

392

Reading Skill Mini-Lesson

USE TYPOGRAPHIC CLUES

Tell students that words in boldface or italic type are clues to important information in what they are reading. Display the transparency. Point out that the section title is the same as the italicized term on this page. Have students complete the table by filling in the meaning of *physical change* and several examples they find as they read the section.

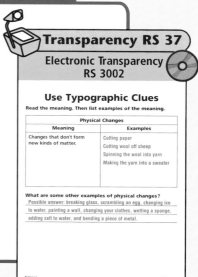

Transparency RS 37

Electronic Transparency RS 3002

Use Typographic Clues
Read the meaning. Then list examples of the meaning.

Physical Changes	
Meaning	**Examples**
Changes that don't form new kinds of matter.	Cutting paper Cutting wool off sheep Spinning the wool into yarn Making the yarn into a sweater

What are some other examples of physical changes?
Possible answer: breaking glass, scrambling an egg, changing ice to water, painting a wall, changing your clothes, wetting a sponge, adding salt to water, and bending a piece of metal.

Science

Knitting a wool cap is another example of a physical change. The thick wool is cut from sheep in spring. This doesn't hurt them, and they grow a new coat before winter. The wool is combed into soft strands, which are pulled into threads and twisted to make yarn. A knitter then knits the wool yarn into a cap. In the cap, the wool looks different from the way it looked on the sheep, but it is still wool. It is the same kind of matter.

 MAIN IDEA AND DETAILS What happens to matter when there is a physical change?

▲ Yarn can be knitted by hand or by machine.

The wool in the cap has been changed physically, but it is still wool.

393

What is the sequence of steps in making a wool sweater from wool? The wool is cut off the sheep. The cut wool is combed into soft strands. The wool strands are then pulled into threads of yarn. A knitter knits the wool into a sweater.

▶ **4 Key Science Concepts**

What changes in the wool during the physical change? The appearance of the wool changes.

Why is changing the wool from the sheep into a hat a physical change? Because the matter itself doesn't change.

Main Idea and Details

▶ **5 Answer:** Nothing; the matter is still the same kind of matter.

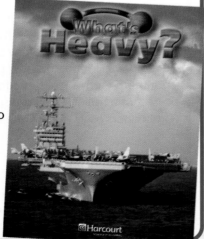

6 Develop Science Vocabulary

mixture Help students understand a mixture through the following activity. Have a group of five or six students form a tight group. Explain that the group represents a mixture. Each person represents a substance, such as sand or water. Each substance still has all its properties. Call out a certain property, such as the color of a shirt one student is wearing, or the color of a student's hair, if it is unique. Students who possess that property should return to their seats. This model represents how mixtures can be separated because the properties of the substances are still present.

7 Interpret Visuals

How would you separate the cereal mixture shown on this page? You could pick the berries out of the cereal and separate them by color. The cereal flakes would be left behind.

Why is the necklace the girl is making a mixture? It is made of different-colored beads.

8 Main Idea and Details (Focus Skill)

Answer: A mixture is a substance made of two or more kinds of matter.

Mixtures

6 ► In the Investigate, you made two mixtures—one of sand and water, and one of salt and water. A **mixture** is a substance that is made up of two or more kinds of matter. Making a mixture is a physical change. You put different types of matter together, but no new types of matter are formed.

Separating the parts of a mixture is a physical change, too. You can separate sand and water by pouring the mixture through filter paper. The water runs through, leaving the sand behind. You can separate salt and water by leaving the mixture in a warm place. The water evaporates, leaving the salt.

▲ This girl has a mixture of beads.

8 ► (Focus Skill) **MAIN IDEA AND DETAILS** What is a mixture?

7 ►

This bowl holds a mixture of cereal, strawberries, and bananas.

394

Social Studies Link

California Gold Rush

Have students use reference materials to research the California gold rush during the middle of the nineteenth century. Students should pay particular attention to how the gold was found and how people separated the gold from the ore in which it was found. Students can prepare posters or a bulletin board display showing the steps the Forty-Niners used to separate the pure gold from the rock.

A solution of drink mix and water is a tasty treat.

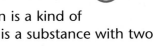

▲ A solution of detergent and water gets dishes clean.

Solutions

In the Investigate, when you first stirred salt into water, you could not see the salt. The salt dissolved, or mixed with the water. You made a solution. A **solution** is a mixture in which different kinds of matter mix evenly. Your mixture of salt and water was a solution. Since the sand didn't dissolve in the water, that mixture wasn't a solution.

 MAIN IDEA AND DETAILS Why is a solution a kind of mixture?

395

solution Make sure students understand that a solution is a mixture. Point out that it is a special kind of mixture in which the different substances mix so evenly that the solution looks like one substance. You can't separate a solution by hand, but solutions can be separated by using the properties of the different substances.

10 ▶ Key Science Concepts

Why is salt water a solution? Because the salt and water are mixed so evenly that you can't see the salt any more.

11 ▶ Critical Thinking

Suppose you have a container of clear liquid that looks like water. What experiment could you do to show whether it is just water or a solution? Students may suggest that you could let the water evaporate. If it is a solution, whatever is dissolved will be left in the container. If it is pure water, everything will evaporate.

12 ▶ Main Idea and Details (Focus Skill)

Answer: A solution is a kind of mixture because it is a substance with two or more different types of matter.

Reaching All Learners

Challenge

Below · On-Level · Advanced · ESL

Language and Vocabulary

The word *solution* has several meanings. Help students identify the scientific meaning by comparing the common meanings.

Beginning Write the word *solution* on the board. Pantomime thinking about a problem and coming up with an answer. Write 2 + 2 = 4 on the board, and point to the 4 as the solution. Then make a solution by mixing sugar with water.

Intermediate Have pairs of students make a drawing or diagram showing the differences between the meanings.

Advanced Have students write a sentence using the word *solution* in the correct scientific meaning.

For strategies and lesson support, see *ESL Support* pp. 156–159.

Key Science Concepts

What is a chemical change? a change in which new kinds of matter are formed

What is one test for a chemical change? You can't get the original matter back very easily. (Point out that this is not an absolute test because some chemical changes can be reversed fairly easily.)

Interpret Visuals

How can you tell that the rusting object is going through a chemical change? The rust is not the same kind of matter as the metal, and you can't get the metal back.

How do you know that the rotting wood is not a physical change? The rotted wood is not the same kind of matter as the original wood and it can't be made to look like the original wood.

Critical Thinking

Painting metal or keeping it in a garage protects it from rusting. What does this suggest about why metal rusts? Students may suggest that something in the outside air causes a chemical change in the metal.

Main Idea and Details

Answer: cooking, burning, rotting, rusting

Chemical Changes

Changes that form different kinds of matter are chemical changes. Cooking causes chemical changes. Suppose you stir flour, sugar, eggs, milk, and butter together to make a cake. After you bake the cake, it has properties that are completely different from the properties of the ingredients.

Burning is also a chemical change. When wood burns, it combines with oxygen in the air. Ashes and smoke form. Those are different kinds of matter than the wood. You can't get the wood back.

MAIN IDEA AND DETAILS Name at least four examples of chemical changes.

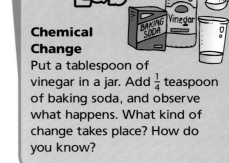

Chemical Change
Put a tablespoon of vinegar in a jar. Add $\frac{1}{4}$ teaspoon of baking soda, and observe what happens. What kind of change takes place? How do you know?

Rotting is a chemical change.

Rusting is a chemical change. It happens when oxygen in the air combines with iron in metal.

396

 5 minutes

Chemical Change

Materials: vinegar, jar, teaspoon, baking soda
Students should see a lot of bubbles forming quickly. A gas (a different form of matter) is being made and released. Help students see the difference between this change and boiling water. The gas wasn't present in either the vinegar or baking soda, so a different kind of matter was formed.

PROFESSIONAL DEVELOPMENT **Science Background**

Surprising Chemical Changes Some chemical changes don't appear to make much change in the appearance of the matter, so students may think they are still physical changes.
- When a tree, a plant, or a person grows, changes aren't visible right away. But new matter is formed as nutrients combine to form the matter out of which the living organism is made. This is a chemical change.
- Cooking a piece of meat or frying an egg may not result in much change in appearance, but the heat causes matter within the food to recombine into new matter or to break down into simpler kinds of matter.

1. MAIN IDEA AND DETAILS Copy and complete this graphic organizer.

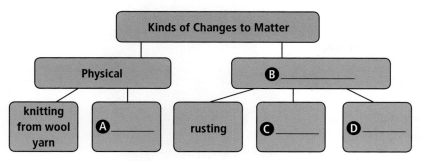

Kinds of Changes to Matter

Physical — **B** _____

knitting from wool yarn — **A** _____ — rusting — **C** _____ — **D** _____

2. SUMMARIZE Use the completed graphic organizer to write a lesson summary.

3. DRAW CONCLUSIONS Mr. Gonzalez put up a wall made of bricks and mortar. Was the change physical or chemical? Explain.

4. VOCABULARY Explain why all solutions are mixtures but not all mixtures are solutions.

Test Prep

5. Which of these is a chemical change?
 A. burning gasoline in a car
 B. putting on fingernail polish
 C. making a chain from strips of paper
 D. grinding wheat to make flour

Links

Writing

Expository
Write a **paragraph** or two in which you compare and contrast mixtures and solutions. Make illustrations to help with the explanation.

Math

Solve a Problem
A mixture contains two times as many red beads as white beads. There are six white beads. How many red beads are in the mixture? On paper, show how you solved the problem.

For more links and activities, go to **www.hspscience.com**

397

Lesson Quick Study

The Lesson Quick Study in **Reading Support and Homework** provides the opportunity for students to practice inquiry skills, review lesson vocabulary, apply reading skills, and use critical thinking and problem solving. Students can use the second page of the Lesson Quick Study to complete the graphic organizer from the Reading Review. The graphic organizer is also available on overhead and electronic transparencies.

Reading Support and Homework

p. RS 85

Lesson 3 - How Does Matter Change?

1. Inquiry Skill Practice–Communicate

An artist takes a large marble block and starts to carve it. After a few hours, the artist has a horse carved out of the marble. **Write a sentence to communicate what kind of change the marble went through.** Possible answer: The marble went through a physical change. The marble continues to be marble even if now it is in the form of a horse.

2. Use Vocabulary

Write a complete sentence that uses the terms *mixture* **and** *solution* **correctly.**
 Check students' sentences.

3. Reading Skill Practice–Main Idea and Details

Read the selection. Underline the main idea. List at least two details about the main idea.

 Matter can go through both physical and chemical changes. Suppose you want to build a play house with wood. After some time of hard work, the pile of wood you started out with is a play house. The change you observed, from wood planks to a play house, is a physical change. A terrible disaster happens. Lightning hits your play house, and a flame of fire destroys it. Your play house is now ashes. This change in the wood is a chemical change.
 Possible answers: Wood goes through a physical change when the wood planks take a new shape as a play house. Wood goes through a chemical change when the wood is burnt and becomes ashes.

p. RS 86

4. Main Idea and Details

Use this space to complete the graphic organizer shown in the Reading Review of the Student Edition.

Kinds of Changes to Matter

Physical Changes — **Chemical Changes**

knitting from wool yarn — Possible answers: cutting paper, making a mixture, making a solution, separating a mixture, folding, bending — rusting — Possible answers: cooking, rotting, burning — Possible answers: cooking, rotting, burning

5. Critical Thinking and Problem Solving

 Mrs. Lupe has lettuce, tomatoes, onion, salt, and vinegar. What solution and mixture can she make using her ingredients?
 Possible answer: Mrs. Lupe can make a mixture, or a salad with lettuce, tomatoes, and onion. She can make a solution with the salt and vinegar. She can then make another mixture by pouring the vinegar and salt solution over the salad.

---

3 Assess and Extend

Graphic Organizer

Transparency GO 37
Electronic Transparency
IS 3002

1. A Possible answers: cutting paper, making a mixture, making a solution, separating a mixture, folding, bending **B** Chemical Changes **C** and **D Possible answers**: cooking, rotting, burning

2. Possible answer: A physical change is one in which matter looks different, but no new kind of matter forms. Examples include cutting paper and knitting a sweater from wool yarn. A chemical change is one in which new matter forms. Examples include cooking, rotting, burning, and rusting.

3. A physical change; the bricks and mortar are still the same kinds of matter.

4. A solution is a kind of mixture. In solutions, the parts mix evenly. That isn't true of all mixtures. All mixtures can be separated by physical means, such as sand and water.

5. A, burning gasoline in a car

Links

Writing Stories and illustrations should correctly distinguish between mixtures and solutions.

 Students can consult *Writing Models* in **Teaching Resources** as they complete the link. Rubrics are also provided.

Math Students may show the solution as the addition sentence $6 + 6 = 12$ or as the multiplication sentence $2 \times 6 = 12$.

LESSON 3 ■ 397

Technology

- Describe how scientists develop synthetic materials.
- Compare and contrast natural and synthetic materials.

1 Introduce

Preview/Set a Purpose

Have students preview the article by skimming the text. Ask students what they think the purpose of the article is.

2 Teach

Chapter Concepts

An understanding of physical and chemical properties of materials will naturally lead to questions about how the properties of synthetic materials compare with the properties of natural materials.

What does the waterproof synthetic material share with the water lilies' leaves? When both materials get wet, water rolls off the surface instead of soaking in.

Does the waterproof synthetic material have the same chemical properties as the water lilies' leaves? Explain. Students may say they do not have the same chemical properties because they are not made from the same substances. The lily leaves are found in nature and have the chemicals needed to make their own food. The synthetic material is made by humans to function as clothing.

Inquiry Skills

Predict In science, one discovery or invention can lead to other discoveries or inventions. Divide the class into small groups to talk about how synthetic materials might be used in the future. Challenge them to identify other materials in nature that might inspire scientists to develop new synthetic materials. Invite groups to share their thoughts with the rest of the class.

SCIENCE *Spin* from WEEKLY READER®

Technology

Better Than Nature Can Make?

398

PROFESSIONAL DEVELOPMENT

Science Background

Nylon One of the most common synthetic materials is nylon. Nylon was developed by scientists who were trying to mimic the natural material silk. You may want to share the following information about nylon with your class:

- Nylon was first made by E.I. du Pont de Nemours & Company.
- Scientists took 10 years to develop nylon before it was released in 1938.
- Some properties of nylon include its strength, elasticity, and resistance to friction.
- Today, nylon is used for many things, including pantyhose, jackets, mosquito netting, surgical sutures (stitches), thread, insulation for wires, tire cords, and rope.

Silk

Cotton

Wool

3 Wrap Up and Assess

Think About It

1. Students may answer that people started making synthetic materials to improve on the qualities of natural materials or to have a larger supply of material. They may also say that synthetic materials are generally more affordable than natural materials.

2. Student answers will vary. Accept all reasonable answers.

Many times, scientists come up with new ideas by looking at nature. For example, swimsuit makers made a fabric for Olympic athletes after studying the skin of sharks.

Recently, scientists in Turkey, a country in Europe, also turned to nature for ideas. Scientists there came up with an idea for a new fabric by looking at water lilies. Water lilies are plants that grow in ponds and have big leaves that float on the surface.

Looking at Lilies

The scientists were inspired by how waterproof a water lily's leaves are. They wanted to make a material that shed water similar to the way the plant's leaves shed water.

The scientists then began working with different materials, such as plastic, to form a new kind of material. Like the plant, when this new material gets wet, the water does not soak in but stays on the surface and rolls off.

The new material is synthetic. Synthetic is another way of saying something that is made by people. The new waterproof material will be useful for many people, especially firefighters, who need to keep dry while they work.

Think About It

1. Why do you think people started making synthetic materials?

2. Do you think synthetic materials should replace natural materials? Why or why not?

Find out more! Log on to
www.hspscience.com

Writing Link

Expository Writing Synthetic materials are used for many different purposes today. They are often used in place of natural materials. Have students write a letter to a friend comparing and contrasting natural materials and synthetic materials. Ask students to consider a specific purpose and conclude if one material is better than another for that purpose.

Inspire Inquiry

Inquiry starts with wonder and with asking questions. Sometimes the questions are just about things people want to know. Sometimes they are problems that people want to solve.

■ Have students suggest reasons scientists may have first tried to mimic natural materials when making synthetic materials in laboratories.

■ Ask students to brainstorm questions about synthetic materials. Write their questions on the board.

■ Discuss with students how they could answer the questions they asked. Provide interested students with time to research synthetic materials and find answers to their questions. Invite students to share their findings with the whole class.

People

- Describe Evangelista Torricelli's contribution to science.
- Discuss how the barometer helps people predict the weather.

1 Introduce

Preview/Set a Purpose

Ask students, **What tools do meteorologists use to predict the weather?** Make a list on the board. If students mention a barometer, circle it. If no one names a barometer, ask if they have heard of one.

2 Teach

The Work of Scientists

Lead students to conclude that scientists invent tools to help them study the natural world.

What did Torricelli's invention do? It helped scientists predict the weather by measuring air pressure.

What did Torricelli's barometer look like? It was a glass tube with mercury in it.

What would the barometer do in good weather? The mercury would go up the glass tube in good weather.

3 Wrap Up and Assess

Think About It

Invite students to make connections between Torricelli's work and the work of modern scientists.

Can you think of another tool that uses mercury? a thermometer **What does it measure?** temperature

How was Torricelli similar to a modern materials scientist? He studied changes in mercury. Materials scientists study how materials react to different conditions.

SCIENCE Spin from WEEKLY READER

People

The Father of the Barometer

Evangelista Torricelli was a scientist who lived about 360 years ago. He is best known for an invention that helps to predict the weather. That invention is the barometer.

Most people before Torricelli did not know that air has weight. This idea is known as "air pressure." A barometer is used to measure air pressure.

Modern Barometer ▶

Torricelli's barometer was a glass tube filled with a liquid metal called mercury. When air pressure is high, during good weather, the mercury moves up the tube. When air pressure was low, usually on stormy days, the mercury is lower in the tube.

Career   Materials Scientist

How long do think the rubber soles of your new sneakers will last? Chances are, a materials scientist knows the answer. These scientists study how different materials react to changes. They study how rubber might react to cold or how long before it wears out.

Find out more! Log on to **www.hspscience.com**

400

PROFESSIONAL DEVELOPMENT

Science Background

Students may wonder why mercury moves up the glass tube when air pressure is high and why it stays down when air pressure is low.

- Air pressure is a result of gravity pulling down on air molecules. When air is warm, the air molecules are farther apart, so air pressure is less. When air is colder, they are closer together, so air pressure is greater.
- In a barometer, the glass tube sits in a dish of mercury. As air presses down on the mercury in the dish, the mercury is forced up the glass tube. As the pressure increases, the mercury goes higher in the tube.
- The glass tube in a barometer has had all the air removed, so air is not pressing down on the mercury in the glass tube.

You Can Do It!

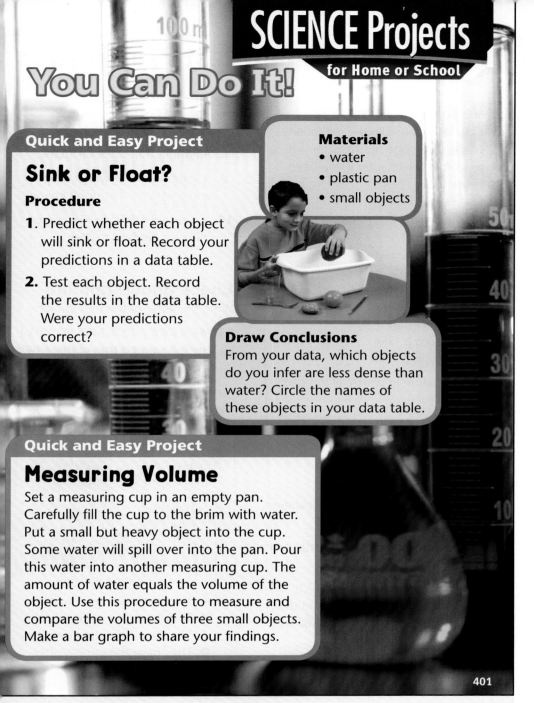

Sink or Float?

Procedure

1. Predict whether each object will sink or float. Record your predictions in a data table.

2. Test each object. Record the results in the data table. Were your predictions correct?

Materials
- water
- plastic pan
- small objects

Draw Conclusions

From your data, which objects do you infer are less dense than water? Circle the names of these objects in your data table.

Measuring Volume

Set a measuring cup in an empty pan. Carefully fill the cup to the brim with water. Put a small but heavy object into the cup. Some water will spill over into the pan. Pour this water into another measuring cup. The amount of water equals the volume of the object. Use this procedure to measure and compare the volumes of three small objects. Make a bar graph to share your findings.

401

You Can Do It!

Quick and Easy Project

Sink or Float?

Objectives

■ Use observations of mass and volume to predict whether objects will sink or float.

• Tips and Hints

Test the objects ahead of time to be sure students will have a variety of results. Suggest that students record their results on a table.

• Draw Conclusions

Students should circle the names of the objects that float. These objects are less dense than water.

Extend the Activity

Have students experiment to find an object that floats just below the surface of the water. Students can also increase the density of the water by adding salt to see if it changes the way the objects sink or float.

Design Your Own Investigation

Measuring Volume

Objectives

■ Find the volume of objects by measuring the amount of water that they displace.

Inspire Inquiry

Use this activity as an at-home investigation or suggestion for a science fair project. Have students use the investigation as a starting point for developing their own questions and ideas for research. Ask students to share their plans with you and the class. Work together to make the procedure work smoothly.

A reproducible copy of this page is provided in *Teaching Resources*.

Chapter 11

Vocabulary Review (5 pts. each)

1. solution
2. gas
3. mass
4. evaporation
5. volume
6. liquid
7. density
8. matter
9. solid
10. mixture

Check Understanding (5 pts. each)

11. B, They have the same volume.
12. F, solid and liquid
13. C, physical properties
14. G, salt and water
15. D, burning wood
16. H, Change its shape.

Inquiry Skills (5 pts. each)

17. Place each object on a pan balance.
18. The box of books has more mass, because books are denser than pillows.

Vocabulary Review

Match the terms to the definitions below. The page numbers tell where to look in the chapter if you need help.

matter p. 374
mass p. 378
volume p. 379
density p. 379
solid p. 385
liquid p. 386
gas p. 387
evaporation p. 388
mixture p. 394
solution p. 395

1. A mixture in which all the parts mix evenly
2. A state of matter with no definite shape or volume
3. The amount of matter in something
4. The process during which water moves into the air
5. The amount of space matter takes up
6. The state of matter in which volume stays the same and the takes the shape of its container
7. The mass of something compared with its volume
8. Anything that takes up space
9. A state of matter with a shape and a volume that don't change
10. A substance with two or more different kinds of matter

Check Understanding

Write the letter of the best choice.

11. **MAIN IDEA AND DETAILS** Which of the following is true of these two jars and their contents?

A. They have the same mass.
B. They have the same volume.
C. They have the same density.
D. They have the same matter.

Harcourt School Publishers
Online Assessment

Harcourt School Publishers Online Assessment provides even more options. For a preview, go to:
www.hspscience.com

Portfolio Assessment

Have students select their best work from the following suggestions:

■ **Investigate**, pp. 373, 383, 391
■ **Links**, pp. 381, 378, 397
■ **Science Project**, p. 401

See **Assessment Guide** pp. xx–xxiv.

12. COMPARE AND CONTRAST Which states of matter have a volume that doesn't change?
   F. solid and liquid
   G. liquid and gas
   H. solid and gas
   J. solid, liquid, and gas

13. Sarah notices that a metal fence rail feels cold and hard. What is Sarah observing?
   A. chemical changes
   B. densities
   C. physical properties
   D. states of matter

14. Which of these is a solution?
   F. peanut butter and jelly
   G. salt and water
   H. cereal and milk
   J. celery and carrot sticks

15. Which of the following is a chemical change?
   A. dissolving soap in water
   B. filling a balloon with air
   C. grating cheese
   D. burning wood

16. A ball of modeling clay sinks in a pan of water. What change could make the clay float?
   F. Remove some of the water.
   G. Increase the clay's density.
   H. Change its shape.
   J. Add more water to the pan.

Inquiry Skills

17. How could you measure which of two objects has more mass?

18. There are two identical boxes. One box is filled to the top with books. The other box is filled to the top with foam pillows. Which box would you predict has more mass? Explain your answer.

Critical Thinking

19. You can put sand into a container, and it takes the shape of the container. What state of matter is sand? Why?

20. You have a mixture of two kinds of buttons. Some are large. Some are small.

Part A How can you separate the mixture without picking out the buttons one at a time?

Part B Is the button mixture a solution? Tell why or why not.

Critical Thinking (5 pts. each)

19. Sand is a solid. Each individual grain has its own shape and volume.

20. Possible answer: Part A: Use a net or screen with holes a little larger than the small buttons but smaller than the large buttons. The small buttons will go through the holes. The large buttons will stay on the screen. Part B: No; the buttons can be separated.

Chapter Test

See *Assessment Guide* pages AG 85-90 for a Chapter Test and Performance Task, with rubric. Assessment options appear on page 370H.

Performance Assessment

Mixtures and Solutions

Work with three or four other students. Using water, two cups, tape, sugar, rice, paper clips, dry beans, and a spoon, make a mixture and a solution. Label each one correctly. Explain how the mixture and the solution differ. Suggest a way to separate the mixture by using forceps, a magnifying glass, and other materials you think may help.

Rubric for Performance Assessment

Preparation Each group will need a container of water, two cups, masking tape to label the cups, sugar, rice, paper clips, dry beans, and a spoon. Each student should record his or her own observations, procedure, and explanation on how to separate the mixture.

Scoring Rubric—Performance Indicators

_____ Students make a solution by using the sugar and water and label it correctly.

_____ Students make and label a mixture by using any materials but not both sugar and water.

_____ Students accurately explain how the mixture and the solution differ.

_____ Students accurately suggest a way to separate the mixture.

Observations and Rubric Scores

   3   2   1   0

CHAPTER 12 LESSON PLANNER

Lesson	Pacing	Vocabulary	Objectives & Reading Focus	Resources & Technology
1 What is Energy? pp. 406–413	2 days	energy kinetic energy potential energy	■ Gather temperature data over a period of time and present it in a graph. ■ Define energy. ■ Explain the difference between kinetic energy and potential energy. **COMPARE AND CONTRAST** Look for what makes forms of energy different. `alike` —— `different`	■ Lab Manual pp. LM 144–146 ■ Transparencies DI 38, IS 38, RS 38, Go 38 ◉ Electronic Transparencies ■ Activity Video/DVD 3003 ◉ ESL Support pp. 162–165 ■ Reading Support and Homework pp. RS 88–89

2 How Can Energy Be Used?
pp. 414–419
	3 days	combustion
		temperature
			■ Measure the amount of energy transferred from sunlight to an object.
			■ Identify the sources of types of energy people use for different purposes.
			■ Define temperature.
			
			MAIN IDEA AND DETAILS Look for details about ways people use energy.
			
			`Main Idea`
			`detail` `detail` `detail`
				■ Lab Manual pp. LM 147–149
				■ Transparencies DI 39, IS 39, RS 39 GO 39
				◉ Electronic Transparencies
				■ Activity Video/DVD 3004
				◉ ESL Support pp. 166–169
				■ Reading Support and Homework pp. RS 90–91

3 Why Is Energy Important?
pp. 420–425
	2 days	resource
		fossil fuels
		nonrenewable resource
		renewable resource
			■ Investigate the power of wind to move objects.
			■ Describe ways people can conserve energy resources.
			■ Explain the difference between renewable and nonrenewable energy resources.
			
			MAIN IDEA AND DETAILS Look for details about saving energy.
			
			`Main Idea`
			`detail` `detail` `detail`
				■ Lab Manual pp. LM 150–152
				■ Transparencies DI 40, IS 40, RS 40, GO 40
				◉ Electronic Transparencies
				■ Activity Video/DVD 3005
				◉ ESL Support pp. 170–173
				■ Reading Support and Homework pp. RS 92–93

End of Chapter pp. 426–431	2 days		■ Evaluate relationships of science, technology, and society. ■ Review chapter concepts	■ Intervention, On-Level, and Above-Level Readers ■ Assessment Guide pp. AG 91–96

Plan Ahead for Activities

Investigate

Observing Temperature p. 407

Materials: thermometer, clock

Time: 5-10 minutes

(**Inquiry Focus: Infer**)

Prep Tip: Pick a sunny spot for the thermometer where it won't be disturbed by others.

The Heat Is On p. 415

Materials: clear plastic cup, thermometer, ice cubes

Time: 3 hours

(**Inquiry Focus: Infer**)

Prep Tip: Allow students to remove the thermometer from the cup in order to read it, but remind them to read it and return it quickly.

Make a Paper Windmill p. 421

Materials: white paper, scissors, ruler, pencil with eraser, pushpin

Time: 20 minutes

(**Inquiry Focus: Model**)

Prep Tip: Students may have difficulty securing the corners and attaching the wheel at the same time. You might suggest using tape to hold the corners in place, and then use the pushpin to attach the wheel to the pencil.

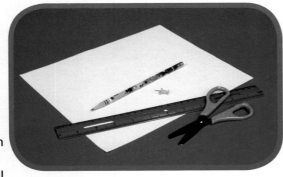

Insta-Lab

Energy in Motion
p. 410

 10 minutes

Materials: rubber ball, meter stick

Tip: Discourage students from climbing in order to drop the ball from a higher height.

A Model Thermometer
p. 417

 5 minutes

Materials: water, clay

Tip: To save time, perform this Insta-Lab as a whole-class activity.

Save Fossil Fuels
p. 423

 10 minutes

Materials: pen and paper

Tip: You may want to provide reference sources, such as books on energy or on conservation, to help students with their tables.

REACHING ALL LEARNERS

Page R51 provides additional information

Reading Support

Below-Level/Intervention

When used along with the hands-on experiences from the **Student Edition**, the Intervention Reader promotes science success for all students.
Reading Level 1.5–2.0

The Intervention Reader presents identical chapter content and vocabulary at a below-grade reading level. The reader uses a visual glossary, simplified language, and comprehension aids especially designed for struggling readers. The **Intervention Reader Teacher Guide** provides additional strategies and support.

On-Level/Enrichment

This reader promotes success on state science tests by reinforcing test content objectives, chapter vocabulary, and reading skills.
Reading Level 2.5–3.5

Trade Books for Students

These books provide in-depth information on chapter content. For more information about each selection, see the Bibliography beginning on page R48.

Easy
Energy by Christine Webster, Capstone, 2005

Average
The Light Bulb by Marc Tyler Nobleman, Capstone, 1998

Challenge
Why Does a Battery Make it Go? by Jackie Holderness, Copper Beech Books, 2002

Advanced/Challenge

This interesting nonfiction reader enriches and extends chapter concepts.
Reading Level 4.0–5.5

Alternative Teaching Strategies

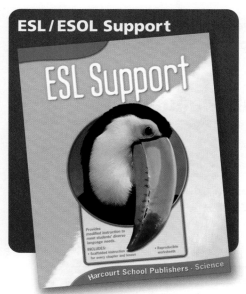
This guide provides additional support for the strategies and activities that appear throughout this chapter.

Intervention and Reteaching

Strategies for reteaching key lesson concepts provide options for addressing a variety of learning styles.

Intervention Reader p. 409

On-Level Reader p. 418

How Do Fossil Fuels Form? p. 423

 Using the E-Book

This chapter is also available online and has provisions for children with special needs. Adjustable text size and audio text can be used with children who have vision impairments or learning difficulties.

www.hspscience.com

Science Concepts Across the Grades

Grade 2	Grade 3	Grade 4
Related Chapters		
Chapter 11 Light and Heat **Lesson 1** What Is Energy?	**Chapter 12 Energy** **Lesson 1** What Is Energy? **Lesson 2** How Can Energy Be Used? **Lesson 3** Why Is Energy Important?	**Chapter 11 Changes in Matter** **Lesson 1** What Is Matter Made of? **Lesson 2** What Are Physical Changes in Matter? **Lesson 3** How Does Matter React Chemically?
Learning Goals		
▶ Understand and describe ways energy and matter interact. ▶ Recognize that light can pass through some objects and not others. ▶ Identify heat sources and explain the transfer of heat and how heat is measured.	▶ Identify heat sources and explain the transfer of heat and how heat is measured. ▶ Identify the sources of types of energy people use for different purposes. ▶ Explain the difference between renewable and nonrenewable energy resources.	▶ Understand that the atom is the smallest particle of matter. ▶ Know that elements are substances made of one kind of atom. ▶ Describe states of matter and changes of state. ▶ Understand physical and chemical changes.

RESOURCES FOR INQUIRY

Daily Practice

Daily Inquiry pp. 372, 382, 390
Teaching Transparencies **DI 38–40**
Electronic Transparencies **DI 3003–3005**

Inquiry Tool Kit

Harcourt Investigations

Harcourt School Publishers offers an alternative program that provides more opportunities for inquiry-based science experiences. The program provides a series of investigations that promote guided, structured, and independent inquiry using student journals, lab manuals, science readers and other materials.

Visit **www.hspscience.com** for more information.

Guided Inquiry

Investigate pp. 373, 383, 391; *Lab Manual* pp. **LM 144–146, 147–149, 150–153**

Inquiry Skill Mini Lesson pp. 373, 383, 391; *Teaching Transparencies* **IS 38–40**; *Electronic Transparencies* **IS 3003–3005**

Insta-Lab pp. 410, 417, 423

Unit Experiment pp. 369A–B; *Lab Manual* pp. **LM 131–133**

Independent Inquiry

Investigate Further *Lab Manual* pp. **LM 374, 384, 392**

Lab Manual

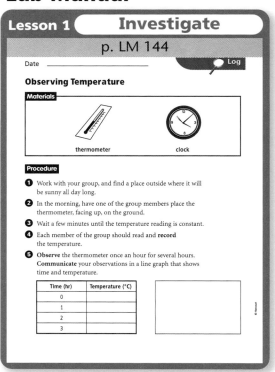

Use with **Student Edition** p. 67.

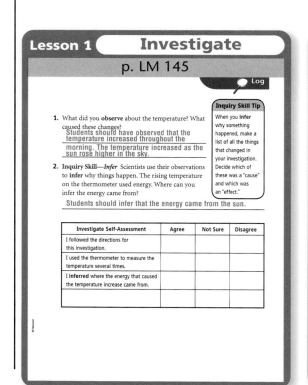

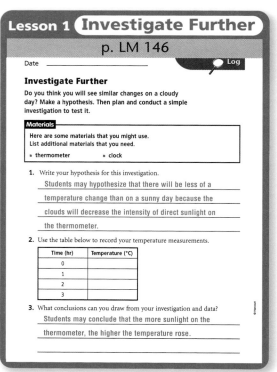

Science Projects for Home or School
p. 429 *Teaching Resources* p. TR 22

Unit Experiment pp. 369A-B; Lab Manual pp. LM 9–11 and Science Fair Projects *Lab Manual* pp. LM 196–201

Lab Manual (cont.)

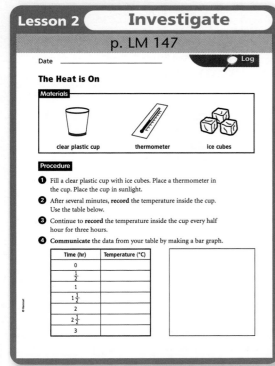

Lesson 2 | Investigate
p. LM 147

Date _____
Log

The Heat is On

Materials

clear plastic cup | thermometer | ice cubes

Procedure

1 Fill a clear plastic cup with ice cubes. Place a thermometer in the cup. Place the cup in sunlight.

2 After several minutes, **record** the temperature inside the cup. Use the table below.

3 Continue to **record** the temperature inside the cup every half hour for three hours.

4 **Communicate** the data from your table by making a bar graph.

Time (hr)	Temperature (°C)
0	
$\frac{1}{2}$	
1	
$1\frac{1}{2}$	
2	
$2\frac{1}{2}$	
3	

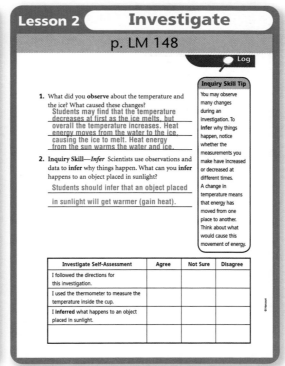

Lesson 2 | Investigate
p. LM 148

Log

1. What did you **observe** about the temperature and the ice? What caused these changes?
Students may find that the temperature decreases at first as the ice melts, but overall the temperature increases. Heat energy moves from the water to the ice, causing the ice to melt. Heat energy from the sun warms the water and ice.

2. **Inquiry Skill—*Infer*** Scientists use observations and data to **infer** why things happen. What can you **infer** happens to an object placed in sunlight?
Students should infer that an object placed in sunlight will get warmer (gain heat).

Inquiry Skill Tip
You may observe many changes during an investigation. To **infer** why things happen, notice whether the measurements you make have increased or decreased at different times. A change in temperature means that energy has moved from one place to another. Think about what would cause this movement of energy.

Investigate Self-Assessment	Agree	Not Sure	Disagree
I followed the directions for this investigation.			
I used the thermometer to measure the temperature inside the cup.			
I **inferred** what happens to an object placed in sunlight.			

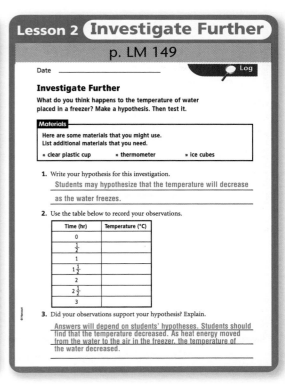

Lesson 2 | Investigate Further
p. LM 149

Date _____
Log

Investigate Further
What do you think happens to the temperature of water placed in a freezer? Make a hypothesis. Then test it.

Materials
Here are some materials that you might use. List additional materials that you need.

▪ clear plastic cup ▪ thermometer ▪ ice cubes

1. Write your hypothesis for this investigation.
Students may hypothesize that the temperature will decrease as the water freezes.

2. Use the table below to record your observations.

Time (hr)	Temperature (°C)
0	
$\frac{1}{2}$	
1	
$1\frac{1}{2}$	
2	
$2\frac{1}{2}$	
3	

3. Did your observations support your hypothesis? Explain.
Answers will depend on students' hypotheses. Students should find that the temperature decreased. As heat energy moved from the water to the air in the freezer, the temperature of the water decreased.

Use with **Student Edition** p. 415.

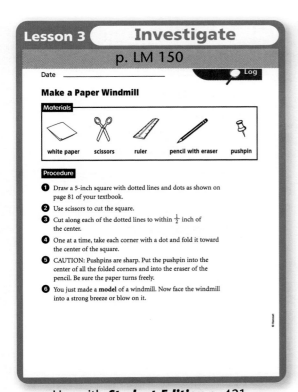

Lesson 3 | Investigate
p. LM 150

Date _____
Log

Make a Paper Windmill

Materials

white paper | scissors | ruler | pencil with eraser | pushpin

Procedure

1 Draw a 5-inch square with dotted lines and dots as shown on page 81 of your textbook.

2 Use scissors to cut the square.

3 Cut along each of the dotted lines to within $\frac{1}{2}$ inch of the center.

4 One at a time, take each corner with a dot and fold it toward the center of the square.

5 CAUTION: Pushpins are sharp. Put the pushpin into the center of all the folded corners and into the eraser of the pencil. Be sure the paper turns freely.

6 You just made a **model** of a windmill. Now face the windmill into a strong breeze or blow on it.

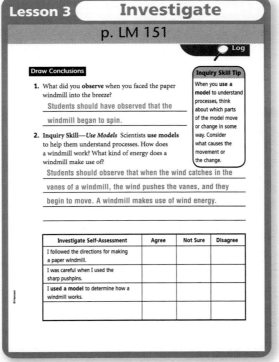

Lesson 3 | Investigate
p. LM 151

Log

Draw Conclusions

1. What did you **observe** when you faced the paper windmill into the breeze?
Students should have observed that the windmill began to spin.

2. **Inquiry Skill—*Use Models*** Scientists **use models** to help them understand processes. How does a windmill work? What kind of energy does a windmill make use of?
Students should observe that when the wind catches in the vanes of a windmill, the wind pushes the vanes, and they begin to move. A windmill makes use of wind energy.

Inquiry Skill Tip
When you **use a model** to understand processes, think about which parts of the model move or change in some way. Consider what causes the movement or the change.

Investigate Self-Assessment	Agree	Not Sure	Disagree
I followed the directions for making a paper windmill.			
I was careful when I used the sharp pushpins.			
I **used a model** to determine how a windmill works.			

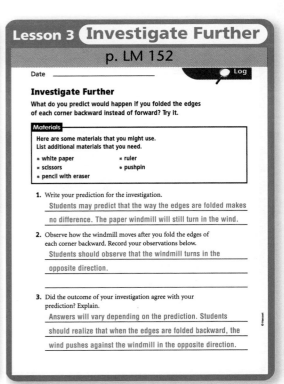

Lesson 3 | Investigate Further
p. LM 152

Date _____
Log

Investigate Further
What do you predict would happen if you folded the edges of each corner backward instead of forward? Try it.

Materials
Here are some materials that you might use. List additional materials that you need.

▪ white paper ▪ ruler
▪ scissors ▪ pushpin
▪ pencil with eraser

1. Write your prediction for the investigation.
Students may predict that the way the edges are folded makes no difference. The paper windmill will still turn in the wind.

2. Observe how the windmill moves after you fold the edges of each corner backward. Record your observations below.
Students should observe that the windmill turns in the opposite direction.

3. Did the outcome of your investigation agree with your prediction? Explain.
Answers will vary depending on the prediction. Students should realize that when the edges are folded backward, the wind pushes against the windmill in the opposite direction.

Use with **Student Edition** p. 421.

READING SUPPORT AND HOMEWORK

Pages available online.
www.hspscience.com

Reading Support and Homework also includes Vocabulary Power, and Vocabulary Cards and Activities.

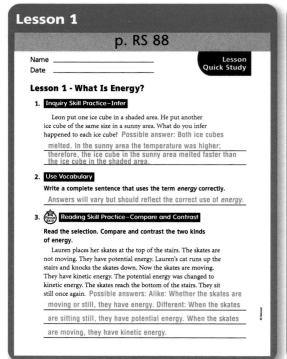

Lesson 1
p. RS 88

Name _____
Date _____

Lesson Quick Study

Lesson 1 - What Is Energy?

1. **Inquiry Skill Practice–Infer**

   Leon put one ice cube in a shaded area. He put another ice cube of the same size in a sunny area. What do you infer happened to each ice cube? Possible answer: Both ice cubes melted. In the sunny area the temperature was higher; therefore, the ice cube in the sunny area melted faster than the ice cube in the shaded area.

2. **Use Vocabulary**

   Write a complete sentence that uses the term *energy* correctly. Answers will vary but should reflect the correct use of *energy*.

3. **Reading Skill Practice–Compare and Contrast**

   Read the selection. Compare and contrast the two kinds of energy.

   Lauren places her skates at the top of the stairs. The skates are not moving. They have potential energy. Lauren's cat runs up the stairs and knocks the skates down. Now the skates are moving. They have kinetic energy. The potential energy was changed to kinetic energy. The skates reach the bottom of the stairs. They sit still once again. Possible answers: Alike: Whether the skates are moving or still, they have energy. Different: When the skates are sitting still, they have potential energy. When the skates are moving, they have kinetic energy.

Use with *Student Edition* pp. 406–413.

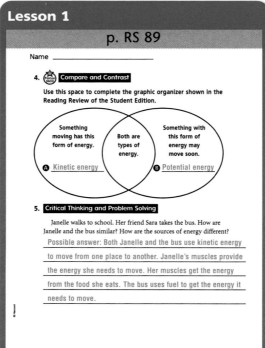

Lesson 1
p. RS 89

Name _____

4. **Compare and Contrast**

   Use this space to complete the graphic organizer shown in the Reading Review of the Student Edition.

   - A Kinetic energy — Something moving has this form of energy.
   - Both are types of energy.
   - B Potential energy — Something with this form of energy may move soon.

5. **Critical Thinking and Problem Solving**

   Janelle walks to school. Her friend Sara takes the bus. How are Janelle and the bus similar? How are the sources of energy different? Possible answer: Both Janelle and the bus use kinetic energy to move from one place to another. Janelle's muscles provide the energy she needs to move. Her muscles get the energy from the food she eats. The bus uses fuel to get the energy it needs to move.

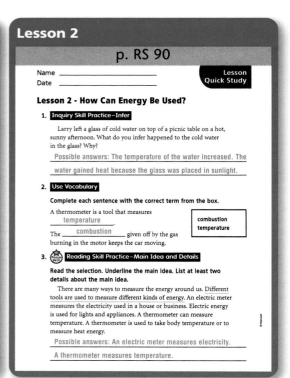

Lesson 2
p. RS 90

Name _____
Date _____

Lesson Quick Study

Lesson 2 - How Can Energy Be Used?

1. **Inquiry Skill Practice–Infer**

   Larry left a glass of cold water on top of a picnic table on a hot, sunny afternoon. What do you infer happened to the cold water in the glass? Why? Possible answers: The temperature of the water increased. The water gained heat because the glass was placed in sunlight.

2. **Use Vocabulary**

   Complete each sentence with the correct term from the box.

   A thermometer is a tool that measures temperature.

   The combustion given off by the gas burning in the motor keeps the car moving.

   [box: combustion / temperature]

3. **Reading Skill Practice–Main Idea and Details**

   Read the selection. Underline the main idea. List at least two details about the main idea.

   There are many ways to measure the energy around us. Different tools are used to measure different kinds of energy. An electric meter measures the electricity used in a house or business. Electric energy is used for lights and appliances. A thermometer can measure temperature. A thermometer is used to take body temperature or to measure heat energy.

   Possible answers: An electric meter measures electricity. A thermometer measures temperature.

Use with *Student Edition* pp. 414–419.

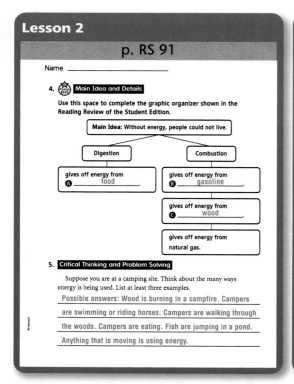

Lesson 2
p. RS 91

Name _____

4. **Main Idea and Details**

   Use this space to complete the graphic organizer shown in the Reading Review of the Student Edition.

   Main Idea: Without energy, people could not live.

   - Digestion
     - A gives off energy from food
   - Combustion
     - B gives off energy from gasoline
     - C gives off energy from wood
     - gives off energy from natural gas.

5. **Critical Thinking and Problem Solving**

   Suppose you are at a camping site. Think about the many ways energy is being used. List at least three examples. Possible answers: Wood is burning in a campfire. Campers are swimming or riding horses. Campers are walking through the woods. Campers are eating. Fish are jumping in a pond. Anything that is moving is using energy.

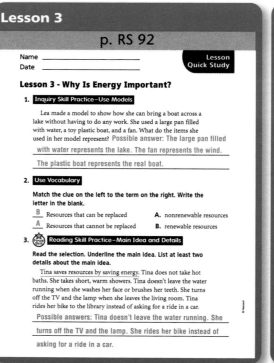

Lesson 3
p. RS 92

Name _____
Date _____

Lesson Quick Study

Lesson 3 - Why Is Energy Important?

1. **Inquiry Skill Practice–Use Models**

   Lea made a model to show how she can bring a boat across a lake without having to do any work. She used a large pan filled with water, a toy plastic boat, and a fan. What do the items she used in her model represent? Possible answer: The large pan filled with water represents the lake. The fan represents the wind. The plastic boat represents the real boat.

2. **Use Vocabulary**

   Match the clue on the left to the term on the right. Write the letter in the blank.

   B Resources that can be replaced   A. nonrenewable resources
   A Resources that cannot be replaced   B. renewable resources

3. **Reading Skill Practice–Main Idea and Details**

   Read the selection. Underline the main idea. List at least two details about the main idea.

   Tina saves resources by saving energy. Tina does not take hot baths. She takes short, warm showers. Tina doesn't leave the water running when she washes her face or brushes her teeth. She turns off the TV and the lamp when she leaves the living room. Tina rides her bike to the library instead of asking for a ride in a car.

   Possible answers: Tina doesn't leave the water running. She turns off the TV and the lamp. She rides her bike instead of asking for a ride in a car.

Use with *Student Edition* pp. 420–425.

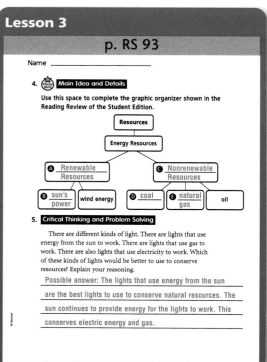

Lesson 3
p. RS 93

Name _____

4. **Main Idea and Details**

   Use this space to complete the graphic organizer shown in the Reading Review of the Student Edition.

   - Resources
     - Energy Resources
       - A Renewable Resources
         - B sun's power
         - wind energy
       - C Nonrenewable Resources
         - D coal
         - E natural gas
         - oil

5. **Critical Thinking and Problem Solving**

   There are different kinds of light. There are lights that use energy from the sun to work. There are lights that use gas to work. There are also lights that use electricity to work. Which of these kinds of lights would be better to use to conserve resources? Explain your reasoning. Possible answer: The lights that use energy from the sun are the best lights to use to conserve natural resources. The sun continues to provide energy for the lights to work. This conserves electric energy and gas.

ASSESSMENT OPTIONS

Formal Assessment
- Chapter Review and Test Preparation SE pp. 430–431
- Chapter Test AG pp. 91–94

Standardized Test Preparation
- Reading Review and Test Preparations SE pp. 413, 419, 425

Online Test Generator
- multiple-choice items ■ free-response items
- prepared tests/teacher-built tests

Ongoing Assessment
- Assess Prior Knowledge—Chapter Opener
- Daily Inquiry Transparencies
- Teacher Edition questions throughout
- Focus Skill questions throughout SE
- Reaching All Learners throughout TE
- Reading Review SE pp. 413, 419, 425
- Observation Checklist AG

Performance Assessment
- Long-Option AG pp. 11–12
- Short-Option TE p. 91

Student Self–Assessment
- Investigate Self-Assessment *Lab Manual*
- Self-Assessment AG

Portfolio Assessment
- Using Portfolio Assessment AG
- Suggested work samples TE p. 430

Chapter Test

p. AG 91

Name _____
Date _____

Chapter Assessment

Energy

Vocabulary 4 points each

Match each term in Column B with its meaning in Column A.

Column A		Column B
E	1. Resource that can be replaced	A. energy
C	2. Another word for *burning*	B. resource
A	3. The ability to make something move or change	C. combustion
H	4. The energy of position	D. fossil fuels
G	5. Resource that cannot be replaced	E. renewable resource
B	6. Something in nature that people use	F. kinetic energy
F	7. The energy of motion	G. nonrenewable resource
D	8. Coal, oil, and gas	H. potential energy

Science Concepts 4 points each

Write the letter of the best choice.

D 9. Where does most of Earth's energy come from?
 A. electricity
 B. fossil fuels
 C. the moon
 D. the sun

p. AG 92

Name _____

G 10. What type of energy does a moving car have?
 F. electrical energy H. light energy
 G. kinetic energy J. potential energy

A 11. Which of the following is a way to save energy resources?
 A. Use a blanket instead of turning on the heater.
 B. Keep the house cool by turning on the air conditioning.
 C. Turn on the lights during the day.
 D. Leave the light on when you exit a room.

F 12. Which of the following are fossil fuels?
 F. coal and natural gas H. light and oil
 G. water and coal J. heat and natural gas

D 13. Which resource is renewable?
 A. coal C. oil
 B. gas D. wind

G 14. Which ball has **no** kinetic energy?

 F. ball 1 H. ball 3
 G. ball 2 J. ball 4

p. AG 93

Name _____

C 15. What kind of energy do plants need to grow?
 A. chemical C. light
 B. electrical D. sound

F 16. What tool measures wind energy?
 F. anemometer H. sound meter
 G. light meter J. thermometer

Inquiry Skills 8 points each

17. Tyler and his sister went to the beach. Tyler sat in the sun, and his sister sat in the shade. **Infer** what happened to each person's skin temperature. Explain.

 Possible answer: Tyler's skin temperature increased, but

 his sister's did not. Tyler received more heat energy from

 sunlight.

18. In Molly's town everyone drives a car to go anywhere. People leave their appliances on all the time, use their heaters or air conditioners every day, and do not recycle materials. **Infer** what will happen to the world if everyone acts the way people in Molly's town do.

 Possible answer: Using so much energy will cause the world

 to run out of fossil fuels, which are not renewable.

p. AG 94

Name _____

Critical Thinking 10 points each

19. List five ways that you can conserve energy at home or at school.

 Possible answer: I can turn off the lights when I leave a

 room. I can turn off the water while I brush my teeth. I

 can recycle paper at home and school. I can use a blanket

 instead of turning on the heater. I can open the blinds and

 curtains during the day instead of turning on the lights.

20. Carly is sitting at the top of the slide.

What type of energy does she have? Is it possible for her to change her energy? If she changes her energy, what type of energy will it become? Explain your answers.

 She has potential energy because she is just sitting at the

 top of the slide. Potential energy is the energy of position.

 If she slides down the slide, she can change her energy from

 potential energy into kinetic energy. Kinetic energy is the

 energy of motion.

Performance Task

p. AG 95

Name _____
Date _____

Performance Assessment
Student Task

Types of Energy

Materials

magazines or newspapers   construction paper   glue

scissors

Procedure

❶ Choose one of the following types of energy.
 • heat • chemical • electric
 • mechanical • sound • light

❷ Look through the magazines and newspapers for pictures that show how this type of energy is used.

❸ Glue the pictures to a piece of construction paper.

❹ Show your pictures to the class, and have the class guess which energy source you chose.

❺ Then tell about each picture. Explain how the energy source is being used.

Rubric

p. AG 96

Performance Assessment
Teacher's Directions

Types of Energy

Materials	Performance Task sheet, magazines or newspapers, construction paper, glue, scissors
Time	30 minutes
Suggested Grouping	pairs or small groups
Inquiry Skills	observe, gather data, interpret data
Preparation Hints	If you want to cover each type of energy, divide the class into six groups. Write each type of energy on a slip of paper, and put the slips in a bag. Have each group select a slip.
Introduce the Task	Review the list of energy types. Ask students to give an example of how each type is used. Then tell them that they will choose one type of energy and will look through magazines and newspapers for examples of how it is used. Allow students also to draw pictures to illustrate the type of energy being used.
Promote Discussion	When students finish, ask them to show their displays to the class. Have the class guess which type of energy is being used in each display. Then have students explain how the energy is being used in each picture.

Scoring Rubric

Performance Indicators

_____ Identifies pictures that show examples of the type of energy chosen.
_____ Makes a display that correctly shows examples of the type of energy chosen.
_____ Shows a variety of examples.
_____ Explains how the type of energy is being used in each example.

Observations and Rubric Score

3	2	1	0

Assess Prior Knowledge

Use the photograph to get students interested in the chapter topic. Ask students to study the photo and look for sources of energy.

Have students discuss their ideas about the question: **What forms of energy are present in this scene?** Note their answers as a key to prior knowledge and misconceptions. (See also the Science Background.) Students may identify the sunlight as being solar energy.

Later, as students read in Lesson 2 about different forms of energy and how they are used, students should note that the wheat also contains energy that people need in order to live and grow.

Generate Science Questions

Have students write down a list of questions they have about energy. Organize students into small groups and have them suggest ways they can find answers to their questions. In this chapter, students will learn about the importance of energy in its various forms.

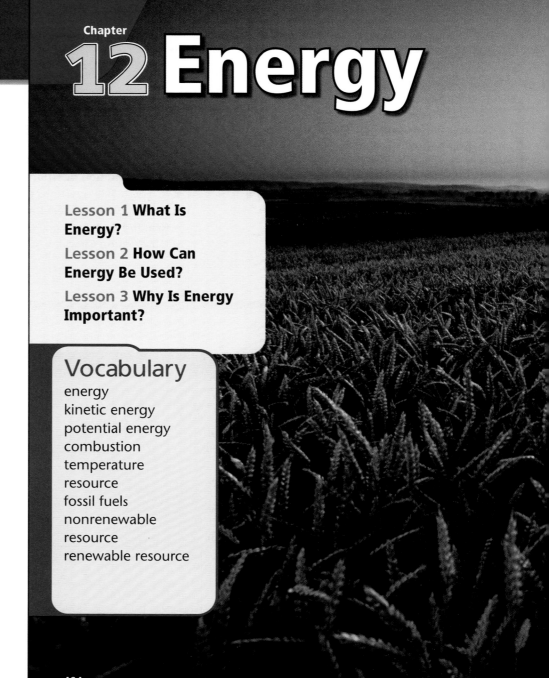

Chapter

12 Energy

Lesson 1 **What Is Energy?**

Lesson 2 **How Can Energy Be Used?**

Lesson 3 **Why Is Energy Important?**

Vocabulary

energy
kinetic energy
potential energy
combustion
temperature
resource
fossil fuels
nonrenewable resource
renewable resource

404

Professional Development

To prepare for effective instruction, you may wish to consult these resources:

The **Activity Video/DVD** provides previews of the activities, offers classroom-management techniques, and presents expected results.

The **Science eBook** provides chapter content online, with greater depth via additional content and activities.

The **Science Background** throughout this Teacher Edition provides content support.

Visit **www.hspscience.com** for additional Professional Development resources.

 Science Background **To Address Misconceptions**

What is combustion?

Assess Prior Knowledge *Ask:* What happens when something burns?

Students May Think that a flame must be present for something to burn.

Scientists Explain that burning, or combustion, is a chemical reaction between a substance and oxygen. Visible flames often accompany the reaction, but not always. For example, gasoline fumes burn inside a car's engine and release heat energy, but there are no flames.

What You Can Do Ask students to draw or bring in pictures of things burning and place them on the bulletin board. Supplement with examples that don't involve flames.

What do YOU wonder?

The sun gives off energy that helps this wheat grow. What other types of energy can you think of?

405

Vocabulary

Opportunities for developing chapter vocabulary include:

- Develop Science Vocabulary strategies at point-of-use in the teaching plan
- Vocabulary questions in each Reading Review and the Chapter Review and Test
- Vocabulary sections on the Quick Study pages in **Reading Support and Homework**
- Vocabulary Cards and activities and Vocabulary Power worksheet in **Reading Support and Homework**

Students can use the **Vocabulary Power** worksheet below to preview and explore more about the chapter vocabulary.

Reading Support and Homework
p. RS 87

Energy

A. **Explore Word Meanings**

A *renewable resource* is a resource that can be replaced. A *nonrenewable resource* is a resource that cannot be replaced. Use these definitions to determine which of the resources in the box can be described as renewable and which can be described as nonrenewable. Write your answers under the headings.

| wind | oil | sunlight | natural gas | coal | water |

Renewable Resources	Nonrenewable Resources
wind	oil
sunlight	natural gas
water	coal

B. **Context Clues**

Read each sentence. Think about the meaning of the underlined word. Write the meaning on the line.

7. A tennis ball in motion has <u>kinetic energy</u>, as does a dog jumping to catch it.

    Possible answer: the energy of motion

8. Items in motion have kinetic energy, but items that rest in position have <u>potential energy</u>.

    Possible answer: the energy of position

Reading Focus Skills

The content of each lesson is organized to focus on a key reading skill. The skill is reinforced by questions that appear at the end of each section and the graphic organizer at the end of the lesson. Additional practice is also provided in **Reading Support and Homework**.

The Reading Focus Skills for this chapter are:	
Lesson 1	Compare and Contrast
Lesson 2	Main Idea and Details
Lesson 3	Main Idea and Details
All Lessons	Draw Conclusions and Summarize

Strategies for other reading skills also appear in the Reading Mini-Lessons throughout the chapter.

ESL/ESOL Support

Spanish-speaking students may already be familiar with English words such as these cognates:

energy/ energía

kinetic/ cinética

kinetic energy/ energía cinética

potential/ potencial

potential energy/ potencial energético

resource/ recurso

Objectives

Gather temperature data over time, and present it in a graph.

■ Define *energy*.

■ Explain the difference between kinetic energy and potential energy.

Transparency DI 38
Electronic Transparency DI 3003

Daily Inquiry

Hot Cotton

 thermometer

Other Materials: water, cotton

Review Skill Measure, Compare, and Infer

What to Do

■ Wrap a dry piece of cotton around the end of a thermometer. Read the temperature on the thermometer.

■ Next, take the temperature of the water. Then, dip a piece of cotton in the water. Wrap the wet cotton around the end of the thermometer. Read the temperature.

■ How did the water change the temperature of the cotton?

1 Introduce

Build on Prior Knowledge

Use the Fast Fact for a discussion starter about the lesson topic.

What other things produce light energy?

What other forms of energy do fireworks produce?

When *Minutes* Count . . .

If time is short, consider these options.

Conduct the Investigate as a **whole-class demonstration.** Have students observe the temperature reading each hour.

Use the Activity Video/DVD to model.

What Is Energy?

Fast Fact

A Real Light Show People use chemicals to make fireworks. The burning chemicals in the fireworks produce light and sound energy. In the Investigate, you will find out about another kind of energy.

406

 Science Background

Energy In the scientific sense, *energy* means "the ability to make something move or change." Every example of energy can be classified as either kinetic or potential. Kinetic energy is the energy of motion. Something that is moving has, obviously, the ability to move. In other words, it has energy. An object has potential energy due to either its position or the arrangement of its parts. A car at the top of a hill has potential energy because of its position—it might roll down the hill. A coiled spring has potential energy because of its arrangement—it might uncoil.

 Webliography
Keyword energy
www.hspscience.com

Observing Temperature

Materials • thermometer • clock

Procedure

1. With your group, find a place outside that is sunny all day long.

2. In the morning, have a group member place the thermometer on the ground, face up.

3. Wait a few minutes until the temperature reading stops changing.

4. Each member of the group should read and **record** the temperature.

5. **Observe** the thermometer once an hour for several hours. **Communicate** your observations in a line graph that shows time and temperature.

Step 2

Step 5

Draw Conclusions

1. What changes did you **observe**? What caused these changes?

2. **Inquiry Skill** Scientists use their **observations** to **infer** why things happen. The rising temperature on the thermometer was caused by energy. Where can you **infer** that the energy came from?

Investigate Further

Do you think you would see similar changes on a cloudy day? Make a hypothesis. **Plan and conduct a simple investigation** to test it.

407

---

2 Teach

Video Segment 3003

Time 5-10 minutes each hour

Grouping groups of 4

Lab Manual pages can be used to record results. Inquiry Skill Tips and Self-Assessment are also provided.

Tips and Guided Inquiry

A thermometer placed in direct sunlight may give a reading higher than the temperature of the air around it.

Why should each member of the group read and record the temperature? When each member collects data, there is less chance of incorrect readings or records.

Why should you take readings every hour instead of just whenever you get a chance? Taking regular readings allows students to calculate the rate of temperature changed.

Expected Results

Step 5: As the thermometer remains in the sun, the reading should rise or remain high.

Draw Conclusions

1. The hotter it was outside, the higher the temperature got. The amount of sun in the sky caused the changes.

2. from the sun

Inquiry Skill Mini-Lesson

Infer Remind students that inferring is making an assumption based on observations combined with prior knowledge and logical reasoning. Display the Transparency and discuss the questions. Limit student answers for the first question to just what is observable in the pictures, without any inferences or suppositions.

Inquiry Skill practice is provided in *Reading Support and Homework*.

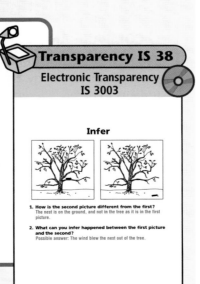

Transparency IS 38

Electronic Transparency IS 3003

Infer

1. **How is the second picture different from the first?** The nest is on the ground, and not in the tree as it is in the first picture.

2. **What can you infer happened between the first picture and the second?** Possible answer: The wind blew the nest out of the tree.

Investigate Further

Students can use this page in the *Lab Manual* for **Independent Inquiry**.

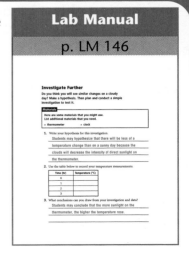

Lab Manual

p. LM 146

Investigate Further
Do you think you will see similar changes on a cloudy day? Make a hypothesis. Then plan and conduct a simple investigation to test it.

Materials
Here are some materials that you might use. List additional materials that you need.
• thermometer • clock

1. Write your hypothesis for this investigation. Students may hypothesize that there will be less of a temperature change than on a sunny day because the clouds will decrease the intensity of direct sunlight on the thermometer.

2. Use the table below to record your temperature measurements.

Time (hr)	Temperature (°C)
0	
1	
2	
3	

3. What conclusions can you draw from your investigation and data? Students may conclude that the more sunlight on the thermometer, the higher the temperature rose.

2 Teach
continued

VOCABULARY For Vocabulary Cards and activities, see *Reading Support and Homework.*

SCIENCE CONCEPTS Have students think of questions they may have about the science concepts. List the questions on the board. Have students review and discuss the questions as they complete the lesson.

 READING FOCUS SKILL

COMPARE AND CONTRAST Tell students that the information in this lesson is organized to help them compare and contrast science ideas. Use the Reading Mini-Lesson below to discuss a strategy that students can use to compare and contrast.

1 Develop Science Vocabulary

energy Remind students that a word can have more than one meaning. Explain that many words have an ordinary, everyday meaning and a very specific scientific meaning. Briefly discuss the everyday meanings of *energy*—"zip, pep, verve, get-up-and-go"—and then discuss the scientific meaning.

2 Key Science Concepts

Some things have the ability to move and some things don't. If a bicycle is moving, what can you say about it? It has the ability to move. **What is the scientific name for the ability to move?** energy **What can you say about any moving object?** It has energy.

3 Interpret Visuals

What do these two pictures have in common? Both show something moving —either the clapper or the wheel.

VOCABULARY	**SCIENCE CONCEPTS**	**READING FOCUS SKILL**
energy p. 408 kinetic energy p. 410 potential energy p. 410	▶ what energy is ▶ what the relationship between kinetic energy and potential energy is	 **COMPARE AND CONTRAST** Look for ways in which forms of energy are different.

alike ———— different

Some Sources of Energy

Think about a moving car. As long as the car is moving, it must be getting energy. Gasoline is burned to supply the energy that makes the car

1 move. **Energy** is the ability to make something move or change.

2 Now think about a boy riding a bike. The bike is moving, so the bike must be getting energy—but from where? The boy's muscles supply the energy to pedal the bike. Moving the pedals makes the bike move.

3 Moving water supplies the energy to turn the water wheel.

Lightning is a type of electric energy.

408

Reading Skill Mini-Lesson

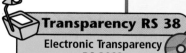 **COMPARE AND CONTRAST**

Lead a brief discussion of fuel as a source of stored energy. Encourage students to name different types of fuel they know about. Introduce the concept that food is a source of stored energy. Then display the Transparency and have students complete the chart.

Transparency RS 38

Electronic Transparency
RS 3003

Compare and Contrast

	Stored Energy	
	Food	Fuel
How They Are the Same	a way of storing energy	a way of storing energy
How They Are Different	eaten by people and animals	burned to make heat, light, or electricity

The boy needs energy to move his muscles. This energy comes from food. You need the energy from food to move your muscles. You also need energy to grow and change.

A seed sprouts and grows into a plant. The energy a plant needs to grow comes from sunlight.

Most of the energy on Earth comes from the sun. Its heat and light supply most of the energy we need.

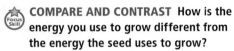 **COMPARE AND CONTRAST** How is the energy you use to grow different from the energy the seed uses to grow?

You know there is sound energy in this clock, because the clapper is moving.

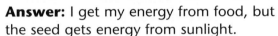

Electric energy causes this sign to light up.

 What types of energy does this picture show?

6

409

4 ▶ **Interpret Visuals**

Does every picture on this page show something moving? No; the neon sign isn't moving. **Does a neon sign ever move?** no **Does a neon sign change in some way?** Yes; it lights up when it's turned on.

5 ▶ **Inquiry Skills**

Predict What would happen to a plant if you kept it in a dark room all the time? It would die.

6 ▶ **Interpret Visuals**

Answer: sun and wind

7 ▶ **Compare and Contrast** (Focus Skill)

Answer: I get my energy from food, but the seed gets energy from sunlight.

Energy

Harcourt

8 ► Develop Science Vocabulary

kinetic energy Explain that *kinetic energy* is a compound term, and remind students that they already know the meaning of one of the words. Then explain that *kinetic* comes from the Greek word *kinein*, which means "to move." Some students may know that a mobile gets its name from the fact that it moves. Tell students that another name for a mobile is *kinetic sculpture.* If students remember that *kinetic* has to do with motion, they'll remember that kinetic energy is the energy of motion.

9 ► Interpret Visuals

How are these pictures related to each other? They all show the same thing at different times. **Which way does the time sequence move?** from left to right

10 ► Develop Science Vocabulary

potential energy Explain that *potential energy* is another compound term. Students are already familiar with the word *energy*, and some may be familiar with the term *potential.* It occurs often in everyday speech, from saying a student "has potential" to saying the runner on second base "represents the potential tying run." The word *potential* means "possible." Something that is in a position where it could possibly move—fall off a shelf, roll down a hill— has potential energy.

11 ► Key Science Concepts

Refer students to the pictures of the jack-in-the-box spring on the previous page. **Potential energy is the energy of position. What about the spring's position gives it potential energy?** The spring is bunched up. **An object with potential energy might possibly move. How might the spring move?** It might stretch out very quickly.

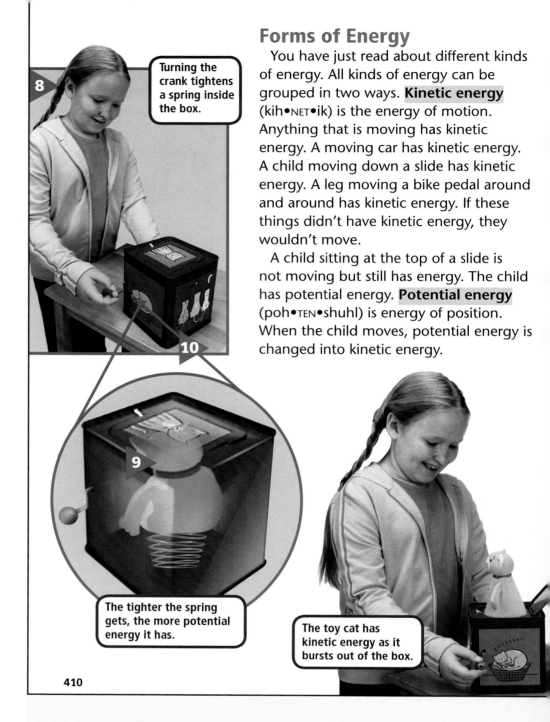

Turning the crank tightens a spring inside the box.

The tighter the spring gets, the more potential energy it has.

The toy cat has kinetic energy as it bursts out of the box.

410

Forms of Energy

You have just read about different kinds of energy. All kinds of energy can be grouped in two ways. **Kinetic energy** (kih•NET•ik) is the energy of motion. Anything that is moving has kinetic energy. A moving car has kinetic energy. A child moving down a slide has kinetic energy. A leg moving a bike pedal around and around has kinetic energy. If these things didn't have kinetic energy, they wouldn't move.

A child sitting at the top of a slide is not moving but still has energy. The child has potential energy. **Potential energy** (poh•TEN•shuhl) is energy of position. When the child moves, potential energy is changed into kinetic energy.

Reaching All Learners

ESL / ESOL Support

Language and Vocabulary

Students may be unfamiliar with the *-ing* ending.

Beginning Write the following pairs on the board: *moving down a slide/ sliding, moving a pedal/pedaling.* Ask students to circle the word part that tells that something is happening now.

Intermediate Write the following phrases on the board: *moving down a slide, moving a pedal.* For each phrase, have students write a single word that has the same meaning.

Advanced Write the following words on the board: *sliding, pedaling.* Have students devise sentences that contain these words.

For strategies and lesson support, see *ESL Support* pp. 14–17.

A battery has potential energy. This energy can be transferred to other forms. When the battery is used to make something move, it releases kinetic energy.

⭐ **COMPARE AND CONTRAST** What is the difference between kinetic energy and potential energy?

 **12**

Energy in Motion

Hold a rubber ball 500 cm above the ground. Drop the ball. How high does it bounce? Now drop the ball from 1 m, 1.5 m, and 2 m. Record your observations.

Science Up Close

How a Battery Works

Inside the battery are two powders. Each is mixed with a liquid to make a paste. The pastes are kept apart by a tube of fabric.

The two pastes have potential energy. When you put the battery in a circuit, the energy is changed into electric current.

One end of the battery touches a paste. The other end connects to the brass tube.

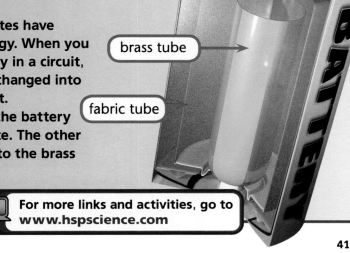

powder

brass tube

fabric tube

💻 For more links and activities, go to **www.hspscience.com**

411

 ⏱ 10 minutes

Energy in Motion

Materials: rubber ball, meter stick

Students should notice that as the height from which the ball is dropped increases, so does the height to which it bounces. Invite interested students to repeat the procedure a number of times, dropping the ball from a number of different heights, while taking and recording accurate measurements of the height of each bounce. Students can then organize and search the data to see if they can find a pattern.

Science Up Close

ONLINE EXPERIENCE
For animations and activities, visit
www.hspscience.com

▶ 12 Interpret Visuals

Tell students that a diagram like this is a cutaway diagram. How do you think it got that name? It looks as if a section of the battery has been cut away. **When would an author use a cutaway diagram?** when trying to show what the interior of something looks like or how the interior parts work

▶ 13 Compare and Contrast ⭐

Answer: Kinetic energy is the energy of motion, but potential energy is energy of position

14 ▶ Inquiry Skills

Draw Conclusions After the book falls, it lies flat on the floor. What kinds of energy does it have? It doesn't have any energy. **Why not?** It isn't moving, so it doesn't have kinetic energy. and it doesn't have the potential to move from trhe position it's in (unless the floor is very slanted), so it doesn't have potential energy.

15 ▶ Key Science Concepts

How could a book that's on a shelf have potential energy? If it's sitting on an edge, it could have the potential to tip over.

16 ▶ Compare and Contrast (Focus Skill)

Answer: The book sitting on the shelf has potential energy, but the falling book has kinetic energy.

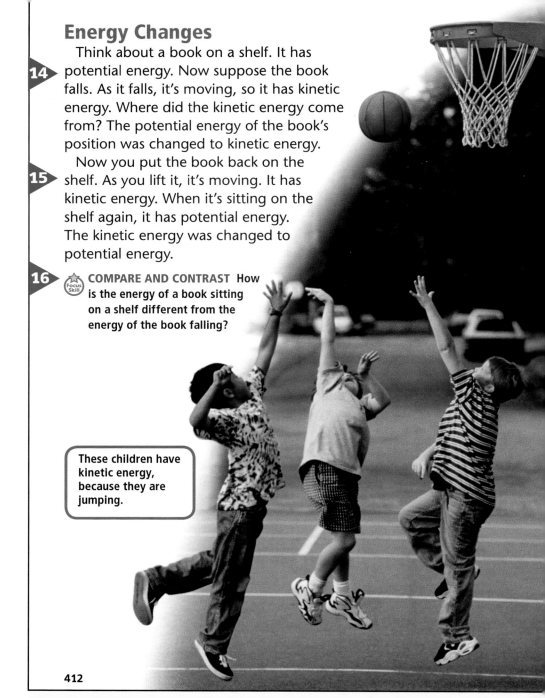

Energy Changes

14 ▶ Think about a book on a shelf. It has potential energy. Now suppose the book falls. As it falls, it's moving, so it has kinetic energy. Where did the kinetic energy come from? The potential energy of the book's position was changed to kinetic energy.

15 ▶ Now you put the book back on the shelf. As you lift it, it's moving. It has kinetic energy. When it's sitting on the shelf again, it has potential energy. The kinetic energy was changed to potential energy.

16 ▶ (Focus Skill) **COMPARE AND CONTRAST How is the energy of a book sitting on a shelf different from the energy of the book falling?**

These children have kinetic energy, because they are jumping.

412

(PROFESSIONAL DEVELOPMENT) **Science Background To Address Misconceptions**

Conserving Energy A fundamental law of the universe is that energy cannot be created or destroyed. Take the example of the car at the top of the hill. The car was moving as it drove up the hill. Therefore, it had kinetic energy. It stopped, and the kinetic energy was changed to potential energy. As the car rolls down the hill, it is moving, so it has kinetic energy. Where did the kinetic energy come from? The potential energy it had at the top of the hill is changed to kinetic energy. (The kinetic energy it had driving up the hill came from potential energy in the gasoline, which derived from the bodies of the plants and animals that formed the gasoline. But that is beyond the scope of this lesson.)

1. COMPARE AND CONTRAST Copy and complete this graphic organizer.

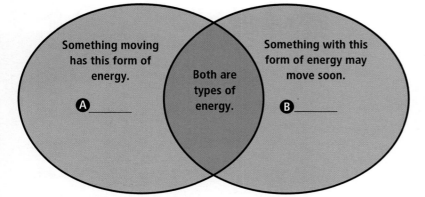

Something moving has this form of energy.

Ⓐ_____

Both are types of energy.

Something with this form of energy may move soon.

Ⓑ_____

2. SUMMARIZE Write two sentences that tell what this lesson is mainly about.

3. DRAW CONCLUSIONS A bike on its kickstand has potential energy. How could you change the energy to kinetic energy?

4. VOCABULARY Use each of the lesson vocabulary terms in a sentence that correctly shows its meaning.

Test Prep

5. Which type of energy do we get from the sun?

A. potential

B. electrical

C. light

D. kinetic

Links

Writing

Expository
Write a **friendly letter** telling a friend or relative what you learned about the different forms of energy.

Physical Education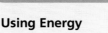

Using Energy
Make up a 30-second physical fitness routine that uses kinetic and potential energy. Do your routine for the class, and identify the kind of energy each move uses.

 For more links and activities, go to www.hspscience.com

413

Lesson Quick Study

The Lesson Quick Study in **Reading Support and Homework** provides the opportunity for students to practice inquiry skills, review lesson vocabulary, apply reading skills, and use critical thinking and problem solving.

Students can use the second page of the Lesson Quick Study to complete the graphic organizer from the Reading Review. The graphic organizer is also available on overhead and electronic transparencies.

Reading Support and Homework

p. RS 88	p. RS 89

---

3 Assess and Extend

Graphic Organizer

Transparency GO 7

Electronic Transparency IS 3003

1. Ⓐ Students should write "Something moving has this energy" in the Kinetic Energy box. Students should write "Something with this energy may move soon" in the Potential Energy box. Students should write "This energy can change into the other form of energy" in the box labeled Both.

2. Possible answer: Energy is the ability to make something move or change. There are two kinds of energy: kinetic and potential.

3. by tipping it over

4. Possible answers: We all need energy to move and grow. Something that is moving has kinetic energy. Energy of position is called potential energy.

5. C, light

Links

Writing If students have trouble getting started, suggest they look back at the graphic organizer and lesson summary they wrote earlier.

 Students can consult the *Writing Models* in *Teaching Resources* as they complete the Link. Rubrics are also provided.

Physical Education Student routines should show a variety of activities. Each activity should be correctly identified as displaying either kinetic (moving) or potential (preparing to move) energy.

Objectives

■ Measure the amount of energy transferred from sunlight to an object.

■ Identify the sources of types of energy people use for different purposes.

■ Define *temperature*.

Transparency DI 39
Electronic Transparency DI 3004

Daily Inquiry

Temperature Swap

Tool Kit

thermometer

Review Skill Measure, Observe

■ Fill a cup with 50 mL of cold water and another with 50 mL of warm water. Measure and record the water temperature.

What to Do

■ Mix the contents of the two cups together. What do you think the temperature of the mixed solution will be? Try it and find out. What happens to the temperature when you mix cold water with warm water?

1 Introduce

Build on Prior Knowledge

Use the Fast Fact for a discussion starter about the lesson topic.

What are some devices other than a barbecue grill that move heat energy to food?

What forms of energy besides heat do people use?

When *Minutes* Count . . .

If time is short, consider these options.

Conduct the Investigate as a **whole-class demonstration.** Be sure students note the temperature at each reading.

Use the Activity Video/DVD to model the Investigate. After previewing, students can conduct the Investigate in small groups.

How Can Energy Be Used?

Fast Fact

Something's Cooking People have been using thermal energy to cook food for tens of thousands of years. In the Investigate, you will observe thermal energy at work.

414

PROFESSIONAL DEVELOPMENT   **Science Background**

Using Energy Whether moving or at rest, humans use energy every moment. The heart beats constantly, the diaphragm moves the lungs constantly, and each individual cell constantly grows or changes. All this requires energy. The energy people use comes from the sun. Green plants use the energy in sunlight to produce long moleculesthat contain some of the energy from the sunlight. When people eat plants, their bodies absorb that energy. Animals absorb energy from the plants they eat, too. This energy reaches people when they eat meat.

Webliography
Key Word energy
www.hspscience.com

The Heat Is On

Materials • clear plastic cup • ice cubes • thermometer

Procedure

1. Fill a clear plastic cup with ice cubes. Place a thermometer in the cup. Place the cup in sunlight.

2. After several minutes, **record** the temperature inside the cup.

3. Continue to **record** the temperature inside the cup every half hour for three hours.

4. **Communicate** the data from your table by making a bar graph.

Step 1

Step 2

Draw Conclusions

1. What did you **observe** about the temperature and the ice? What caused these changes?

2. **Inquiry Skill** Scientists use **observations** and data to **infer** why things happen. What can you **infer** happens to an object placed in sunlight?

Investigate Further

What do you think happens to the temperature of water placed in a freezer? Make a **hypothesis.** Then test it.

415

Inquiry Skill Mini-Lesson

Infer Remind students that inferring is making an assumption based on observations combined with prior knowledge and logical reasoning. Display the Transparency and discuss the questions.

Inquiry Skill practice is provided in *Reading Support and Homework*.

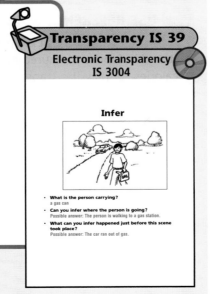

Transparency IS 39

Electronic Transparency
IS 3004

Infer

- **What is the person carrying?**
  a gas can
- **Can you infer where the person is going?**
  Possible answer: The person is walking to a gas station.
- **What can you infer happened just before this scene took place?**
  Possible answer: The car ran out of gas.

2

Time 3 hours

Grouping individuals

Video Segment 3004

Lab Manual pages can be used to record results. Inquiry Skill Tips and Self-Assessment are also provided.

Tips and Guided Inquiry

Students may have trouble reading somes types of thermomter in direct sunlight. Tell them it's okay to remove the thermometer from the cup in order to read it, as long as they read it and return it quickly.

Why should you use a clear cup for this investigation? Students will probably realize that a clear cup allows more sunlight to reach the water than an opaque cup would.

What other kind of graph could you make besides a bar graph? Some students may say that because the data show how a single element changes over time, a line graph could display the data as well as or better than a bar graph does.

Expected Results

Step 3: The temperature of the cup's contents should rise as long as the cup remains in direct sunlight.

Draw Conclusions

1. The temperature increased as the ice melted. Heat energy caused these changes.

2. I can infer that an object placed in sunlight will get warmer (gain heat).

Investigate Further

Students can use this page in the *Lab Manual* for **Independent Inquiry.**

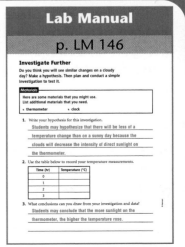

Lab Manual

p. LM 146

Investigate Further
Do you think you will see similar changes on a cloudy day? Make a hypothesis. Then plan and conduct a simple investigation to test it.

Materials
Here are some materials that you might use.
List additional materials that you need.
• thermometer • clock

1. Write your hypothesis for this investigation.
   Students may hypothesize that there will be less of a temperature change than on a sunny day because the clouds will decrease the intensity of direct sunlight on the thermometer.

2. Use the table below to record your temperature measurements.

Time (hr)	Temperature (°C)
0	
1	
2	
3	

3. What conclusions can you draw from your investigation and data?
   Students may conclude that the more sunlight on the thermometer, the higher the temperature rose.

2 Teach
continued

VOCABULARY For Vocabulary Cards and activities, see *Reading Support and Homework.*

SCIENCE CONCEPTS Have students turn the concept statement into a question and then use their prior knowledge to suggest responses. List the responses on the board. Have students review and revise the responses as they discuss the lesson.

 READING FOCUS SKILL

MAIN IDEA AND DETAILS Tell students that the information in this lesson is organized to help them recognize a main idea and the details that support it.

1 Key Science Concepts

What is the definition of *energy*? the ability to make something move or change

If something doesn't have energy, what can you say about it? It doesn't have the ability to move or change.

What do YOU wonder?

Have students look back at the photo on the chapter opener. **How does this picture illustrate the ideas on this page?** The wheat is absorbing the energy from the sun. When people eat the wheat, they absorb some of that energy.

2 Inquiry Skills

Infer If you eat a piece of meat instead of a plant, does it have energy? Yes **Where did the energy come from?** from the plants the animal ate

3 Critical Thinking

Do you need energy when you are asleep? yes **Why?** Some parts of the body, such as the heart, lungs, and blood are moving. Also, individual cells are growing and changing.

VOCABULARY	SCIENCE CONCEPTS	READING FOCUS SKILL
combustion p. 417 temperature p. 418	▶ how people use energy	MAIN IDEA AND DETAILS Look for details about ways people use energy.

1 Using Energy

Energy makes things move or change. Without it, we could not live.

2 The sun provides energy to plants to grow. You then get energy from eating the plants for food. After you eat, energy from the food moves through your body. The energy keeps you healthy and helps you grow.

3 Energy in your muscles lets you move. When you run or jump, energy moves from your leg muscles to make your body move.

It takes a lot of energy to make this big, heavy train move.

778

416

Reading Skill Mini-Lesson

 **USE REFERENCE SOURCES**

Explain to students that energy stored in food is measured in calories. Display the Transparency, and have students copy the chart. Ask students to refer to a nutrition guide and complete their charts by showing the amount of energy in foods they ate yesterday.

Transparency RS39

Electronic Transparency RS 3004

Use Reference Sources

Suppose this table shows some of the foods John ate in one day. Use the information given to fill in the blank boxes.

How Much Energy is in the Foods You Eat?			
Type of Food	Calories per Serving	Number of Servings	Number of Calories
cereal	100	1	100
skim milk	80	2	160
turkey slices	100	2.5	250
bread	40	2	80
banana	90	1	90
chicken	240	1	240
rice	60	2	120
green beans	25	2	50
Total Number of Calories John Ate			1090

Machines get energy in many ways. One way to get energy is from combustion. **Combustion** (kuhm•BUHS•chuhn) is another word for "burning." When fuels burn, they give off heat.

A car engine burns gasoline. The gasoline gives off energy that makes the car move. Some stoves burn gas. The gas gives off energy that cooks your food. Wood burning in a fireplace also gives off energy.

 MAIN IDEA AND DETAILS What happens during combustion?

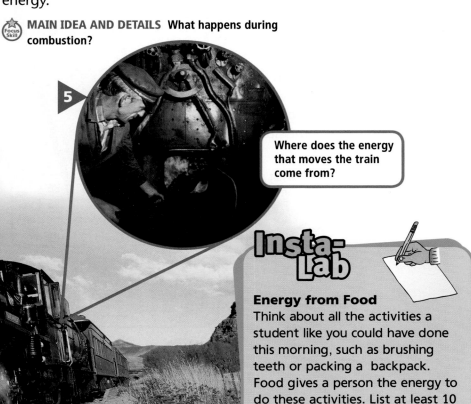

Where does the energy that moves the train come from?

Insta-Lab

Energy from Food

Think about all the activities a student like you could have done this morning, such as brushing teeth or packing a backpack. Food gives a person the energy to do these activities. List at least 10 activities someone might do each morning. Explain how someone might feel if he or she didn't have the energy from the foods.

417

4 ▶ **Develop Science Vocabulary**

combustion Provide students with more examples of combustion by explaining that combustion can take place at different speeds. In the barbecue grill shown in the lesson opener, the glowing coals are combusting slowly. In the firebox shown on this page, the combustion is happening quickly. When a stick of dynamite explodes, it combusts very, very quickly.

5 ▶ **Interpret Visuals**

Tell students this kind of picture is a callout. **What do the lines running back to the engine mean? They show the position in the engine of the object pictured in the callout photo. Answer:** from the burning of wood or coal in the firebox

6 ▶ **Main Idea and Details**

Answer: Heat energy is given off.

Insta-Lab

 5 minutes

A Model Thermometer

Materials: pencil, paper

Students should note that getting to school is more difficult without energy from food. Point out that concentration and memory are also affected without proper food energy.

Reaching All Learners

 **ESL / ESOL Support**

Language and Vocabulary

Students may have difficulty pronouncing the *-tion* ending after an *s*.

Beginning Write the following words on the board: *combustion, question, motion, direction*. Ask students to circle the part of each word that is pronounced "chun or "shun."

Intermediate Write sentences that use the words *combustion, question, motion,* and *direction*. Have students say each sentence aloud.

Advanced Write the following words on the board: *combustion, question, motion, direction*. Have students write a paragraph that contains these words and then read their sentences aloud.

For strategies and lesson support, see *ESL Support* pp. 166–169.

7 Develop Science Vocabulary

temperature Most students are familiar with the concept of temperature, and many have had their temperatures taken. Help students understand the difference between temperature and heat. Tell them that temperature is a measure of something (heat), just as their age is a measure of something (how long they've been alive).

8 Interpret Data

Turning the thermometer into a number line may help students grasp the relative temperatures shown. Have students place a sheet of blank paper over this page and trace the markings on the thermometer. They can then plot the temperature points onto their number lines. **Answer:** boiling water

9 Interpret Visuals

Answers: light; Possible answer: a photographer **Answer:** Possible answers: a pilot, a balloonist, a weather forecaster

10 Main Idea and Details (Focus Skill)

Answer: Possible answers: heat energy, light energy, sound energy, wind energy, electrical energy

---

Measuring Energy

You have read that there are different types and uses of energy. There are different ways to measure energy, too. The way energy is measured depends on the type of energy.

You have probably seen a thermometer like the one shown on this page. Thermometers are used to measure temperature.

7 Temperature is the measure of how hot or cold something is. Not all energy is measured with a thermometer, though. For example, wind speed is measured with an anemometer.

10 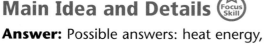 MAIN IDEA AND DETAILS What are some kinds of energy that can be measured?

9

This machine measures wind energy.

What type of energy do you think this light meter measures?

---

8 Math in Science

Different Temperatures
Which requires more thermal energy, melting butter or boiling water?

100°C
212°F
water boils

37°C
98.6°F
human body

0°C
32°F
water freezes

F   C

36°C
95°F
butter melts

Reaching All Learners — Enrichment

On-Level Reader

Target: Students who need reinforcement and enrichment of science concepts and vocabulary.

Enrichment Strategy: The On-Level Reader reinforces and enriches lesson content and vocabulary by using different visuals and examples. The reader also reinforces the Reading Focus Skills in each lesson.

Assess: Use strategies in the back of the reader to assess student understanding.

All About Energy
Harcourt

1. **MAIN IDEA AND DETAILS** Copy and complete this graphic organizer.

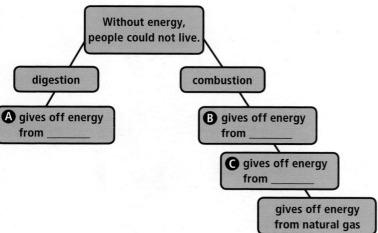

Without energy, people could not live.

digestion

combustion

A gives off energy from _____

B gives off energy from _____

C gives off energy from _____

gives off energy from natural gas

2. **SUMMARIZE** Write a summary of this lesson by writing the most important idea from each page.

3. **DRAW CONCLUSIONS** Matt tells his friend that he uses the sun's energy, even at night. How can this be?

4. **VOCABULARY** What word is a synonym of *combustion*?

Test Prep

5. Which type of energy does a thermometer measure?

   A. electric energy
   B. kinetic energy
   C. light energy
   D. sound energy

Links

Writing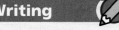

Expository
Find out how a light meter measures energy. Then write a **description** of what you learn. Share the description with a family member.

Math

Make a Graph
The average temperature of the human body is 37°C. Find the average body temperatures of three other animals of your choice. Make a bar graph to show your findings.

For more links and activities, go to **www.hspscience.com**

419

3 Assess and Extend

Graphic Organizer

Transparency GO 39
Electronic Transparency GO 3004

1. **A** food; **B** gasoline; **C** wood

2. Possible answer: Without energy, we could not live. Energy is given off during combustion. Each kind of energy can be measured.

3. Matt's body needs energy to stay alive. He gets energy from the food he eats. Since the food he eats uses the sun as an energy source, he uses the sun even at night.

4. Possible answer: *burning*

5. **B**, heat energy

Links

Writing Student descriptions should explain how light meters measure light energy at a certain point by converting the light energy to electrical energy which can be measured by the light meter.

 Students can consult *Writing Models* in **Teaching Resources** as they complete the link. Rubrics are also provided.

Math Check that the bar graphs are properly labeled and values match those found in student research for a variety of animals.

Lesson Quick Study

The Lesson Quick Study in **Reading Support and Homework** provides the opportunity for students to practice inquiry skills, review lesson vocabulary, apply reading skills, and use critical thinking and problem solving.

Students can use the second page of the Lesson Quick Study to complete the graphic organizer from the Reading Review. The graphic organizer is also available on overhead and electronic transparencies.

Reading Support and Homework

p. RS 90

Lesson 2 - How Can Energy Be Used?

1. **Inquiry Skill Practice–Infer**
   Larry left a glass of cold water on top of a picnic table on a hot, sunny afternoon. What do you infer happened to the cold water in the glass! Why?
   Possible answers: The temperature of the water increased. The water gained heat because the glass was placed in sunlight.

2. **Use Vocabulary**
   Complete each sentence with the correct term from the box.
   A thermometer is a tool that measures temperature.
   The combustion given off by the gas burning in the motor keeps the car moving.
   | combustion |
   | temperature |

3. **Reading Skill Practice–Main Idea and Details**
   Read the selection. Underline the main idea. List at least two details about the main idea.
   There are many ways to measure the energy around us. Different tools are used to measure different kinds of energy. An electric meter measures the electricity used in a house or business. Electric energy is used for lights and appliances. A thermometer can measure temperature. A thermometer is used to take body temperature or to measure heat energy.
   Possible answers: An electric meter measures electricity. A thermometer measures temperature.

p. RS 91

4. **Main Idea and Details**
   Use this space to complete the graphic organizer shown in the Reading Review of the Student Edition.
   Main Idea: Without energy, people could not live.
   Digestion   Combustion
   gives off energy from **food**
   gives off energy from **gasoline**
   gives off energy from **wood**
   gives off energy from natural gas.

5. **Critical Thinking and Problem Solving**
   Suppose you are at a camping site. Think about the many ways energy is being used. List at least three examples.
   Possible answers: Wood is burning in a campfire. Campers are swimming or riding horses. Campers are walking through the woods. Campers are eating. Fish are jumping in a pond. Anything that is moving is using energy.

Objectives

- Investigate the power of wind to move objects.
- Describe ways people can conserve energy resources.
- Explain the difference between renewable and nonrenewable energy resources.

Transparency DI 40

Electronic Transparency DI 3005

Daily Inquiry

Made in the Shade

 thermometers

Review Skill Measure, Observe, Compare, Record Data, Display Data

What to Do

- Work with a partner. Place one thermometer in the shade. Place another thermometer in direct sunlight.
- Every minute, measure and record the temperatures shown on both thermometers.
- Make a graph that displays the temperatures of the two thermometers.

1 Introduce

Build on Prior Knowledge

Use the Fast Fact for a discussion starter about the lesson topic.

Where would we be in this picture?

Is the area around us bright or dark?

When *Minutes* Count . . .

If time is short, consider these options.

Conduct the Investigate as a **whole-class demonstration.** Be sure students can see the windmill turn.

Use the Activity Video/DVD to model the Investigate. After previewing, students can conduct the Investigate in small groups.

Lesson **3**

Why Is Energy Important?

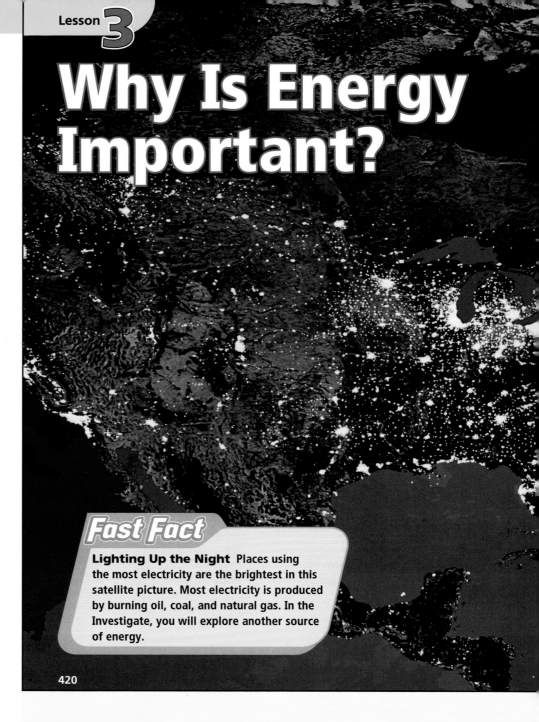

Lighting Up the Night Places using the most electricity are the brightest in this satellite picture. Most electricity is produced by burning oil, coal, and natural gas. In the Investigate, you will explore another source of energy.

420

 PROFESSIONAL DEVELOPMENT   **Science Background**

Fossil Fuels Millions of years ago, as plants and animals died, some of their remains settled together on the bottoms of lakes or swamps. Over time, more and more earth formed on top of the remains. Deep underground, the remains were subjected to tremendous heat and pressure that converted them into what we call fossil fuels—oil, coal, and natural gas. Because it would take millions of years for more of these fuels to form, they are considered nonrenewable. Solar, wind, and geothermal power are considered renewable. They can provide energy indefinitely; however, current technology doesn't allow them to produce energy as cheaply and efficiently as fossil fuels.

Webliography
Keyword fossil fuels
www.hspscience.com

Make a Paper Windmill

Materials • white paper • ruler • scissors • pushpin • pencil with eraser

Procedure

1. Draw a 12.75-cm square with dotted lines and dots, as shown.

2. Use scissors to cut out the square.

3. Cut along each of the dotted lines to within 1.25 cm of the center.

4. Take each corner that has a dot, and fold it toward the center of the square to make a vane.

5. CAUTION: Pushpins are sharp! Put the pushpin through the center of all the folded corners and into the eraser of the pencil. Be sure the vanes turn freely.

6. You have just made a model of a windmill. Face your windmill into a strong breeze, or blow on it.

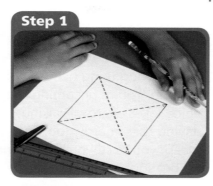
Step 1

Step 4

Draw Conclusions

1. What did you observe when you faced the paper windmill into the breeze?

2. **Inquiry Skill** Scientists use models to help them understand processes. How does a windmill work? What kind of energy turns a windmill?

Investigate Further

Fold each corner with a dot backward instead of forward. What do you predict will happen to your windmill in a breeze? Try it.

421

Inquiry Skill Mini-Lesson

Use Models Display the Transparency and have students answer the questions. Encourage students to brainstorm as many ideas as possible in response to the second question.

Inquiry Skill practice is provided in *Reading Support and Homework*.

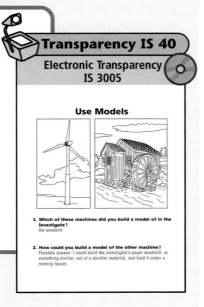

Transparency IS 40

Electronic Transparency IS 3005

Use Models

1. Which of these machines did you build a model of in the Investigate?
the windmill

2. How could you build a model of the other machine?
Possible answer: I could build the Investigate's paper windmill, or something similar, out of a sturdier material, and hold it under a running faucet.

2

Video Segment 3005

Time 20 minutes

Grouping individuals

Lab Manual pages can be used to record results. Inquiry Skill Tips and Self-Assessment are also provided.

Tips and Guided Inquiry

Students may have difficulty securing the corners while attaching the wheel to a pencil at the same time. Suggest they use tape to hold the corners in place and use a pushpin to attach the wheel to a pencil.

Why are you building a model of a windmill instead of a full-size windmill? Students will realize that a full-size windmill would be too large, too expensive, and too difficult to build.

In what kinds of situations would a scientist use a model instead of the real thing? Students may mention other situations in which the real thing would not be practical, such as building a wind tunnel to test a model plane, or when it would not be possible, such as using a computer model to study the galaxy.

Expected Results

Step 5: The windmill will turn.

Draw Conclusions

1. The windmill began to move (spin).

2. When wind catches in the vanes of a windmill, the wind pushes the vanes, and they begin to move. A windmill makes use of wind energy.

Investigate Further

Students can use this page in the *Lab Manual* for **Independent Inquiry**.

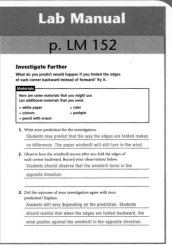

Lab Manual

p. LM 152

Investigate Further
What do you predict would happen if you folded the edges of each corner backward instead of forward? Try it.

Materials
Here are some materials that you might use. List additional materials that you need.
• white paper   • ruler
• scissors   • pushpin
• pencil with eraser

1. Write your prediction for the investigation.
Students may predict that the way the edges are folded makes no difference. The paper windmill will still turn in the wind.

2. Observe how the windmill moves after you fold the edges of each corner backward. Record your observations below.
Students should observe that the windmill turns in the opposite direction.

3. Did the outcome of your investigation agree with your prediction? Explain.
Answers will vary depending on the prediction. Students should realize that when the edges are folded backward, the wind pushes against the windmill in the opposite direction.

2 Teach
continued

VOCABULARY For Vocabulary Cards and activities, see *Reading Support and Homework*.

SCIENCE CONCEPTS Ask students to preview the lesson and suggest places where the concepts may be addressed.

 READING FOCUS SKILL

MAIN IDEA AND DETAILS Tell students that the information in this lesson is organized to help them recognize a main idea and the details that support it.

1 ▶ Critical Thinking

What are some other ways that communities use energy? Possible answers: to heat and/cool homes, for street lights and traffic lights, to run machines in a hospital

2 ▶ Interpret Visuals

Answer: from the food they are eating

3 ▶ Main Idea and Details

Answer: to cook food, to light homes, to power cars

VOCABULARY
resource p. 423
fossil fuels p. 423
nonrenewable resources p. 424
renewable resources p. 424

SCIENCE CONCEPTS
▶ how important energy is
▶ why it's important to save energy

READING FOCUS SKILL

MAIN IDEA AND DETAILS
Look for details about saving energy.

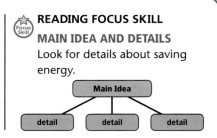

The Importance of Energy

Every living thing needs energy. You are still growing. You're becoming bigger and taller, which takes energy. Walking, running, and playing uses energy, too. Even when you are asleep, you're still breathing and your heart is still beating. That takes energy, too.

1 Communities also need energy. We use energy to cook our food. We use it to light our homes. We use it to run our cars.

3 **MAIN IDEA AND DETAILS** What are three ways communities use energy?

These people are eating foods that will give them energy.

422

Reading Skill Mini-Lesson

 DISTINGUISH FACT FROM OPINION

Lead a brief discussion about facts and opinions. Remind students that a statement that can be proved either true or false is a fact. If a statement can't be proved either true or false, it's an opinion.

Display the Transparency. Read each sentence, and have the class discuss whether it expresses a fact or an opinion.

Transparency RS 40

Electronic Transparency RS 3005

Distinguish Fact from Opinion

Statement	Fact or Opinion
1. Fossil fuels take millions of years to form.	fact
2. Renewable resources are better than nonrenewable resources.	opinion
3. The Sun's energy can be used to make electricity.	fact
4. Communities should try to use less energy.	opinion
5. Wind power is really cool.	opinion
6. Wind power is a renewable resource.	fact

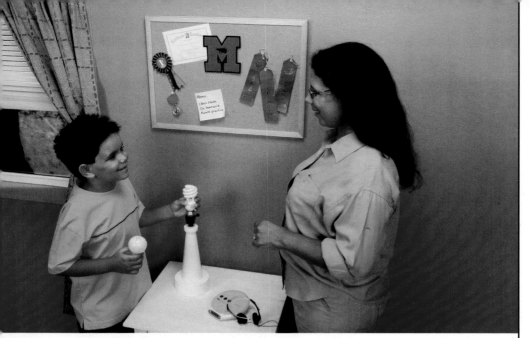

Ways to Save Energy

Coal, oil, and natural gas are all energy resources. A **resource** is something in nature that people can use. Energy resources are used to produce energy.

Coal, oil, and natural gas are called **fossil fuels**. They come from the remains of long-ago plants and animals. Fossil fuels can't be replaced. When they are used up, there will be no more. So it's important to save them and make them last longer. You save resources when you reduce the amount of energy you use.

 MAIN IDEA AND DETAILS Why is it important to save energy?

▲ This boy is replacing an old light bulb with a new one. The new kind of bulb gives off the same amount of light as the old bulb but uses less energy.

Save Fossil Fuels
With a partner, design and make a table about fossil fuels. List as many fossil fuels as you can. Then list all the ways you can think of for people to use less of each fossil fuel. Share your table with your classmates.

423

4 ▶ Develop Science Vocabulary

resource Students may not readily grasp just how broad this term is. Ask student volunteers for examples, such as the energy resources mentioned here, food resources such as wheat and corn, mineral resources such as iron and aluminum, or other resources such as clay (pottery) and sand (glass).

fossil fuels Remind students that fossils are the remains of things that lived long ago. The word comes from the Latin word *fodere*, meaning "to dig up." Like fossils, fossil fuels have to be dug out of the earth.

5 ▶ Inquiry Skills

Infer **How long do fossils take to form?** millions of years **How long do fossil fuels take to form?** millions of years **Why do we say that when fossil fuels are used up, there won't be any more?** because it will be millions of years before more are formed

6 ▶ Main Idea and Details

Answer: so that energy resources will last as long as possible

  15 minutes

Save Fossil Fuels

Materials: pen and paper

You may want to provide reference sources, such as books on energy or on conservation, to help students with their tables.

7 Develop Science Vocabulary

nonrenewable resources and renewable resources Write the root *new* on the board. Then add the prefix *re-* and have students name and define the new word. (renew: "make new again") Add the suffix *-able*, and have students name and define this new word. (renewable: "able to be made new again") Ask students for examples of energy resources that are renewable. (wind, water, solar, geothermal) Now, add the prefix *non-*, and have students discuss the new word. (nonrenewable: "not able to be made new again")

8 Interpret Visuals

How did the photographer manage to get two photos' worth of information into this one photo? by putting an individual use of geothermal energy— people in the water— in the foreground and a community's use of geothermal energy— the smokestacks in the city—in the background.

9 Main Idea and Details (Focus Skill)

Answer: oil, coal, natural gas

Other Energy Resources

It took millions of years for fossil fuels to form. They are said to be **nonrenewable resources**, because more fossil fuels cannot be made. *Nonrenewable* means "unable to be replaced."

Some resources are **renewable resources**, or resources that can be replaced. In the Investigate, you saw that wind can move things. Wind can turn windmills to produce electricity. Solar energy, or the sun's energy, can also be used to produce electricity.

9 (Focus Skill) **MAIN IDEA AND DETAILS** What are three nonrenewable resources?

This water is warmed by geothermal (jee•oh•THER•muhl) energy, or heat from deep within Earth. That same heat provides power to the city.

424

Reaching All Learners — ESL / ESOL Support

Language and Vocabulary

Students may not be familiar with the prefix *non-*.

Beginning Write on the board the words *nonrenewable, nonfiction, nonstop*. Have students circle the part of each word that is the same. Explain that this part, *non-*, means "not."

Intermediate Ask students to respond with words that mean "not renewable" (nonrenewable), "not fiction" (nonfiction), and "not stopping" (nonstop).

Advanced Have students use each of these words in a sentence: *nonrenewable, nonfiction, nonstop*.

For strategies and lesson support, see *ESL Support* pp. 170–173.

1. **MAIN IDEA AND DETAILS** Copy and complete this graphic organizer.

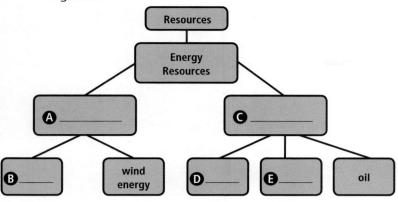

Resources

Energy Resources

 A _____

C _____

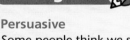 B _____

wind energy

D _____

E _____

oil

2. **SUMMARIZE** Use your completed graphic organizer to write a lesson summary.

3. **DRAW CONCLUSIONS** As water plunges over Niagara Falls, it turns machines that produce electricity. Is moving water a renewable energy resource or a nonrenewable energy resource? Explain.

4. **VOCABULARY** Use each lesson vocabulary word in a sentence that correctly shows its meaning.

Test Prep

5. Which of the following is a nonrenewable energy resource?

A. electricity
B. coal
C. water
D. wind

Links

Writing

Persuasive
Some people think we should rely more on renewable energy resources than we do now. Write a **letter** to your local newspaper, stating your opinion.

Literature

Saving Resources
Read a book about ways to save resources. Write a summary of the book to share with a first grader.

💻 **For more links and activities, go to www.hspscience.com**

425

Lesson Quick Study

The Lesson Quick Study in *Reading Support and Homework* provides the opportunity for students to practice inquiry skills, review lesson vocabulary, apply reading skills, and use critical thinking and problem solving.

Students can use the second page of the Lesson Quick Study to complete the graphic organizer from the Reading Review. The graphic organizer is also available on overhead and electronic transparencies.

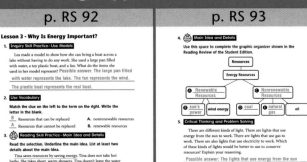

Reading Support and Homework

p. RS 92

p. RS 93

---

3 Assess and Extend

Graphic Organizer

Transparency GO 40
Electronic Transparency GO 3005

1. Ⓐ renewable resources; Ⓑ the sun's power or geothermal power; Ⓒ nonrenewable resources; Ⓓ coal; Ⓔ natural gas

2. Possible answer: People need energy. Our energy resources are very important. Nonrenewable resources, like oil, coal, and natural gas, can't be made again, so we need to make them last as long as possible. Other energy resources, such as wind power and the sun's power, are renewable.

3. Renewable; water pours continuously over the falls.

4. Possible answers: A resource is something found in nature that people use. A nonrenewable resource can't be replaced after it's used up. Oil, coal, and natural gas are sometimes called fossil fuels. A renewable resource can always be replaced

5. Ⓑ, coal

Links

Writing If students have trouble getting started, suggest they discuss their opinions aloud before trying to set them to paper.

 Students can consult *Writing Models* in **Teaching Resources** as they complete the link. Rubrics are also provided.

Literature Students may need assistance choosing an appropriate book. Emphasize the need to summarize the book by listing only the major points being made.

Technology

Objectives

- Discuss how scientists work to improve the lives of heart patients.
- Describe how the AbioCor works.

1 Introduce

Preview/Set a Purpose

Have students preview the article by reading the headings and looking at the pictures. Ask students to identify the main idea of the article.

2 Teach

Chapter Concepts

An understanding of how energy is transformed will naturally lead to questions about how the AbioCor uses energy to operate.

What type of energy does the internal battery have before it is used by the AbioCor? Students may answer that the internal battery has potential energy or chemical energy stored in it.

Describe how energy changes in the AbioCor. Potential energy from the outside battery transforms into electrical energy when it travels through the coil. The electrical energy changes into potential energy in the internal battery. The potential energy in the internal battery changes to kinetic energy when it is used by the artificial heart.

Inquiry Skills

Hypothesize Scientists often use one type of new technology to develop other, related types of technology. Ask small groups of students to hypothesize how the technology used to develop the AbioCor may be used in other types of technology. Have student groups put together oral presentations to share with the class about their hypotheses.

SCIENCE Spin from WEEKLY READER®
Technology

Batteries Included

The doors of an emergency room in a big city hospital burst open. Heart attack! shouts the medic. Soon the patient is in the operating room. But doctors don't want to wait for a heart transplant from another patient. Instead, doctors insert an artificial heart to save the patient's life.

426

PROFESSIONAL DEVELOPMENT Science Background

Artificial Hearts Doctors have used both external and internal artificial hearts to replace diseased hearts in patients. Recent research has focused on internal hearts to help recovering patients. Share the following information about artificial hearts with students:

- The first artificial heart was the Jarvik-7. It was implanted into Barney Clark in 1982. He lived for 112 days. The second recipient lived 620 days.
- The Jarvik-7 had two major problems: The patient had to be hooked to an external air compressor, and there was an increased risk of stroke.
- The ventricular assist device (VAD) is a pump that can be used in people who have a partially damaged heart. The VAD does not require the heart to be replaced. Instead, it helps the damaged part of the heart work better.

Although it hasn't happened yet, this type of scene could happen if the makers of the *AbioCor* are successful. The *AbioCor* is a battery-operated, replacement heart that weighs about two pounds.

A Life-Saver

Scientists spent about 30 years designing the *AbioCor*. The replacement heart is different from earlier types of devices. This device fits completely inside the body of a patient. There is no need for wires to connect through the skin to an outside power source. This way a patient can be free to walk around without being hooked up to any machines.

Although the heart is not yet approved by the government, it is being tested in some patients. The first patient received an *AbioCor* about four years ago. Scientists hope that the government might soon approve the heart to be used in hospitals.

THINK ABOUT IT

1. What other lifesaving devices might batteries be used in?
2. Why would patients want a replacement heart that runs on batteries instead of being plugged into a power source?

How It Works

The *AbioCor* gets its power from two lithium batteries. One battery is inside the patient and the other battery is outside the patient. Each battery has a set of coils. The outside battery pack can constantly recharge the inside battery. The outside battery does this by sending electricity from its coil, through the skin, to the coil of the inside battery.

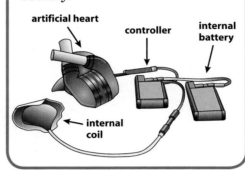

artificial heart
controller
internal battery
internal coil

Find out more! Log on to
www.hspscience.com

427

3 Wrap Up and Assess

3 Wrap Up and Assess

Think About It

1. Student answers will vary. Accept all reasonable answers.
2. Students may answer that by using batteries instead of being plugged in, patients can move around more easily and maintain a more normal lifestyle.

Writing Link

Expository Writing Have students write a report that describes the AbioCor and explains how it is different from a human heart transplant and earlier replacement hearts.

Inspire Inquiry

Inquiry starts with wonder and with asking questions. Sometimes the questions are just about things people want to know. Sometimes they are problems that people want to solve.

■ Brainstorm with students a list of advantages and disadvantages the AbioCor has over other options for people with heart problems.

■ Ask students to list any questions they have about AbioCor or other replacement organs developed by scientists. Write their questions on the board.

■ Discuss with students how they could answer the questions that they asked. Invite interested students to research more about artificial organs, including AbioCor. Encourage students to share their findings with the rest of the class.

Objectives

- Knows how problems can be solved by people applying scientific processes to create inventions.
- Understands the need for inventors to consider how their inventions will affect other people.

1 Introduce

Preview/Set a Purpose

Ask students to name as many inventions as they can. List them on the board. Next to each, write how the invention helps people. Ask students to write three sentences answering the question: **How can new technology help people?**

2 Teach

The Work of Scientists

Ask students to think about how and why Ryan Patterson invented the special glove.

Why did Ryan Patterson want to make a glove that changes sign language into written language? He wanted to help people who are deaf communicate better.

What materials did Ryan need to make his glove? He needed a glove, computer chips, wires, and a monitor.

How might this invention help people who are deaf? They might be able to communicate better with people who don't know sign language.

3 Wrap Up and Assess

Think About It

Ask students how inventors use existing ideas and materials to make a new product.

What parts of Ryan's glove did other people invent? They invented all the parts.

What was new about Ryan's invention? Ryan combined the parts in a new way to make a new use for them.

SCIENCE Spin from WEEKLY READER
People

A Handy Idea

Ryan Patterson invented a special glove to help people that are deaf. Many people who are deaf use sign language to communicate. The glove can change sign language motions into written alphabet letters. The alphabet letters show up on a display screen.

Each finger of the glove has a computer chip on it. Tiny wires lead from the fingers to a small screen. The chips chang the finger spelling to alphabet letters. The letters are displayed on the screen. This 18-year-old inventor ha won many national science contests.

 Find out more! Log on to **www.hspscience.com**

428

PROFESSIONAL DEVELOPMENT — Science Background

More Inquiry

Have students work in groups of three or four to brainstorm ideas for a new invention. Explain that many new inventions are either improvements to existing products, or devices made to solve a certain problem.

- Invite each group to decide on a problem that needs to be solved or a product that needs improvement. For ideas, have students conduct interviews or surveys of their families and schoolmates.
- Allow time for groups to brainstorm ideas for inventions.
- Have students make a list of all the ideas from their group. Next to each idea, students should write how the invention would be helpful to people.
- Encourage students to list the materials they will need for their invention.

SCIENCE Projects

for Home or School

You Can Do It!

Leaping Coin

Procedure

1. Put the bottle in a freezer for 10–15 minutes. Next dip the mouth part of the bottle in the water.

2. Wet the quarter by dipping it into the water. Put the quarter over the bottle's mouth.

3. Put your hands around the sides of the bottle, and keep them still. Record your observations.

Materials
- glass bottle
- quarter
- small bowl of water

Draw Conclusions
Why do you think this happened to the quarter?

Design Your Own Investigation

Learn About Solar Energy

What is solar energy? How can you measure it? Can you build a device that uses solar energy for power? Design one or more investigations that will help you find out more about solar energy. Then gather the materials you need, and carry out your investigations.

429

You Can Do It!

Quick and Easy Project

Light Bulb Energy

Objectives

- Use an unusual tool to detect the rising of heated air.

• Tips and Hints

Warn students not to touch the bulbs when they are on, because the bulbs will be very hot.

• Draw Conclusions

The pinwheel began to turn because it was being pushed by rising air that had been heated by the light bulb.

• Extend the Activity

Have interested students experiment with developing pinwheel that will turn the fastest when held over the light bulb.

Design Your Own Investigation

What Is Solar Energy?

Objectives

- Design and conduct simple investigations to determine the nature of solar energy and find a way to measure it.

Inspire Inquiry

Use the activity as an at-home investigation or suggestion for a science fair project. Have students use the investigation as a starting point for developing their own questions and ideas for research. Ask students to share their plans and ideas with you and the class and work together to help make the investigation procedure better.

Reproducible copies of these activities are provided in Teaching Resources.

LESSON 3 ■ 429

Chapter 12

Vocabulary Review (5 pts. each)

1. fossil fuels
2. renewable
3. potential energy
4. combustion
5. resource
6. energy
7. nonrenewable
8. kinetic energy

Check Understanding (5 pts. each)

9. B, the food you eat
10. F, potential energy
11. D, CD 4
12. I, a thermometer
13. B, light energy
14. G, oil
15. D, water
16. G fossil fuels

Vocabulary Review

Use the terms below to complete the sentences. The page numbers tell you where to look in the chapter if you need help.

energy p. 408
kinetic energy p. 410
potential energy p. 410
combustion p. 417
resource p. 423
fossil fuels p. 423
nonrenewable resource p. 424
renewable resource p. 424

1. Oil, coal, and natural gas are resources called _____.

2. A resource that can be replaced is said to be _____.

3. Energy of position is _____.

4. Gasoline gives off energy during _____.

5. Something in nature that people can use is a _____.

6. The ability to make something move or change is _____.

7. A resource that can't be replaced are _____.

8. Energy of motion is _____.

Check Understanding

Write the letter of the best choice.

9. Where does the energy you need to grow come from?
   A. from potential energy
   B. from the food you eat
   C. from fossil fuels
   D. from wind energy

10. Which kind of energy does a book sitting on a shelf have?
    F. potential energy
    G. light energy
    H. speed energy
    I. kinetic energy

11. Which CD has kinetic energy?
    A. CD 1   C. CD 3
    B. CD 2   D. CD 4

Harcourt School Publishers
Online Assessment

Harcourt School Publishers Online Assessment provides even more options. For a preview, go to:
www.hspscience.com

Portfolio Assessment

Have students select their best work from the following suggestions:

- **Links,** pp. 413, 419, 425
- **Investigate,** pp. 407, 415, 421
- **Insta-Lab,** pp. 410, 423
- **Science Projects,** p. 429

See **Assessment Guide** pp. AGxx-AGxxiv.

12. MAIN IDEA AND DETAILS Which tool measures how hot or cold something is?

    F. an anemometer

    G. a light meter

    H. a sound meter

    I. a thermometer

13. Which kind of energy do people need to see things?

    A. sound energy

    B. light energy

    C. kinetic energy

    D. electrical energy

14. COMPARE AND CONTRAST Which resource can't be replaced?

    F. air

    G. oil

    H. water

    I. wind

15. Which resource is constantly being renewed?

    A. coal

    B. fossil fuels

    C. natural gas

    D. water

16. Which of the following takes millions of years to form?

    F. a plant

    G. a fossil fuel

    H. an energy need

    I. a hot spring

Inquiry Skills

17. Suppose it's a sunny July morning in your town. What hypothesis can you make about what will happen to the temperature? How could you check your hypothesis?

18. Suppose you have two ice cubes. You place one of the ice cubes outside in the direct sunlight and the other ice cube outside under the shade. Infer what will happen to each ice cube.

Critical Thinking

19. What changes can solar energy cause to a person lying in the sun?

20. List five ways you use energy in your home.

431

Inquiry Skills (5 pts. each)

17. Answers will vary, but for most places in North America, the temperature will rise during the day.

18. It would take longer for ice in the shade to melt.

Critical Thinking

(5 pts. each)

19. Solar energy can cause a person's skin to feel warm, to sweat, and to burn.

20. Possible answers: to see at night; to watch television; to heat water

Chapter Test

See **Assessment Guide** pages AG92-96 for a Chapter Test and Performance Task, with rubric. Assessment options appear on page 404H.

Performance Assessment

Water Power

Have students build a water trough of aluminum foil, place it on a tilted cookie sheet and place the pin wheels from the Investigate at the bottom. Have students vary the positions and angles of both components so the wheel turns at maximum speed. Have students determine the best location for a hydroelectric plant.

Rubric for Performance Assessment

Preparation Provide aluminum foil, a cookie sheet, and water

Scoring Rubric—Performance Indicators

_____ Makes aluminum-foil "river bed" along which water can flow

_____ Build setup in which flowing water causes a water wheel to turn

_____ Varies the relative positions of the water flow and the water wheel, and determines which is most efficient

_____ Generalizes results to suggest preferred locations for real-world hydroelectric plants

Observations and Rubric Scores

    3   2   1   0

CHAPTER 13 LESSON PLANNER

Lesson	Pacing	Vocabulary	Objectives & Reading Focus	Resources & Technology
1 What Is Electricity? pp. 434–439	3 days	vocab	■ Describe static electricity. ■ Know that electricity must move through a complete circuit to operate a device. ■ Distinguish insulators from conductors and give examples. **MAIN IDEA AND DETAILS** Look for kinds of electricity. Main Idea — detail, detail, detail	■ Lab Manual pp. LM153–155 ■ Transparencies DI41, IS41, RS41, GO 41 ■ Electronic Transparencies ■ Activity Video/DVD 3015 ■ ESL Support pp. 176–179 ■ Reading Support and Homework pp. RS95–96
2 What Are Magnets? pp. 440-445	3 days	magnetic	■ Recognize types and properties of magnets ■ Recognize magnetic materials. ■ Identify practical uses of magnets in everyday life. **COMPARE AND CONTRAST** Find out how magnets of different shapes work. alike — different	■ Lab Manual pp. LM156–158 ■ Transparencies DI42, IS42, RS42, GO 42 ■ Electronic Transparencies DI3016, IS3016, RS3016, GO 3016 ■ Activity Video/DVD 3016 ■ ESL Support pp. 180–183 ■ Reading Support and Homework pp. RS97–98
3 How Are Electricity and Magnets Related? pp. 446-451	3 days	generator	■ Recognize how magnets can be used to do work. ■ Describe the properties and uses of electromagnets. ■ Explain how a generator works. **MAIN IDEA AND DETAILS** Find out how to make an electromagnet. Main Idea — detail, detail, detail	■ Lab Manual pp. LM159–161 ■ Transparencies DI43, IS43, RS43, GO 43 ■ Electronic Transparencies DI3017, IS3017, RS3017, GO 3017 ■ Activity Video/DVD 3017 ■ ESL Support pp. 184–187 ■ Reading Support and Homework pp. RS99–100
End of Chapter pp. 452-457	2 days		■ Evaluate relationships of science, technology, and society ■ Review chapter concepts	■ Intervention, On-Level, and Above-Level Readers ■ Assessment Guide pp. AG97–102

Plan Ahead for Activities

Investigate

Looking for Static Electricity p. 434

Materials: ttissue paper, comb, piece of wool (sweater or blanket)

Time: 15 minutes

(**Inquiry Focus: Hypothesize**)

Prep Tip: This investigation works best in dry weather. Don't allow students to trade or share combs. Head lice may be transmitted.

Which Magnet is Stronger p. 441

Materials: bar magnet, 10 to 20 steel paper clips, horseshoe magnet

Time: 30 minutes

(**Inquiry Focus: Communicate**)

Prep Tip: Allow students some free exploration time with the magnets before the investigation begins. Make sure the paper clips are steel. Discuss the form and use of the data table ahead of time.

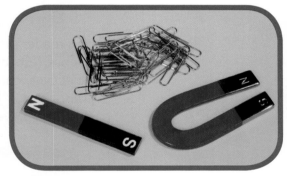

Simple Sorting p. 447

Materials: steel paper clips, bowl, plpastic beads, magnet, stopwatch

Time: 15 minutes

(**Inquiry Focus: Infer**)

Prep Tip: Show students how to use stopwatches ahead of time.

Insta-Lab

Make it Light
p. 437

 5 minutes

Materials: D batteries, flashlight bulbs, pieces of electrical wire about 30 cm long with insulation stripped from the ends

Tip: Consider doing this experiment ina carpeted area in case bulbs are dropped.

Are Horseshoe Magnets Like Bar Magnets?
p. 443

 5 minutes

Materials: 2 horseshoe magnets

Tip: Consider providing bar magnets for students to compare with horseshoe magnets.

Get Ready for an Emergency
p. 450

 15 minutes

Materials: pencil, paper

Tip: Students may want to interview the principal or school safety specialist to get the information they need.

Reading Support

Page R63 provides additional information

Below-Level/Intervention

Electricity and Magnets

The Intervention Reader presents identical chapter content and vocabulary at a below-grade reading level. The reader uses a visual glossary, simplified language, and comprehension aids especially designed for struggling readers. The *Intervention Readers Teacher Guide* provides additional strategies and support.

When used along with the hands-on experiences from the *Student Edition*, the Intervention Reader promotes science success for all students.
Reading Level 1.5–2.0

On-Level/Enrichment

This reader promotes success on state science tests by reinforcing test content objectives, chapter vocabulary, and reading skills.
Reading Level 2.5–3.5

Advanced/Challenge

This interesting nonfiction reader enriches and extends chapter concepts.
Reading Level 4.0–5.5

Trade Books for Students

These books provide in-depth information on chapter content. For more information about each selection, see the Bibliography beginning on page R48.

Easy
What Makes a Magnet? by Franklyn M. Branley, HarperCollins, 1996, Award-Winning Author

Average
Science With Magnets by Helen Edom, Usborne, 1992

Challenge
Flick a Switch: How Electricity Gets to Your Home by Barbara Seuling, Holiday House, 2003

Alternative Teaching Strategies

 **Intervention and Reteaching**

Strategies for reteaching key lesson concepts provide options for addressing a variety of learning styles.

Intervention Reader p. 437

On-Level Reader p. 443

 **Using the E-Book**

This chapter is also available online and has provisions for children with special needs. Adjustable text size and audio text can be used with children who have vision impairments or learning difficulties.

www.hspscience.com

Science Concepts Across the Grades

Grade 2	Grade 3	Grade 4
Related Chapters		
Chapter 13 Motion **Lesson 1** What Are Ways Things Move? **Lesson 2** What Makes Things Move? **Lesson 3** How Do Magnets Move Things?	**Chapter 13 Electricity and Magnets** **Lesson 1** What Is Electricity? **Lesson 2** What Are Magnets **Lesson 3** How Are Electricity and Magnets Related?	**Chapter 14 Making and Using Electricity** **Lesson 1** What Is Electricity? **Lesson 2** How Are Electricity and Magnetism Related? **Lesson 3** What Are Some Sources of Electricity? **Lesson 4** How Do People Use Energy Resources?
Learning Goals		
▶ Know that objects may be moved by being pushed and pulled with magnets. ▶ Describe electricity. ▶ Identify types and properties of magnets.	▶ Describe the properties and uses of electromagnets. ▶ Explain how a generator works. ▶ Explain static and current electricity. ▶ Recognize how electricity moves in circuits.	▶ Define magnets, electromagnets, generators, and motors; Recognize that energy can change form. ▶ Identify the need for energy conservation.

RESOURCES FOR INQUIRY

Daily Practice

Daily Inquiry pp. 434, 440, 446;
  Teaching Transparencies DI 41-43
  Electronic Transparencies DI 3015-3017

Inquiry Tool Kit

Harcourt Investigations

Harcourt School Publishers offers an alternative program that provides more opportunities for inquiry-based science experiences. The program provides a series of investigations that promote guided, structured, and independent inquiry using student journals, lab manuals, science readers and other materials.

Visit **www.hspscience.com** for more information.

Guided Inquiry

Investigate pp. 435, 441, 447;
  Lab Manual pp. LM 153-155,
  156-158, 159-161

Inquiry Skill Mini Lesson pp. 435,
  441, 447;
  Teaching Transparencies **IS 41-43**;
  Electronic Transparencies **IS 3015-3017**

Insta-Lab pp. 437, 443, 450

Unit Experiment pp. 369A-B;
  Lab Manual pp. LM 131-134

Independent Inquiry

Investigate Further
  Lab Manual pp. LM 436, 442, 438

Lab Manual

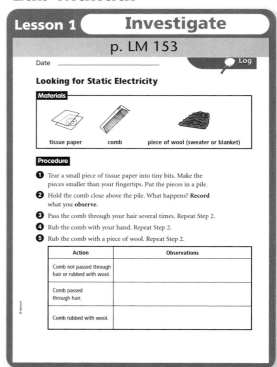

Use with *Student Edition* p. 435.

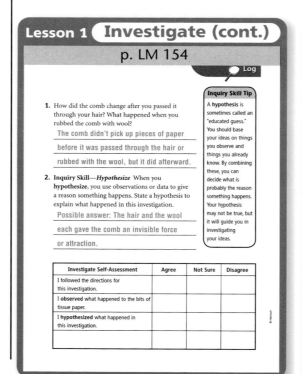

What do YOU wonder?

Electricity is used to keep the lights on at this amusement park. In what other ways is electricity used in an amusement park?

433

Vocabulary

Opportunities for developing chapter vocabulary include:

■ Develop Science Vocabulary strategies at point-of-use in the teaching plan

■ Vocabulary questions in each Reading Review and the Chapter Review and Test

■ Vocabulary sections on the Quick Study pages in *Reading Support and Homework*

■ Vocabulary Cards and activities and Vocabulary Power worksheet in *Reading Support and Homework*

Students can use the **Vocabulary Power** worksheet below to preview and explore more about the chapter vocabulary.

Reading Support and Homework

p. RS 94

Electricity and Magnets

A. **Explore Word Meanings**

Think about the meaning of the underlined words. Answer each question.

1. Static electricity is an electric charge that builds up in an object. What does *static* mean?

   Possible answer: a charge that builds up

2. Current electricity is electricity that moves through a wire. What does *current* mean?

   Possible answer: something that moves continuously

B. **Analogies**

An analogy is made of two pairs of words. The words in each pair are related in the same way. Think about the relationships in the following pairs of words. Then choose a word from the box to complete the analogy.

circuit	magnet	generator

3. *Sticker* is to *paper* as *iron* is to _____ magnet

4. *Hiker* is to *trail* as *electricity* is to _____ circuit

5. *Fire* is to *wood* as *power* is to _____ generator

Reading Focus Skills

The content of each lesson is organized to focus on a key reading skill. The skill is reinforced by questions that appear at the end of each section and the graphic organizer at the end of the lesson. Additional practice is also provided in *Reading Support and Homework*.

The Reading Focus Skills for this chapter are:	
Lesson 1	Main Idea and Details
Lesson 2	Compare and Contrast
Lesson 3	Main Idea and Details
All Lessons	Draw Conclusions and Summarize

Strategies for other reading skills also appear in the Reading Mini-Lessons throughout the chapter.

ESL/ESOL Support

Spanish-speaking students may already be familiar with English words such as these cognates.

attract/atraer

circuit/circuito

conductor/conductor

electromagnet/electrómagnético

generator/generador

magnetic/magnético

static electricity/electricidad estático

Objectives

- Describe static electricity.
- Know that electricity must move through a complete circuit to operate a device.
- Distinguish insulators from conductors and give examples.

Transparency DI 41

Electronic Transparency DI 3015

Daily Inquiry

Inside a Bulb

 Tool Kit hand lens

Other Materials: bulb from a flashlight

Review Skill: Measure, Observe, Display Data

What to Do

- Use your hand lens to examine the inside of a flashlight bulb. What do you see?
- Make a drawing that shows the inside of a flashlight bulb.

1 Introduce

Build on Prior Knowledge

Use the Fast Fact for a discussion starter about the lesson topic.

How might static electricity make this girl's hair stand on end?

The girl is touching a *generator*. What do you think *generate* means?

When *Minutes* Count . . .

If time is short, consider these options.

Conduct the Investigate as a **whole-class demonstration**.

Use the Activity Video/DVD to model. After previewing, conduct the Investigate.

Lesson 1

What Is Electricity?

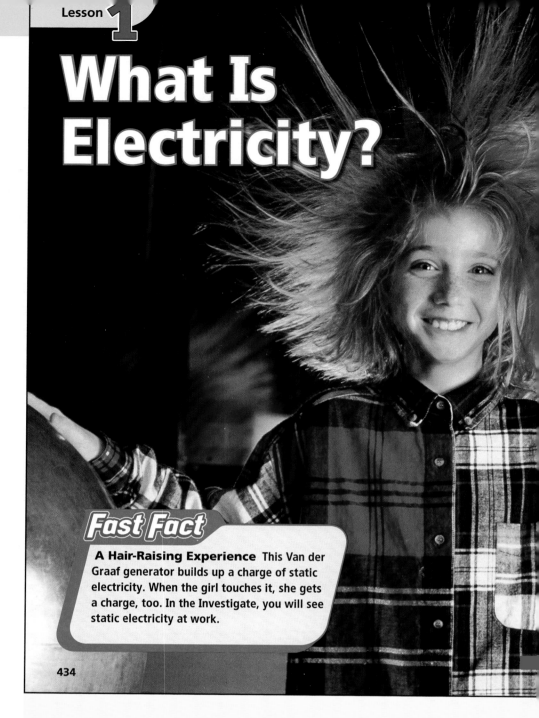

 Fast Fact

A Hair-Raising Experience This Van der Graaf generator builds up a charge of static electricity. When the girl touches it, she gets a charge, too. In the Investigate, you will see static electricity at work.

434

 PROFESSIONAL DEVELOPMENT   **Science Background**

The Van de Graaff Generator The Van de Graaff generator is named for the American physicist Robert J. Van de Graaff, who invented it between 1929 and 1931. It uses a moving belt to generate a charge of static electricity on a hollow metal globe. It is capable of producing as much as 20 million volts.

The girl in the picture is standing on a rubber mat so that the static charge will not flow through her into the ground. Instead, the charge is transferred from the sphere to the girl, and the strands of her clean, dry hair all become charged. Each hair has the same charge. Objects that have the same charge repel, so her hairs move apart.

Webliography
Keyword electricity
www.hspscience.com

Looking for Static Electricity

Materials • tissue paper • comb • piece of wool (sweater or blanket)

Procedure

1 Tear a small piece of tissue paper into tiny bits. Make the pieces smaller than your fingertips. Put the pieces in a pile.

2 Hold the comb close above the pile. What happens? Record what you observe.

3 Pass the comb through your hair several times. Repeat Step 2.

4 Rub the comb with your hand. Repeat Step 2.

5 Rub the comb with a piece of wool. Repeat Step 2.

Draw Conclusions

1. How did the comb change after you passed it through your hair? What happened when you rubbed the comb with wool?

2. **Inquiry Skill** When you hypothesize, you use observations or data to give a reason something happens. State a hypothesis to explain what happened in this investigation.

Step 3

Step 3

Investigate Further

Do you get the same result if you rub the comb with other things, such as silk or plastic wrap? **Plan and conduct an experiment** to find out.

435

Inquiry Skill Mini-Lesson

Hypothesize Display the Transparency. Explain that a hypothesis is a possible explanation for something. When we hypothesize, we try to tell why something happens. Ask students to describe the results shown in the pictures and offer a hypothesis to explain them.

Inquiry Skill practice is provided in **Reading Support and Homework**.

Transparency IS 41

Electronic Transparency IS 3015

Hypothesize

1. Tell how these pictures are alike and different?
   In some, the paper and comb have the same signs on them (+ and −). In some, they are opposite: one is + and the other is −.

2. What do you think the − and + signs stand for?
   Electrical charges; charges of static electricity

3. Write a hypothesis to explain why a comb can pick up pieces of paper.
   A comb can pick up pieces of paper if it has a sign (or charge) that is opposite the sign (or charge) on the paper.

2

Video Segment 3015

Time 15 minutes

Grouping pairs

Alternative Materials

▶ newspaper, piece of silk

Lab Manual pages can be used to record results. Inquiry Skill Tips and Self-Assessment are also provided.

Tips and Guided Inquiry

This investigation works best in dry weather. Don't allow students to trade or share combs. Head lice may be transmitted.

Why must you test the comb with paper pieces before you pass it through your hair? The untreated comb is the control for the experiment. It shows that the comb itself has no effect on the paper.

Expected Results

Steps 2 and 4: The comb does not pick up the pieces. The charge that was induced by the hair in Step 3 is discharged by the hand in Step 4. Steps 3 and 5: The comb picks up the paper pieces. The hair and the wool induce a static charge in the uncharged comb.

Draw Conclusions

1. Rubbing the comb with hair or wool makes it pick up the paper pieces.

2. **Possible answer:** The hair and the wool each gave the comb an invisible force or attraction.

Investigate Further

Students can use this page in the *Lab Manual* for **Independent Inquiry**.

Lab Manual

p. LM 155

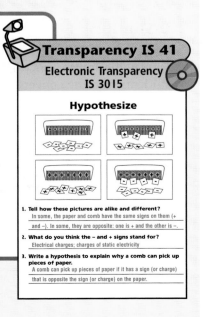

Investigate Further

Do you get the same result if you rub the comb with other things, such as silk or plastic wrap? Plan and conduct an experiment to find out.

Here are some materials that you might use. List additional materials that you need.

• tissue paper   • comb

1. Predict whether the comb will attract the bits of tissue paper after being rubbed with each of the objects. Students should predict whether the comb will attract the bits of tissue paper after being rubbed with each of the objects. Possible objects to test include silk, plastic wrap, a wooden or plastic ruler, a metal spoon, a book, a cotton ball, and a rubber ball.

2. Use the table below to record your observations.

Object	Observations

3. Were your predictions correct? Explain.
   Students should list whether each of their predictions was correct.

2 Teach
continued

VOCABULARY For Vocabulary Cards and activities, see *Reading Support and Homework.*

SCIENCE CONCEPTS Have students turn each statement into a question and use their prior knowledge to suggest responses. List the responses on the board. Have students review and revise them as they discuss the lesson.

 READING FOCUS SKILL

MAIN IDEA AND DETAILS Tell students that the information in this lesson is organized to help them recognize a main idea and the details that support it.

1 Key Science Concepts

Where is static electricity found? in objects and lightning **What are some ways you can observe static electricity?** It can make hair stand on end. It causes a flash of light and a crackling sound in lightning.

2 Develop Science Vocabulary

static electricity Explain that *static* means to stay in one place. Guide students to understand that electricity from an outlet moves through wires, but static electricity stays in one place.

3 Interpret Visuals

Why can't we use lightning to light light bulbs? While there is a lot of electrical energy in a lighting flash, we have no way to capture it or control it.

4 Interpret Data

Pennsylvania gets the most reports of lightning damage. California gets the fewest.

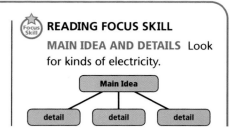

VOCABULARY	SCIENCE CONCEPTS	READING FOCUS SKILL
static electricity p. 436 current electricity p. 437 circuit p. 437	▶ what electricity is ▶ how electricity moves	**MAIN IDEA AND DETAILS** Look for kinds of electricity.

Main Idea → detail / detail / detail

Static Electricity

On a cold day, you may see a person's hair stand up straight. The reason the hair stands up is static electricity. **Static electricity** is an electric charge that builds up in an object.

Lightning is one example of static electricity. A charge builds up in a cloud, and static electricity moves to the ground in the form of a lightning flash. You may even hear a crackling noise.

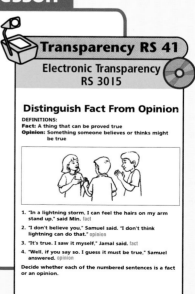

Math in Science
Interpret Data

Which of these states gets the most lightning damage? Which gets the least?

Deaths from Lightning in One Year

(Bar graph — Number of Deaths vs. States: NC 5, MI 1, OH 1, FL 10, OK 2, TX 4)

A lightning flash has enough electricity in it to light a 100-watt bulb for three months.

436

Reading Skill Mini-Lesson

DISTINGUISH FACT FROM OPINION

Display the Transparency. Have students read the conversation aloud or silently. Point out that the sentences are numbered. Tell students to use the definitions to decide whether each numbered statement is a fact or an opinion. Then have them complete the chart.

Transparency RS 41

Electronic Transparency RS 3015

Distinguish Fact From Opinion
DEFINITIONS:
Fact: A thing that can be proved true
Opinion: Something someone believes or thinks might be true

1. "In a lightning storm, I can feel the hairs on my arm stand up," said Min. fact
2. "I don't believe you," Samuel said. "I don't think lightning can do that." opinion
3. "It's true. I saw it myself," Jamal said. fact
4. "Well, if you say so. I guess it must be true," Samuel answered. opinion
Decide whether each of the numbered sentences is a fact or an opinion.

In the mixer, current electricity runs a motor, which makes the beaters turn.

What happens when you plug a lamp into a wall outlet? Electricity flows from wires in the wall through the plug and into the lamp's wires. Electricity that moves through a wire is **current electricity**.

A lamp's bulb glows only when there is a closed circuit. A **circuit** is a path that electricity follows. Electricity moves from the wall outlet, through the lamp, and back to the wall.

People use current electricity to light, heat, and cool homes, to run motors, and to cook food. What other things do you know of that use electricity?

 MAIN IDEA AND DETAILS What is current electricity?

Insta-Lab

Make It Light
Put a nightlight bulb in a bulb holder. Attach two wires to the bulb holder. Touch one wire to one knob of the battery. Touch the other wire to the other knob on the battery. What happens

437

---

5 ▶ **Interpret Visuals**

Ask students what other household appliances have electric motors in them. Possible answers: fan, blender, shaver, washing machine

6 ▶ **Inquiry Skills**

Compare **How are the electricity in lightning and the electricity that runs the mixer different?** The static electricity in lightning can't be contained or controlled. The current electricity can.

7 ▶ **Develop Science Vocabulary**

current electricity On the board, draw parallel lines to represent a wire. Between the lines, put many minus (-) marks. Explain that current electricity is the movement of negative charges through a wire.

circuit Tell students that this word comes from the Latin word *circuitus,* meaning "to go around." Ask them to explain how an electrical circuit relates to the Latin root.

What do YOU wonder?

Ask students to look back at the chapter opener photograph and explain how *current electricity* is used in the amusement park.

8 ▶ **Main Idea and Details** (Focus Skill)

Answer: Current electricity is electricity that moves through a wire.

Reaching All Learners

Intervention **ReExpand**

Target: struggling readers

Intervention Strategy: The Intervention Reader presents the essential lesson content at reading level 1.5–2.0. A visual glossary and other text-style and comprehension aids increase student understanding of the content.

Assess: Use the strategies in the *Intervention Reader Teacher Guide* to assess learning, along with the guided questions in the reader.

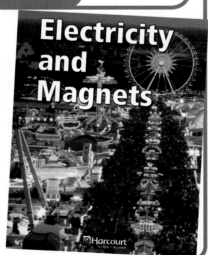

Electricity and Magnets

Harcourt

Insta-Lab ⏱ 5 minutes

Make It Light

Materials: D batteries, flashlight bulbs, pieces of electrical wire about 30 cm long with insulation stripped from the ends

For the bulb to light, the current must move along a closed circuit from one terminal of the battery through a wire to the bulb, through the bulb, and through another wire back to the other terminal of the battery.

⑨ Critical Thinking

Point out that some materials keep heat from moving through them. **Can you think of examples of heat insulators?** insulated cups that keep drinks hot or cold, insulated jackets for cold weather, insulation in houses **How are electric insulators like heat insulators?** They both prevent something from moving through them.

⑩ Inquiry Skills

Observe Show students an ordinary piece of electrical wire. Strip some of the plastic insulation off one end so students can see the metal wire inside. **What is the conductor and what is the insulator in this wire?** The plastic is the insulator and the metal is the conductor.

⑪ Interpret Visuals

What conductors and insulators can you find in the picture? Students may say that electricity flows through metal wire (a conductor) surrounded by plastic (an insulator). The plastic around the wire helps the worker stay safe. Other insulators in the picture include the wooden pole and the worker's gloves.

⑫ Main Idea and Details

Answer: A conductor is a material that electricity moves through. An insulator is a material that electricity will not move through.

How Electricity Moves

⑨ Electricity moves through some things but not through others. Something that electricity moves freely through is called a *conductor*. Copper wire is a good conductor.

⑩ Something that electricity will not move through easily is called an *insulator*. Wood and plastic are examples of insulators. Electricity can be dangerous, so people use insulators to stay safe.

⑫ (Focus Skill) **MAIN IDEA AND DETAILS** What is a conductor? What is an insulator?

How does this worker stay safe? Find the conductors and insulators in this picture.

⑪

438

1. MAIN IDEA AND DETAILS Draw and complete this graphic organizer to identify two kinds of electricity.

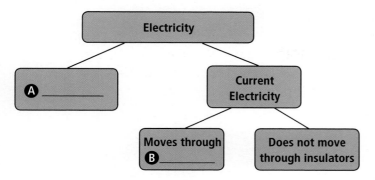

2. SUMMARIZE Use the graphic organizer to write a lesson summary.

3. DRAW CONCLUSIONS Why do wires often have plastic wrapped around them?

4. VOCABULARY Write a sentence to tell what *current electricity* is.

Test Prep

5. Which of the following makes an oven work?

A. a magnet
B. current electricity
C. an open circuit
D. static electricity

Links

Writing

Expository
Electricity that is used the wrong way can be dangerous. Research ways to be safe around electricity. Use your findings to write a **how-to** booklet.

Math 9÷3

Solve Problems
Suppose Sam's computer is on a desk that's centered exactly between two wall outlets. The wall outlets are 3 meters apart. What is the least amount of cord Sam can use to plug his computer into one of the outlets?

For more links and activities, go to www.hspscience.com

439

---

3 Assess and Extend

Graphic Organizer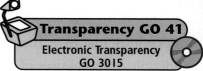
Transparency GO 41
Electronic Transparency GO 3015

1. Ⓐ Static electricity; Ⓑ Conductors

2. There are two kinds of electricity. They are static electricity and current electricity. Current electricity moves through a conductor. It does not move through an insulator.

3. Metal wire is a good conductor. Plastic is an insulator. Wrapping the conductor with an insulator helps keep the user safe.

4. Possible answer: Current electricity is electricity that moves through a conductor, such as a wire.

5. B, current electricity

Links

Writing Some students may wish to research and write about safety during lightning storms.

Students can consult *Writing Models* in **Teaching Resources** as they complete the Link. Rubrics are also provided.

Math 3 meters divided by 2 = 1.5 meters.

Lesson Quick Study

The Lesson Quick Study in **Reading Support and Homework** provides the opportunity for students to practice inquiry skills, review lesson vocabulary, apply reading skills, and use critical thinking and problem solving. Students can use the second page of the Lesson Quick Study to complete the graphic organizer from the Reading Review. The graphic organizer is also available on overhead and electronic transparencies.

Reading Support and Homework

p. RS 95

Lesson 1 - What Is Electricity?

1. **Inquiry Skills Practice–Hypothesize**

Marta placed a blown-up balloon against the wall. The balloon dropped to the floor. Marta then rubbed the balloon against her wool sweater. She placed the balloon against the wall again. This time, the balloon stayed where she put it. Make a hypothesis about Marta's experiment. Possible answer: Rubbing the balloon against the wool gave it a static electric charge. Because the balloon had built up this electric charge, it could stick to the wall.

2. **Use Vocabulary**

Match the clue on the left to the term on the right. Write the letter in the blank.

_B_ electricity that moves through a wire   A. static electricity
_A_ electric charge that builds up in an object   B. current electricity

3. **Reading Skill Practice–Main Idea and Details**

Read the selection. Underline the main idea. List at least two details about the main idea.

Electricity can move through conductors, but not through insulators. Conductors include metals such as copper and gold. These metals are called conductors because they allow electricity to flow through them easily. Insulators include plastic and wood. Plastic and wood are called insulators because they do not allow electricity to flow through them. Possible answers: Conductors allow electricity to flow through them easily. Insulators do not allow electricity to flow through them.

p. RS 96

4. **Main Idea and Details**

Use this space to complete the graphic organizer shown in the Reading Review of the Student Edition.

Electricity
Ⓐ Static Electricity   Current Electricity
Moves through: Ⓑ conductors   Does not move through: Ⓒ insulators

5. **Critical Thinking and Problem Solving**

Suppose you are stirring a pot of hot cocoa on a stove. What kind of long spoon would be better to use, a wooden one or a metal one? Explain your answer.
Possible answer: The wooden spoon would be better to use while stirring the hot cocoa. The metal spoon would get hot because metal is a conductor. The wooden spoon would stay cool because wood is an insulator.

Objectives

- Recognize types and properties of magnets.
- Recognize magnetic materials.
- Identify practical uses of magnets in everyday life.

Transparency DI 42

Electronic Transparency DI 3016

Daily Inquiry

Metric Measures

 ruler

Review Skill: Measure, Compare

What to Do

- Draw a rectangle that is 50 millimeters wide and 150 millimeters long. Cut the rectangle out and place it on your desktop.
- Next, draw a rectangle that is 5 centimeters wide and 15 centimeters long. Cut the rectangle out and place it on your desktop.
- Look at the two rectangles. How do they compare?

1 Introduce

Build on Prior Knowledge

Use the Fast Fact for a discussion starter about the lesson topic.

How is the student in the picture picking up the fish?

Have you ever seen or played with magnets?

What do magnets do?

When *Minutes* Count . . .

If time is short, consider these options.

Conduct the Investigate as a **whole-class demonstration**. Let volunteers pick up the paper clips. Record data on the board and ask all students to make the graph.

Use the Activity Video/DVD to model the Investigate. After previewing, conduct the Investigate in small groups.

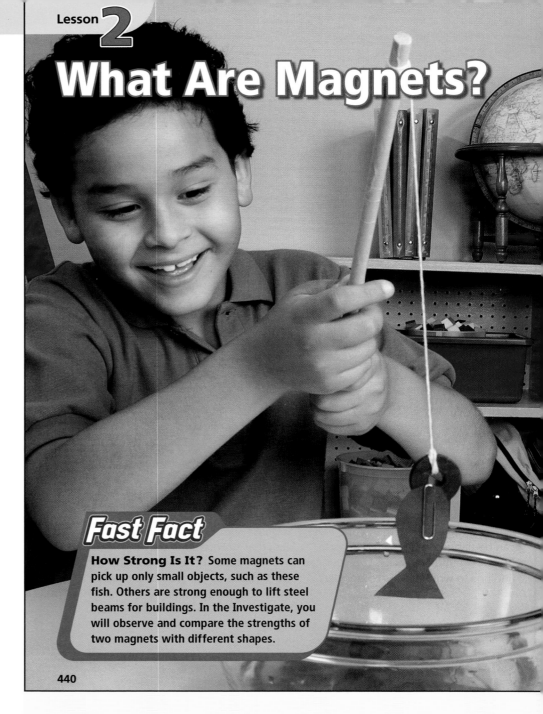

Lesson 2

What Are Magnets?

Fast Fact

How Strong Is It? Some magnets can pick up only small objects, such as these fish. Others are strong enough to lift steel beams for buildings. In the Investigate, you will observe and compare the strengths of two magnets with different shapes.

440

 Science Background

PROFESSIONAL DEVELOPMENT

Earth's Magnetic Field Earth is a giant magnet that is surrounded by a magnetic field. The center of Earth is a solid iron ball that has a temperature as hot as the surface of the sun. A layer of melted metal surrounds the inner core and is known as the outer core. This is the source of Earth's magnetic field. Earth's magnetic field is weak at the surface because the distance from the inner core to the surface is about 6,400 kilometers. A compass contains a small magnet, or needle, that points toward Earth's magnetic north pole. What we call the north pole is actually the south pole because the north pole of a compass is attracted to Earth's south pole. Pass around a compass and allow students to observe the way the needle lines up. The red end of the magnetic needle always turns to north when the compass is held in a level position.

Which Magnet Is Stronger?

Materials • bar magnet • 10 to 20 steel paper clips • horseshoe magnet

Procedure

1. Hold the bar magnet near a paper clip. **Record** what happens.

2. Hold the horseshoe magnet near a paper clip. **Record** what happens.

3. Pick up as many paper clips as one end of the bar magnet will hold. Count them. **Record the data.**

4. Pick up as many paper clips as one end of the horseshoe magnet will hold. Count them. **Record the data.**

Step 2

Kind of Magnet	Number of Paperclips
Bar	
Horseshoe	

Draw Conclusions

1. Which magnet is stronger? How can you tell?

2. **Inquiry Skill** Scientists can **communicate** data in graphs. Make a bar graph to show how many paper clips each magnet held.

Investigate Further

If you hold two magnets together, can they lift as many paper clips as each one can separately? **Plan an investigation** to find out.

441

Inquiry Skill Mini-Lesson

Communicate Display the Transparency and ask students to read the description of Jeri's experiment either aloud or silently. Then discuss as a class the data table and what it shows. Let students work individually or with a partner to make the bar graph and answer the questions.

Inquiry Skill practice is provided in **Reading Support and Homework.**

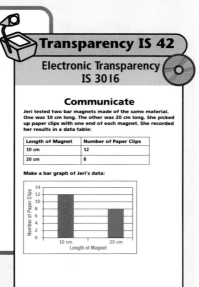

Transparency IS 42

Electronic Transparency IS 3016

Communicate

Jeri tested two bar magnets made of the same material. One was 10 cm long. The other was 20 cm long. She picked up paper clips with one end of each magnet. She recorded her results in a data table:

Length of Magnet	Number of Paper Clips
10 cm	12
20 cm	8

Make a bar graph of Jeri's data:

2 Teach

Video Segment 3016

Time 30 minutes

Grouping pairs

Lab Manual pages can be used to record results. Inquiry Skill Tips and Self-Assessment are also provided.

Tips and Guided Inquiry

Allow students some free exploration time with the magnets before the investigation begins. Make sure to use metal paper clips.

Why is exact counting important? You cannot compare the number of paper clips unless you know exactly how many each magnet picked up. **Are your results the same as another team's? Why or why not?** Different teams will probably get different numbers because they have different magnets or because they did something different when picking up the paper clips.

Expected Results

Steps 1 and 2: The magnets pick up paper clips. Steps 3 and 4: The two types of magnets will pick up different numbers of paper clips. In general, a horseshoe magnet is stronger than a bar magnet of the same size, but results will vary.

Draw Conclusions

1. The stronger magnet is the one that picks up more paper clips.

2. Check the students' bar graphs for form and accuracy.

Investigate Further

Students can use this page in the *Lab Manual* for **Independent Inquiry**.

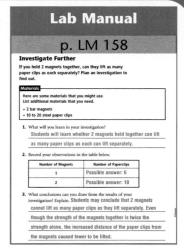

Lab Manual

p. LM 158

Investigate Further

If you hold 2 magnets together, can they lift as many paper clips as each separately? Plan an investigation to find out.

Materials

Here are some materials that you might use. List additional materials that you need.

• 2 bar magnets
• 10 to 20 steel paper clips

1. What will you learn in your investigation?
   Students will learn that 2 magnets held together can lift as many paper clips as each can lift separately.

2. Record your observations in the table below.

Number of Magnets	Number of Paperclips
1	Possible answer: 6
2	Possible answer: 10

3. What conclusions can you draw from the results of your investigation? Explain. Students may conclude that 2 magnets cannot lift as many paper clips as they lift separately. Even though the strength of the magnets together is twice the strength alone, the increased distance of the paper clips from the magnets caused fewer to be lifted.

LESSON 2 ■ 441

2 Teach
continued

VOCABULARY For Vocabulary Cards and activities, see *Reading Support and Homework.*

SCIENCE CONCEPTS Have students turn the statement into a question and use their prior knowledge to suggest a response. List ideas on the board. Have students review and revise them as they discuss the lesson.

READING FOCUS SKILL

COMPARE AND CONTRAST Tell students that the information in this lesson is organized to help them compare and contrast science facts and ideas. Use the Reading Mini-Lesson below to discuss a strategy that students can use to compare and contrast.

1 Key Science Concepts

How do you know if something is magnetic? It picks up, attracts, or pulls on something that has iron in it.

Will a magnet pick up a block of wood? Why or why not? No; wood doesn't have any iron in it.

2 Develop Science Vocabulary

magnetic A person is sometimes described as having a "magnetic personality." Discuss how the word *magnetic* has a similar meaning here. Both people and objects can be attractive, i.e., draw other things or people toward them.

3 Interpret Visuals

How are magnets being used in the pictures? Students may talk about games or activities such as arranging magnetic letters on a refrigerator door (made of steel), using magnetic game pieces on a travel game, or playing a magnetic "donut" game.

VOCABULARY	SCIENCE CONCEPTS	READING FOCUS SKILL
magnetic p. 442	▶ what magnets do	**COMPARE AND CONTRAST** Find out how magnets of different shapes work.

alike ——— different

Magnets

In the Investigate, you used magnets to pick up paper clips. Magnets are made from metal that is magnetic. **Magnetic** things attract objects that have iron in them. Paper clips are made of steel, but steel has iron in it. That's why the magnets lift and hold steel paper clips. A magnet won't pick up plastic paper clips, because they don't contain iron.

▲ This rock is magnetite. It's naturally magnetic.

▲ How are magnets being used here?

442

Reading Skill Mini-Lesson

COMPARE AND CONTRAST

Have students compare and contrast the properties and characteristics of bar magnets and horseshoe magnets. Display the transparency, and have students complete the chart as directed.

 **Transparency RS 42**

Electronic Transparency RS 3016

Compare and Contrast

Complete the chart below to compare and contrast bar magnets and horseshoe magnets. In the first column, circle *Alike* if the two magnets are alike. Circle *Different* if they are different. Explain the reason for your answer in the "Explain" column.

Feature	Alike or Different?	Explain
Shape	Alike (Different)	One is a long bar. The other is bent in a U shape.
Size	Alike (Different)	Students' answers will probably refer to the magnets used in the Investigate.
Appearance	Alike (Different)	They may be different colors or have different finishes.

Magnets will attract only when the north and south poles match up. Which magnets are attracting? Which are repelling?

 For more links and activities, go to www.hspscience.com

All magnets have two ends, called poles—a north pole and a south pole. To see how a magnet works, use two bar magnets. Hold the two north poles together. Can you push them together? You probably can't. Poles that are alike repel each other. *Repel* means "push away." What do you think will happen if you put the two south poles together?

Now hold opposite poles—a north pole and a south pole—together. They pull toward each other, or *attract*. The opposite poles of a magnet attract.

 COMPARE AND CONTRAST How are all magnets alike?

Are Horseshoe Magnets Like Bar Magnets?
Try to push two horseshoe magnets together. What happens? Turn one over and try again. What happens? Explain what you observe.

443

ONLINE EXPERIENCE
For animations and activities, visit **www.hspscience.com**

4 ▶ Interpret Visuals

What do the arrows in the pictures show? the direction in which the magnets push or pull **What do arrows that point away from each other mean?** that the magnets push away **What do the arrows pointing toward each other mean?** that the magnets pull toward each other **What do the N and S show?** the north (N) and south (S) poles of the magnets

Ask students to explain what each picture shows (left to right):

1. When two north poles come together, the magnets push apart.
2. When two south poles come together, the magnets push apart.
3. When a north pole and a south pole come together, the magnets pull toward each other.

 5 minutes

Are Horseshoe Magnets Like Bar Magnets?

Materials: 2 horseshoe magnets

Horseshoe magnets have north and south poles at the ends, just as bar magnets do. If the horseshoe magnets are turned with like poles facing (N to N and S to S), they will push apart. When turned with their opposite poles facing (N to S and S to N), they will pull toward each other.

5 ▶ Compare and Contrast

Answer: All magnets have a north pole and a south pole.

6 ▸ Interpret Visuals

Ask students to examine the pictures and talk about how each device works. (The screwdriver picks up iron-containing screws because its tip is made of a magnetic material. The steel kitchen utensils cling to the magnetic strip of the wall holder. The door stays closed because the magnet holds the steel catch and the doorframe together. The back of the note clip has a magnet on it. The clip sticks to a steel refrigerator door or filing cabinet to hold something in place.)

7 ▸ Key Science Concepts

What magnets do you use at home? At school? Students' answers will vary.

Do you use motors, computers, or compasses at home or at school? Most students will say yes to one or the other.

Did you know they had magnets in them? Most students will say no.

Where are the magnets in these devices? How do they work? Most students will not know, but they may wish to work together in teams to research answers in the library or on the Internet. Here's also a good opportunity to invite an engineer to class as a guest speaker.

8 ▸ Critical Thinking

How might magnets be used in recycling? to separate steel from other metals

9 ▸ Compare and Contrast (Focus Skill)

Answer: Magnets pick up things, move things, and hold things in place.

Some Uses of Magnets

7 Magnets have many uses. They can keep cabinets closed or can hold papers on a refrigerator door. Some of your favorite games might use magnets.

8 Magnets can also be used to make electricity and to sort metals for recycling. Motors, computers, and compasses also use magnets.

9 (Focus Skill) **COMPARE AND CONTRAST** What are some of the different uses of magnets?

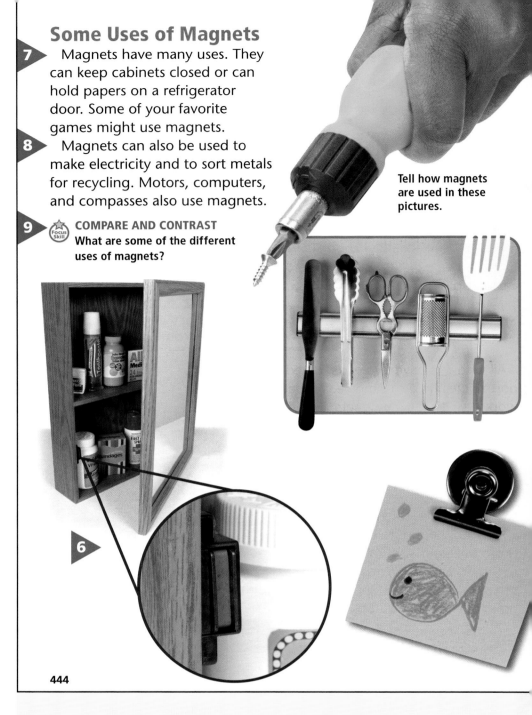

Tell how magnets are used in these pictures.

6

444

---

1. **COMPARE AND CONTRAST** Draw and complete this graphic organizer to compare magnets.

How Magnets Are Alike	How Magnets Are Different
A _____	**C** _____
B _____	**D** _____

2. **SUMMARIZE** Use the completed graphic organizer to write a lesson summary.

3. **DRAW CONCLUSIONS** Juan is using a bar magnet to pick up items in his room. Explain why the magnet he is using won't pick up a rubber ball.

4. **VOCABULARY** Write a sentence to explain what *magnetic* means.

Test Prep

5. What must an object be made of to be attracted to a magnet?
   A. iron
   B. plastic
   C. rubber
   D. wood

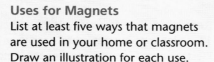 ## Links

Writing

Expository
Some objects are naturally magnetic. Research lodestone. Write a two-paragraph **description** of your findings.

Art

Uses for Magnets
List at least five ways that magnets are used in your home or classroom. Draw an illustration for each use.

 For more links and activities, go to www.hspscience.com

445

3 Assess and Extend

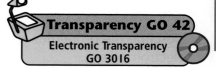
Graphic Organizer — Transparency GO 42 · Electronic Transparency GO 3016

1. **A** Attract things made of iron; **B** Have two poles (N and S); **C** Have different shapes; **D** Have different uses

2. Magnets have different shapes and uses, but they all have two poles and attract things made of iron.

3. A rubber ball doesn't have iron in it, and it isn't magnetic.

4. **Possible answer:** Something that is magnetic attracts objects with iron in them.

5. A, iron

Links

Writing Lodestone, or magnetite, is a mineral composed of the elements iron and oxygen. Like a human-made magnet, it has north and south poles. Its magnetic properties have been known since about 500 B.C..

 Students can consult *Writing Models* in **Teaching Resources** as they complete the link. Rubrics are also provided.

Art Make a bulletin board of students' drawings.

Lesson Quick Study

The Lesson Quick Study in **Reading Support and Homework** provides the opportunity for students to practice inquiry skills, review lesson vocabulary, apply reading skills, and use critical thinking and problem solving. Students can use the second page of the Lesson Quick Study to complete the graphic organizer from the Reading Review. The graphic organizer is also available on overhead and electronic transparencies.

Reading Support and Homework

p. RS 97

Lesson 2 – What Are Magnets?

1. **Inquiry Skills Practice - Communicate**

Think about the items listed at the right. Using what you know about magnets, circle the items a magnet attracts. Then underline the items a magnet does not attract. Explain how you know.

A magnet attracts things that have iron in them.

- a metal washer
- a rubber band
- a needle
- a marble
- a steel screw
- a plastic button
- a wooden block

2. **Use Vocabulary**

Write a complete sentence that uses the term *magnetic* correctly.

Answers will vary but should reflect the correct use of *magnetic*.

3. **Reading Skill Practice—Compare and Contrast**

Read the selection. Compare and contrast steel and aluminum.

In recycling centers, machines help sort the cans. The machines have magnets that separate the steel cans from the aluminum cans. Magnets attract steel but not aluminum. When steel cans, like paint cans, come near the magnet of the machine, they are attracted to it. Aluminum cans, like soda cans, are not attracted to the magnet. So the steel cans go one way, and the aluminum cans go another way. Alike: Both steel and aluminum are used to make cans. Different: Steel cans are attracted to magnets.

Aluminum cans are not attracted to magnets.

p. RS 98

4. **Compare and Contrast**

Use this space to complete the graphic organizer shown in the Reading Review of the Student Edition.

How magnets are alike:	How magnets are different:
A attract things made with iron	**C** have different shapes
B have two poles (north and south)	**D** have different uses (function differently)

5. **Critical Thinking and Problem Solving**

Ralph has two bar magnets. He holds one magnet in one hand and the other magnet in the other hand. He brings the ends of the magnets close to each other. The magnets attract each other. They pull together. Ralph pulls the magnets apart and turns one of them around. He tries to bring the ends close to each other again, but they repel each other, or push away. Why does this happen?

A magnet has a south pole and a north pole. For two magnets to attract each other, the north pole of one must face the south pole of the other. When you put two north poles or two south poles together, they repel each other, or push away. The second time, Ralph is trying to put the two north poles or the two south poles together.

Objectives

- Recognize how magnets can be used to do work.
- Describe the properties and uses of electromagnets.
- Explain how a generator works.

Transparency DI 43

Electronic Transparency DI 3017

Daily Inquiry

Balloon Attraction

 Tool Kit magnifying box

Review Skills: Measure, Observe

What to Do

- Crush packing noodles into small pieces. Place these pieces in the magnifying box. Put the lid on the box. Stroke an inflated balloon on your hair. Move the balloon close to the box. Record your observations.
- What happens when a charged balloon is brought near a box containing pieces of packing foam?

1 Introduce

Build on Prior Knowledge

Use the Fast Fact for a discussion starter about the lesson topic.

How is this scrap metal being lifted?

What do you think an electromagnet might be?

When *Minutes* Count . . .

If time is short, consider these options.

Conduct the Investigate as a **whole-class demonstration.** Have students predict the time it will take you or a student volunteer to separate the objects by hand and then with a magnet.

Use the Activity Video/DVD to model the Investigate. After previewing, students can conduct the Investigate in small groups.

How Are Electricity and Magnets Related?

Fast Fact

Recycling Americans recycle more than 13 million tons of scrap metal each year. Electromagnets are used to sort scrap metal. In the Investigate, you will find out why an electromagnet is useful.

446

Science Background

PROFESSIONAL DEVELOPMENT

Electromagnetism Until the late 1800s, electricity and magnetism were thought to be separate forces. Experimental evidence began to accumulate, suggesting that electricity and magnetism are actually two aspects of the same phenomenon.

In 1905, Einstein's theory of relativity confirmed the dual nature of a single electromagnetic force. We encounter this dual nature in visible light, ultraviolet radiation, microwaves, and radio waves. We use it in practical applications in which magnetic fields generate current electricity (generator) and current electricity produces magnetic fields (electromagnet).

 Webliography
Keywords electricity, magnetism
www.hspscience.com

Simple Sorting

Materials
- steel paper clips
- magnet
- bowl
- stopwatch
- plastic beads

Procedure

1. Put a handful of paper clips in the bowl. Add a handful of beads. Mix them up.

2. Remove the paper clips from the bowl by hand, making sure not to pick up any of the beads. Use a stopwatch to **measure** and **record** how long this takes.

3. Return the paper clips to the bowl of beads. Mix them up again.

4. Now use a magnet to remove the paper clips from the bowl. Use a stopwatch to **measure** and **record** how long this takes.

Step 2

Step 4

Draw Conclusions

1. How do the two times **compare**? Which is the quicker way to separate the steel paper clips from the plastic beads?

2. **Inquiry Skill** Scientists use what they know to **infer**, or conclude. Look at the picture on the left-hand page. What are some things that you can **infer** about the use of an electromagnet?

Investigate Further

Mix various small metal objects together. **Predict** which objects you can separate by using a magnet. Test your prediction.

447

Inquiry Skill Mini-Lesson

Infer Display the Transparency. Ask students to describe what they see in each picture. Then ask them what they can infer, or conclude, about the bars and the screws. Have them answer the questions with their descriptions and inferences.

Inquiry Skill practice is provided in **Reading Support and Homework**.

Transparency IS 43

Electronic Transparency
IS 3017

Infer

A	B	C

1. **Tell what you see in each picture?**
In A and C, nothing has happened when the bar is brought close to the pile. In B, some of the screws have attached to the bar.

2. **What can you infer about the bars?**
A and C are not magnets. B is.

3. **What can you infer about the screws?**
They have iron or some other magnetic metal in them.

2

Video Segment 3017

Time 15 minutes

Grouping groups of 3

Alternative Materials

▶ nonmagnetic objects, such as pasta, rice, or plastic paper clips, instead of beads

Lab Manual pages can be used to record results. Inquiry Skill Tips and Self-Assessment are also provided.

Tips and Guided Inquiry

Show students how to use stopwatches ahead of time.

How do you like separating the paper clips by hand? Possible answer: It's very slow and boring.

Why does using the magnet to separate the paper clips and the beads work? because the magnet attracts the steel paper clips but not the plastic beads

Expected Results

Step 2: Students will pick paper clips out from beads. The process will be slow. Step 4: Students will separate the paper clips with a magnet. The process will be faster.

Draw Conclusions

1. Times will vary, but using the magnet is the quicker way to separate the mixture.

2. Students can infer that using an electromagnet is a convenient way to separate and move certain things.

Investigate Further

Students can use this page in the *Lab Manual* for **Independent Inquiry**.

Lab Manual

p. LM 161

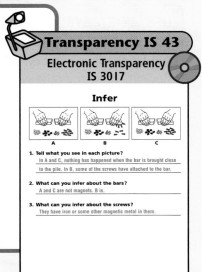

Investigate Further
Mix various small metal objects together. Predict which objects you can separate by using a magnet. Test your prediction.

Materials
Here are some materials that you might use. List additional materials that you need.
- steel paper clips
- bowl
- magnet

1. Write your predictions.
Students should list the objects they believe will be attracted to the magnet.

2. Record which objects were attracted to the magnet and which were not.

Objects attracted to the magnet	Objects not attracted to the magnet

3. Explain how the outcome of this investigation was the same or different from your predictions. Students should explain how their predictions differed from their results. They should realize that only objects made from steel or iron can be picked up and separated from the bowl of metal objects.

2 Teach
continued

VOCABULARY For Vocabulary Cards and activities, see *Reading Support and Homework.*

SCIENCE CONCEPTS Have students turn the statement into a question and use their prior knowledge to suggest a response. List responses on the board. Have students review and revise them as they discuss the lesson.

 READING FOCUS SKILL

MAIN IDEA AND DETAILS Tell students that the information in this lesson is organized to help them recognize a main idea and the details that support it.

1 Key Science Concepts

What are the electromagnets in salvage yards used for? to pick up old cars

2 Critical Thinking

Why are magnets and cranes needed to move the cars? The cars can't be driven, and they are too heavy to lift by hand.

3 Interpret Visuals

Ask students to study the picture.

Is the screw magnetic? no **How can you tell?** It is not picking up the paper clips.

VOCABULARY	SCIENCE CONCEPTS	READING FOCUS SKILL
generator p. 450	▶ how an electromagnet works	**MAIN IDEA AND DETAILS** Look for details about electromagnets.

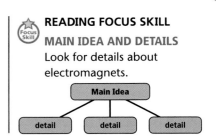

Electromagnets

At a salvage (SAL•vij) yard, there are many recycled cars. The cars don't run anymore, so a person can't drive or move them. However, a very strong magnet attached to a crane can move a car. Together, the crane and magnet can pick up a car and put it somewhere else. There is one problem. After the car is on the magnet, how is it removed? A person cannot pull the car from the magnet. The magnet's pull is too strong.

How does the boy know that the screw isn't magnetic?

Reading Skill Mini-Lesson

USE WORD STRUCTURE: COMPOUND WORDS

Display the transparency. Ask students to identify the word roots that make up the compound word *electromagnet*. Ask them to draw lines to match the compound and its roots with their meanings.

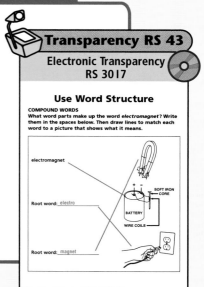

Transparency RS 43

Electronic Transparency RS 3017

Use Word Structure

COMPOUND WORDS
What word parts make up the word *electromagnet*? Write them in the spaces below. Then draw lines to match each word to a picture that shows what it means.

electromagnet

Root word: electro

Root word: magnet

SOFT IRON CORE
BATTERY
WIRE COILS

DANGER
Generator X
Most generators work by burning fuels such as oil or coal. Burning those fuels gives off gases that pollute the air.

People in the United States use a lot of electricity. Televisions, computers, toasters, and lights all use electricity. Power companies have to produce all that electricity. But making electricity can produce air pollution.

An energy company in Georgia is testing a way to make electricity that doesn't give off as much pollution.

Generating Energy

Energy companies make electricity at places called power plants. The plants have huge machines called generators. These machines generate electricity and send it across wires to your home.

The company in Georgia is testing a fuel that is a mixture of grass and coal. The grass, called switchgrass, is a kind of prairie grass that grows in the South.

To make the fuel, the company mixes switchgrass and coal. The mixture is then formed into cubes. As the cubes burn, they produce almost as much energy as the same amount of coal would. However, the cubes give off less pollution than other fuels.

THINK ABOUT IT

1. How is electricity produced?
2. How can you reduce the amount of electricity you use?

Find out more! Log on to
www.hspscience.com

453

3 Wrap Up and Assess

Think About It

1. Generators use the energy from the burning of coal or a mixture of grass and coal to produce electricity.

2. Answers will vary. Possible answers: Turn off lights when they are not in use; have the air conditioner set at a comfortable temperature; or turn off appliances, such as televisions, when not in use.

Writing Link

Persuasive Writing Have students write a business letter describing reasons why saving electricitiy is important. You might wish to supply the students with a business letter template.

Inspire Inquiry

Inquiry starts with wonder and with asking questions. Sometimes the questions are just about things people want to know. Sometimes they are problems that people want to solve.

- Have students suggest the reasons why it is important to find alternative ways to produce electricity.
- Ask students to suggest ways they can save electricity, yet still accomplish a certain task, such as reading a book outside or near a window where the sun is shining instead of turning on a lamp.
- Invite students to research other fuel alternatives besides the one mentioned in this feature. Prior to beginning their research, help students develop a research plan. Ask students to share their findings with the class.

Objectives

- Identify ways that Edith Clarke used math and science to solve problems.
- Discuss how people invent new tools to make calculating easier.

1 Introduce

Preview/Set a Purpose

Ask students, **What does a computer look like?** Ask students if they can find a picture of a computer on the page. Tell them that as they read the article, they will be able to identify the "hidden" computer.

2 Teach

The Work of Scientists

Have students conclude that scientists use numbers to measure, calculate, organize, and display data.

How can a person be a computer? Before there were machines that did calculations, people who did math problems for other people were called "computers."

Why did Edith make a graphical calculator? She wanted to help engineers solve electrical design problems.

What two "firsts" did Edith accomplish? She was the first to make a graphical calculator and the first woman to study electrical engineering at a top school.

3 Wrap Up and Assess

Think About It

Have students infer what it was like to live when the only computers were people.

How would our life be different if we did not have computers? We would not have e-mail, cell phones, or video games.

What do Edith and today's computers have in common? They both do math for other people; they make electrical design easier; they both use numbers to solve problems.

SCIENCE Spin from WEEKLY READER®
People

A Mind for Numbers

Edith Clarke grew up in Maryland in the 1800s. She studied and enjoyed math all her life.

Clarke's first job was as a "computer." This may sound strange, but she actually *computed* math problems for other people. Clarke lived long before modern computers were invented.

Clarke was the first woman to study electrical engineering at one of the top schools in the nation. After graduating, Clarke became a teacher at the University of Texas.

Clarke also was an electrical engineer. She was the first person to make a graphical calculator. This calculator helped engineers to solve electrical design problems.

Career   Electrical Engineer

Ever wonder how your handheld electronic game works? Ask an electrical engineer. Electrical engineers help design, build, and test electronic equipment. There are many types of engineers. For example, a computer engineer helped to design the computer you use in school.

Find out more! Log on to
www.hspscience.com

454

Science Background

Like Edith Clarke, today's computers do a lot of math. In fact, everything a computer does is done in mathematical "language."
- The number system we use every day is the decimal (base 10) system. This system was created in India and originally used the ten fingers to do calculations.
- A computer uses the binary (base 2) number system. This means that all the information in a computer is expressed in zeros and ones.
- The word "bit" comes from the words "Binary digIT."
- Each digit, or bit, in a computer is like a switch that can be either "on" or "off." When you type words into a computer, those words are converted into a series of zeros and ones, or "on"s and "off"s.

You Can Do It!

Make a Magnetic Fishing Game

Materials
- string
- ruler
- magnet
- paper
- paper clips

Procedure

1. Make a "fishing pole" by tying string to one end of a ruler. Tie a magnet to the end of the string.

2. Cut fish shapes from paper. Tape steel paper clips to some.

3. Play the fishing game. Which fish can't you catch?

Draw Conclusions
How can you make the fishing game work better? Predict ways to improve the design. Test your predictions.

Design Your Own Investigation

Static Electricity

Build up static electricity by rubbing a wool cloth over a hard rubber comb for a minute. Turn out the lights in the room. Touch the comb to a light bulb that hasn't been used in the last hour and that isn't plugged in. What happens? Repeat the procedure, touching the comb to different parts of the light bulb. Are your results different?

455

You Can Do It!

Quick and Easy Project
Make a Magnetic Fishing Game

Objectives
- Construct a game based on the principle of magnetic attraction.
- Predict and test designs for improving the game.

• Tips and Hints

Make sure the paper clips are steel. Let students design, color, and cut their own fish shapes from lightweight paper.

• Draw Conclusions

Students may predict that using two magnets instead of one or putting more paper clips on the fish will improve the game. Or they may predict that using something other than paper clips or using different types of paper would be better. Let them test their predictions and evaluate the results.

• Extend the Activity

Make a magnetic question-and-answer game of facts about magnetism and electricity. Write answers on a board with magnetic strips (available in craft stores) glued beside them. Put questions on slips of paper with paper clips taped to the back. Let players try to attach the correct questions beside their answers.

Design Your Own Investigation
Static Electricity

Objectives
- Conduct a demonstration to show that static electricity will not light a bulb.

Inspire Inquiry

Use this activity as a suggestion for a science fair project. Have students use the investigation as a starting point for developing their own questions and ideas.

A reproducible copy of this page is provided in *Teaching Resources*.

Chapter 13

Vocabulary Review (5 pts. each)

1. circuit
2. generator
3. current electricity
4. magnetic
5. static electricity

Check Understanding (5 pts. each)

6. B, conductor
7. H, static electricity
8. A, turn on and off
9. J, poles
10. A, They attract.
11. H, Magnet A is weaker than magnet B.
12. B, electricity
13. F, current
14. D, an electric current
15. J, static electricity
16. A, iron

Inquiry Skills (5 pts. each)

17. She will fail. Both the paper clips and the pins will be attracted to the magnet because they are both made of steel.
18. She could turn one of the magnets over, so the poles would be opposite.

Vocabulary Review

Use the terms below to complete the sentences. The page numbers tell where to look in the chapter if you need help.

static electricity p. 436
current electricity p. 437
circuit p. 437
magnetic p. 442
generator p. 450

1. To run a machine, electricity must move along a closed _____.

2. A machine that uses a magnet to make a current of electricity is called a _____.

3. Current that moves in a wire is called _____.

4. An object that pulls iron toward itself is _____.

5. A charge that builds up in an object is _____.

Check Understanding

Write the letter of the best choice.

6. Which term describes copper?
   A. circuit   C. insulator
   B. conductor   D. magnet

7. **MAIN IDEA AND DETAILS** What is lightning an example of?
   F. a magnet
   G. an electromagnet
   H. static electricity
   J. a circuit

8. **COMPARE AND CONTRAST** What can an electromagnet do that other magnets can't do?
   A. turn on and off
   B. coil around a wire
   C. lift metal objects
   D. generate electricity

Use the picture for questions 9–10.

9. What are the ends of the magnets called?
   F. circuits   H. insulators
   G. conductors   J. poles

10. What happens to the magnets when they are held like this?
    A. They attract.
    B. They cause static electricity.
    C. They make an electromagnet.
    D. They repel.

Harcourt School Publishers Online Assessment

Harcourt School Publishers Online Assessment provides even more options. For a preview, go to:
www.hspscience.com

Portfolio Assessment

Have students select their best work from the following suggestions:
- **Investigate,** p. 441
- **Insta-Lab,** p. 450
- **Links,** pp. 439, 445, 451

See *Assessment Guide* pp. xx-xxiv.

11. Magnet A picks up six paper clips. Magnet B picks up eight paper clips. What conclusion can you draw?

  F. The circuit in Magnet A has been broken.

  G. Magnet B is an electromagnet.

  H. Magnet A is weaker than Magnet B.

  J. Both magnets are weak.

12. A coil of wire moves near a magnet. What is produced?

  A. an outlet

  B. electricity

  C. an electromagnet

  D. static electricity

13. Miguel plugs his desk lamp into an outlet. What type of electricity is the lamp using?

  F. current   **H.** magnetic

  G. lightning   **J.** static

14. What does a generator make?

  A. a magnet

  B. an electromagnet

  C. a circuit

  D. an electric current

15. Your socks are stuck together. You pull them apart and hear a crackle. What is the sound?

  F. attraction

  G. current electricity

  H. lightning

  J. static electricity

16. A magnet attracts an object. What must the object contain?

  A. iron   **C.** rubber

  B. plastic   **D.** wood

Inquiry Skills

17. Dana wants to separate steel paper clips from steel safety pins. She uses a magnet. Predict what will happen, and tell why.

18. As hard as Brooke tries, she can't push two horseshoe magnets together. Infer what she could do to get them to attract.

Critical Thinking

19. Carson built an electromagnet. He used a battery, a nail, and some wire. His electromagnet doesn't work. Give one reason it doesn't work.

20. Miguel held a magnet 2 cm above some steel safety pins. His magnet picked up eight pins. What will happen if Miguel holds the magnet 4 cm above the pins? Why?

Critical Thinking (5 pts. each)

19. Possible answers: A connection may be loose, so the circuit may not be closed. The battery may not be strong enough, or he may need more coils of wire.

20. He will pick up fewer safety pins because the strength of the magnet is less at a greater distance.

Chapter Test

See *Assessment Guide* pages AG97-102 for a Chapter Test and Performance Task, with rubric. Assessment options appear on page 432H.

Performance Assessment

Make It Light

Give the student masking tape, a D battery, a flashlight bulb, and two 30-cm lengths of electrical wire with the insulation stripped from the ends. Ask the student to make the bulb light and to draw a picture of how the materials had to be put together to achieve this. Ask the student to write a one-sentence conclusion. Limit time to 20 minutes.

Rubric for Performance Assessment

Preparation Materials may be gathered ahead of time and placed in a learning center.

Scoring Rubric—Performance Indicators

_____ Attaches bulb, wires, and battery in a complete circuit and succeeds in lighting the bulb.

_____ Draws a picture of a complete circuit.

_____ States that a complete circuit is needed for the bulb to light.

Observations and Rubric Scores

    3   2   1   0

CHAPTER 14 LESSON PLANNER

Lesson	Pacing	Vocabulary	Objectives & Reading Focus	Resources & Technology
1 What Is Heat? pp. 460–465	3 days	temperature heat thermal energy conduction conductor insulator	■ Make a thermometer and use it to measure an increase and decrease in temperature. ■ Define heat and temperature. ■ Compare conductors and insulators. **MAIN IDEA AND DETAILS** Look for things that allow heat to move through them. Main Idea detail detail detail	■ Lab Manual pp. LM162–164 ■ Transparencies DI44, IS44, RS44, GO 44 ■ Electronic Transparencies ■ Activity Video/DVD 3018 ■ ESL Support pp. 190–193 ■ Reading Support and Homework pp. RS102–103
2 What Is Light? pp. 466–471	3 days	reflection refraction shadow	■ Investigate the path of light. ■ Define reflection and refraction. ■ Understand shadows. **SEQUENCE** See what happens next when light changes direction. ☐ → ☐ → ☐	■ Lab Manual pp. LM165–167 ■ Transparencies DI45, IS45, RS45, GO 45 ■ Electronic Transparencies ■ Activity Video/DVD 3019 ■ ESL Support pp. 194–197 ■ Reading Support and Homework pp. RS104–105
3 How Are Light and Color Related? pp. 472–479	3 days	absorbed opaque transparent translucent	■ Investigate how white light can be split into colored light. ■ Describe how objects absorb light in different amounts. ■ Explain how colored lights combine to make other colors. **CAUSE AND EFFECT** Look for different ways materials affect light. Cause → Effect	■ Lab Manual pp. LM168–170 ■ Transparencies DI46, IS46, RS46, GO 46 ■ Electronic Transparencies ■ Activity Video/DVD 3020 ■ ESL Support pp. 198–201 ■ Reading Support and Homework pp. RS106–107
4 What Is Sound? pp. 480–485	3 days	vibrations loudness pitch	■ Investigate how a maraca makes sound. ■ Identify vibrations as the source of sound and define loudness and pitch. ■ Explain how hearing works. **CAUSE AND EFFECT** Look for ways that sounds are made. Cause → Effect	■ Lab Manual pp. LM171–173 ■ Transparencies DI47, IS47, RS47, GO 47 ■ Electronic Transparencies ■ Activity Video/DVD 3021 ■ ESL Support pp. 202–205 ■ Reading Support and Homework pp. RS108–109
End of Chapter pp. 486–491	2 days		■ Evaluate relationships of science, technology, and society ■ Review chapter concepts	■ Intervention, On-Level, and Above-Level Readers ■ Assessment Guide pp. AG103–108

Plan Ahead for Activities

Investigate

Measuring Temperature p. 461

Materials: water, 1-L plastic bottle, red food coloring, clear drinking straw, clay, clear plastic cup, dropper, metric ruler

Time: 75 minutes

Inquiry Focus: Order

Prep Tip: This activity will work best if you choose four very different places such as 1) out in the open in the classroom, 2) in direct sunlight, 3) in the hallway outside the room, 4) in a freezer.

Where's the Light p. 467

Materials: small object, flash light, poster board

Time: 10 minutes

Inquiry Focus: Predict

Prep Tip: Students should use an object that is tall enough to be clearly seen when it is illuminated, but avoid long slender objects such as pencils. If the available flashlights are not very bright, close the blinds or dim the classroom lights.

Making Rainbows p. 473

Materials: prism, crayons, sheet of white paper, sheet of red paper

Time: 10 minutes

Inquiry Focus: Predict

Prep Tip: Students may need practice rotating a prism until the light catches it to create a rainbow. Discuss with students how they can use the crayons to record their observations.

Make a Maraca p. 481

Materials: empty paper-towel roll, stapler, masking tape, dried rice, dried beans

Time: 15 minutes

Inquiry Focus: Compare

Prep Tip: Students may have difficulty hearing the different sounds generated by the maraca if many maracas are being shaken at the same time. If possible, separate students into different parts of the room or the hallway to provide acoustic privacy.

Insta-Lab

Feeling the Heat
p. 464

 10 minutes

Materials: butter, spoon, sponge, small piece of wood, metal jar lid

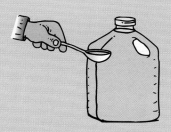

Tip: Remind students to use extreme caution around hot water. Make sure the pan of water is on a stable surface.

What Do You See?
p. 469

 10 minutes

Materials: pencil, cards, mirror

Tip: consider using an inexpensive full length mirror turned horizontally, to allow more students to use the mirror at once.

Cover Up
p. 475

 5 minutes

Materials: plastic wrap, aluminum foil, waxed paper

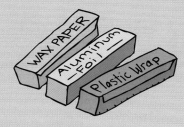

Tip: Allow students to come up with a scale of transparency from 1 to 10 on the board.

Big Ears
p. 484

 5 minutes

Materials: paper

Tip: Have students ask specific questions and see if the other students can answer them with and without the cone.

REACHING ALL LEARNERS

Reading Support

Page R64 provides additional information

Below-Level/Intervention

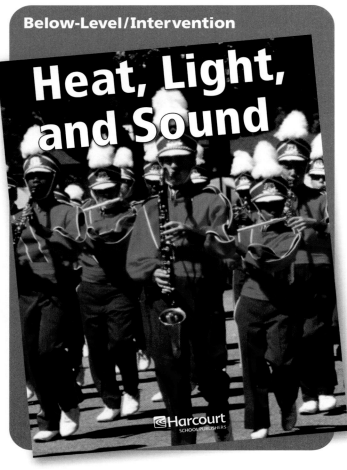

When used along with the hands-on experiences from the **Student Edition**, the Intervention Reader promotes science success for all students.
Reading Level 1.5–2.0

The Intervention Reader presents identical chapter content and vocabulary at a below-grade reading level. The reader uses a visual glossary, simplified language, and comprehension aids especially designed for struggling readers. The **Intervention Readers Teacher Guide** provides additional strategies and support.

On-Level/Enrichment

This reader promotes success on state science tests by reinforcing test content objectives, chapter vocabulary, and reading skills.
Reading Level 2.5–3.5

Advanced/Challenge

This interesting nonfiction reader enriches and extends chapter concepts.
Reading Level 4.0–5.5

Trade Books for Students

These books provide in-depth information on chapter content. For more information about each selection, see the Bibliography beginning on page R48.

Easy
Polar Bear, Polar Bear, What Do You Hear? by Bill Martin Jr., Henry Holt, 1991, Children's Choice

Average
How Does a Trumpet Work?: Projects About Sound by Trevor Day, Copper Beech Books, 2002

Challenge
Science With Light and Mirrors by Kate Woodward, Usborne, 1991

Alternative Teaching Strategies

This guide provides additional support for the strategies and activities that appear throughout this chapter.

 ## Intervention and Reteaching

Strategies for reteaching key lesson concepts provide options for addressing a variety of learning styles.

Intervention Reader p. 463

On-Level Reader p. 470

More Inquiry p. 476

Pitch p. 483

 ## Using the E-Book

This chapter is also available online and has provisions for children with special needs. Adjustable text size and audio text can be used with children who have vision impairments or learning difficulties.

www.hspscience.com

Science Concepts Across the Grades

Grade 2	Grade 3	Grade 4
Related Chapters		
Chapter 11 Light and Heat **Lesson 1** What Is Energy? **Lesson 2** What Is Light? **Lesson 3** What Is Heat? **Chapter 12 Sound** **Lesson 1** What Causes Sound? **Lesson 2** How Does Sound Travel? **Lesson 3** How Do We Make Different Sounds?	**Chapter 14 Heat, Light, and Sound** **Lesson 1** What Is Heat? **Lesson 2** What Is Light? **Lesson 3** How Are Light and Color Related? **Lesson 4** What Is Sound?	**Chapter 12 Sound** **Lesson 1** What Is Sound? **Lesson 2** What Are The Properties of a Wave? **Lesson 3** How Do Sound Waves Travel? **Chapter 13 Light and Heat** **Lesson 1** How does Light Behave? **Lesson 2** How Can Heat Be Transferred? **Lesson 3** How is Heat Produced and Used?
Learning Goals		
▶ Understand how energy and matter interact; Recognize that light can pass through some sources; Explain heat sources and how heat is transfered . ▶ Know what causes sound; Explain how sound travels; Identify the loudness and pitch of sounds, and know how they can be changed.	▶ Tell how warmer objects lose heat to cooler objects when the two come into contact. ▶ Know the properties of conductors and insulators. ▶ Identify how light is reflected, refracted, and absorbed. ▶ Identify vibrations as the source of sound and define loudness and pitch.	▶ Know what produces sound, pitch, and intensity; Know how the human ear functions; Know how a sound wave reacts. ▶ Define reflection, absorption and refaction; Describe how light passes through eyes; Define temperture and heat; Know ways heat is used and transferred.

RESOURCES FOR INQUIRY

Daily Practice

Daily Inquiry pp. 460, 466, 472, 480;
  Teaching Transparencies DI 144-147
  Electronic Transparencies DI 3007-3020

Inquiry Tool Kit

Harcourt Investigations

Harcourt School Publishers offers an alternative program that provides more opportunities for inquiry-based science experiences. The program provides a series of investigations that promote guided, structured, and independent inquiry using student journals, lab manuals, science readers and other materials.

Visit **www.hspscience.com** for more information.

Guided Inquiry

Investigate pp. 461, 467, 473, 481;
  Lab Manual pp. LM 162-164,
  165-167, 168-170, 171-173

Inquiry Skill Mini Lesson pp. 461, 468, 474, 481;
  Teaching Transparencies **IS 144-147**;
  Electronic Transparencies **IS 3007-3020**

Insta-Lab pp. 464, 469, 475, 484

Unit Experiment pp. 139A-B;
  Lab Manual pp. LM 131-134

Independent Inquiry

Investigate Further
  Lab Manual pp. LM 462, 468, 474, 482

Lab Manual

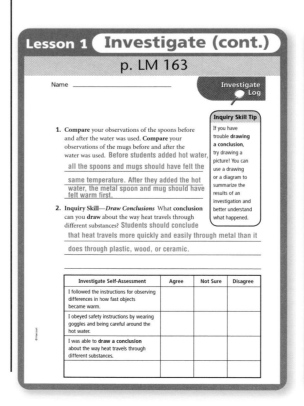

Use with **Student Edition** p. 461.

Independent Inquiry (continued)

Science Projects for Home or School
p. 489 *Teaching Resources* p. TR 24

Unit Experiment pp. 139A-B; Lab Manual pp. LM 9-11 and Science Fair Projects *Lab Manual* LM 214-219

Lab Manual (cont.)

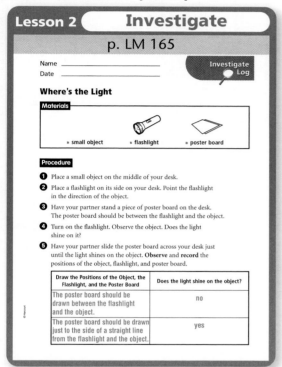

Lesson 2 — Investigate — p. LM 165

Name _____
Date _____

Where's the Light

Materials
- small object
- flashlight
- poster board

Procedure

1. Place a small object on the middle of your desk.
2. Place a flashlight on its side on your desk. Point the flashlight in the direction of the object.
3. Have your partner stand a piece of poster board on the desk. The poster board should be between the flashlight and the object.
4. Turn on the flashlight. Observe the object. Does the light shine on it?
5. Have your partner slide the poster board across your desk just until the light shines on the object. **Observe** and **record** the positions of the object, flashlight, and poster board.

Draw the Positions of the Object, the Flashlight, and the Poster Board	Does the light shine on the object?
The poster board should be drawn between the flashlight and the object.	no
The poster board should be drawn just to the side of a straight line from the flashlight and the object.	yes

Use with **Student Edition** p. 467.

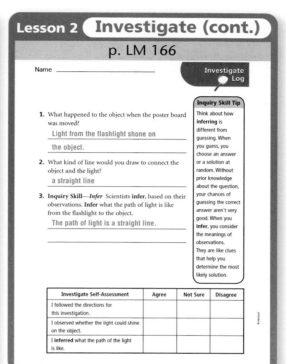

Lesson 2 — Investigate (cont.) — p. LM 166

Name _____

1. What happened to the object when the poster board was moved?
   Light from the flashlight shone on the object.

2. What kind of line would you draw to connect the object and the light?
   a straight line

3. Inquiry Skill—*Infer* Scientists **infer**, based on their observations. **Infer** what the path of light is like from the flashlight to the object.
   The path of light is a straight line.

Inquiry Skill Tip
Think about how **inferring** is different from guessing. When you guess, you choose an answer or a solution at random. Without prior knowledge about the question, your chances of guessing the correct answer aren't very good. When you **infer**, you consider the meanings of observations. They are like clues that help you determine the most likely solution.

Investigate Self-Assessment	Agree	Not Sure	Disagree
I followed the directions for this investigation.			
I observed whether the light could shine on the object.			
I **inferred** what the path of the light is like.			

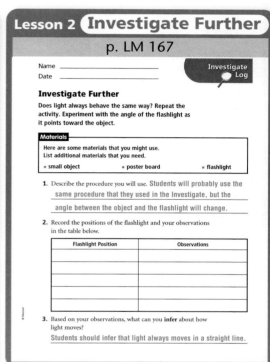

Lesson 2 — Investigate Further — p. LM 167

Name _____
Date _____

Investigate Further
Does light always behave the same way? Repeat the activity. Experiment with the angle of the flashlight as it points toward the object.

Materials
Here are some materials that you might use. List additional materials that you need.
- small object
- poster board
- flashlight

1. Describe the procedure you will use. Students will probably use the same procedure that they used in the Investigate, but the angle between the object and the flashlight will change.

2. Record the positions of the flashlight and your observations in the table below.

Flashlight Position	Observations

3. Based on your observations, what can you **infer** about how light moves?
   Students should infer that light always moves in a straight line.

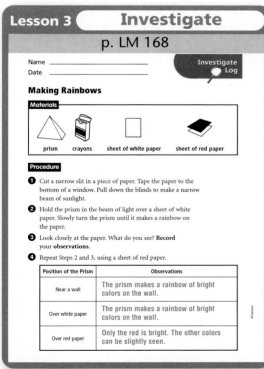

Lesson 3 — Investigate — p. LM 168

Name _____
Date _____

Making Rainbows

Materials
- prism
- crayons
- sheet of white paper
- sheet of red paper

Procedure

1. Cut a narrow slit in a piece of paper. Tape the paper to the bottom of a window. Pull down the blinds to make a narrow beam of sunlight.
2. Hold the prism in the beam of light over a sheet of white paper. Slowly turn the prism until it makes a rainbow on the paper.
3. Look closely at the paper. What do you see? **Record** your **observations**.
4. Repeat Steps 2 and 3, using a sheet of red paper.

Position of the Prism	Observations
Near a wall	The prism makes a rainbow of bright colors on the wall.
Over white paper	The prism makes a rainbow of bright colors on the wall.
Over red paper	Only the red is bright. The other colors can be slightly seen.

Use with **Student Edition** p. 473.

Lesson 3 — Investigate (cont.) — p. LM 169

Name _____

1. How does a prism change sunlight?
   A prism changes sunlight's direction and makes light into colors.

2. How was the light you saw on the white paper different from the light you saw on the red paper?
   On white paper, all the colors can be seen.
   On red paper, some colors can't be seen.
   Red is the brightest color on red paper.

3. Inquiry Skill—*Predict* Scientists **predict** what might happen based on patterns or experiences. What do you **predict** you would see if you used the prism to shine sunlight on a piece of blue paper?
   Blue can be seen, but the other colors can't be seen, or can't be seen well.

Inquiry Skill Tip
When you **predict** what will happen in an investigation, think about the pattern of things that have happened before. Then decide what would happen if that pattern were to continue with just one variable changed.

Investigate Self-Assessment	Agree	Not Sure	Disagree
I followed the directions for making rainbows.			
I held the prism so that sunlight would shine through it.			
I **predicted** what I would see if I used the prism to shine sunlight on a piece of blue paper.			

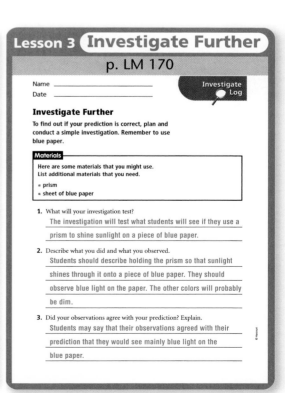

Lesson 3 — Investigate Further — p. LM 170

Name _____
Date _____

Investigate Further
To find out if your prediction is correct, plan and conduct a simple investigation. Remember to use blue paper.

Materials
Here are some materials that you might use. List additional materials that you need.
- prism
- sheet of blue paper

1. What will your investigation test?
   The investigation will test what students will see if they use a prism to shine sunlight on a piece of blue paper.

2. Describe what you did and what you observed.
   Students should describe holding the prism so that sunlight shines through it onto a piece of blue paper. They should observe blue light on the paper. The other colors will probably be dim.

3. Did your observations agree with your prediction? Explain.
   Students may say that their observations agreed with their prediction that they would see mainly blue light on the blue paper.

RESOURCES FOR INQUIRY

Lab Manual (cont.)

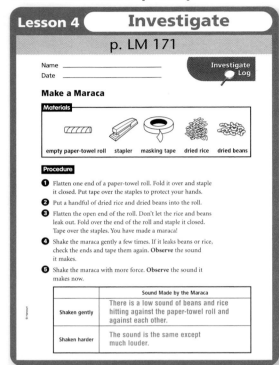

Name _____

Date _____

Investigate Log

Make a Maraca

Materials

empty paper-towel roll — stapler — masking tape — dried rice — dried beans

Procedure

❶ Flatten one end of a paper-towel roll. Fold it over and staple it closed. Put tape over the staples to protect your hands.

❷ Put a handful of dried rice and dried beans into the roll.

❸ Flatten the open end of the roll. Don't let the rice and beans leak out. Fold over the end of the roll and staple it closed. Tape over the staples. You have made a maraca!

❹ Shake the maraca gently a few times. If it leaks beans or rice, check the ends and tape them again. **Observe** the sound it makes.

❺ Shake the maraca with more force. **Observe** the sound it makes now.

Sound Made by the Maraca	
Shaken gently	There is a low sound of beans and rice hitting against the paper-towel roll and against each other.
Shaken harder	The sound is the same except much louder.

Use with **Student Edition** p. 481.

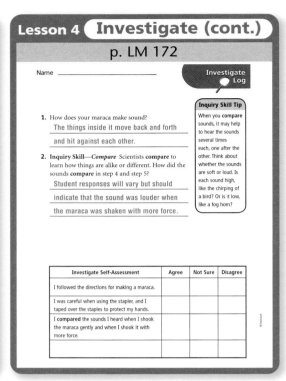

Name _____

Investigate Log

1. How does your maraca make sound?

   The things inside it move back and forth and hit against each other.

2. **Inquiry Skill—Compare** Scientists **compare** to learn how things are alike or different. How did the sounds **compare** in step 4 and step 5?

   Student responses will vary but should indicate that the sound was louder when the maraca was shaken with more force.

Inquiry Skill Tip

When you **compare** sounds, it may help to hear the sounds several times each, one after the other. Think about whether the sounds are soft or loud. Is each sound high, like the chirping of a bird? Or is it low, like a fog horn?

Investigate Self-Assessment	Agree	Not Sure	Disagree
I followed the directions for making a maraca.			
I was careful when using the stapler, and I taped over the staples to protect my hands.			
I compared the sounds I heard when I shook the maraca gently and when I shook it with more force.			

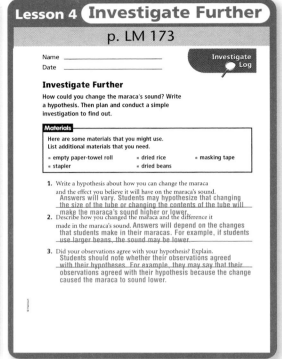

Name _____

Date _____

Investigate Log

Investigate Further

How could you change the maraca's sound? Write a hypothesis. Then plan and conduct a simple investigation to find out.

Materials

Here are some materials that you might use. List additional materials that you need.

- empty paper-towel roll
- dried rice
- masking tape
- stapler
- dried beans

1. Write a hypothesis about how you can change the maraca and the effect you believe it will have on the maraca's sound.
   Answers will vary. Students may hypothesize that changing the size of the tube or changing the contents of the tube will make the maraca's sound higher or lower.

2. Describe how you changed the maraca and the difference it made in the maraca's sound. Answers will depend on the changes that students make in their maracas. For example, if students use larger beans, the sound may be lower.

3. Did your observations agree with your hypothesis? Explain.
   Students should note whether their observations agreed with their hypotheses. For example, they may say that their observations agreed with their hypothesis because the change caused the maraca to sound lower.

READING SUPPORT AND HOMEWORK

Pages available online.
www.hspscience.com

Reading Support and Homework also includes Vocabulary Power, and Vocabulary Cards and Activities.

Lesson 1 Quick Study
p. RS 102

Name _____
Date _____

Lesson Quick Study

Lesson 1 - What Is Heat?

1. **Inquiry Skill Practice–Draw A Conclusion**

| a plastic container |
| an iron wire |

Think about the objects listed in the box to the right. Draw a conclusion about which object is a conductor. Explain why you think so. **An iron wire; iron is a metal, and heat moves through most metals easily.**

2. **Use Vocabulary**

Match the clue on the left to the term on the right. Write the letter on the blank.

D An object that heat can move through easily — A. temperature
C The movement of heat — B. heat
A The measure of how hot or cold something is — C. thermal energy
E An object that does not conduct heat well — D. conductor
B A form of energy that moves between objects because of differences in temperature — E. insulator

3. **Reading Skill Practice–Main Idea and Details**

Read the selection. Underline the main idea. List at least three details about the main idea.

Maria uses a cooking pot to heat her food. A cooking pot is a conductor. Maria places the cooking pot on top of the stovetop. The stovetop is heated by a flame. The hot flame heats the cooking pot. The cooking pot heats Maria's food. **Possible answers: The stovetop is heated by a flame. The hot flame heats the cooking pot. The cooking pot heats Maria's food.**

Use with *Student Edition* pp. 460–465.

Lesson 1 (cont.)
p. RS 103

Name _____

4. **Main Idea and Details**

Use this space to complete the graphic organizer shown in the Reading Review of the Student Edition.

Main Idea: Some things allow heat to pass through them better than others.

Possible answers are given.

Examples of Conductors:
A. copper
iron

Examples of Insulators:
B. wood
cloth

5. **Critical Thinking and Problem Solving**

A pizzeria makes pizzas in a very hot and large oven. When the pizza needs to be turned or taken out of the oven, the cook uses a long wooden paddle. Why do you think the cook uses a wooden paddle rather than a shined metal paddle?

Possible answer: Wood is an insulator. It does not let heat pass through it easily. Metal is a conductor. It lets heat pass through it easily. Wood is better to use because since heat does not transfer easily through the wood, the cook will not get burned.

Lesson 2 Quick Study
p. RS 104

Name _____
Date _____

Lesson Quick Study

Lesson 2 - What Is Light?

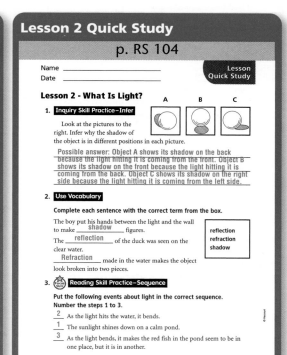

1. **Inquiry Skill Practice–Infer**

Look at the pictures to the right. Infer why the shadow of the object is in different positions in each picture.

Possible answer: Object A shows its shadow on the back because the light hitting it is coming from the front. Object B shows its shadow on the front because the light hitting it is coming from the back. Object C shows its shadow on the right side because the light hitting it is coming from the left side.

2. **Use Vocabulary**

Complete each sentence with the correct term from the box.

The boy put his hands between the light and the wall to make ___shadow___ figures.

The ___reflection___ of the duck was seen on the clear water.

___Refraction___ made in the water makes the object look broken into two pieces.

| reflection |
| refraction |
| shadow |

3. **Reading Skill Practice–Sequence**

Put the following events about light in the correct sequence. Number the steps 1 to 3.

2 As the light hits the water, it bends.

1 The sunlight shines down on a calm pond.

3 As the light bends, it makes the red fish in the pond seem to be in one place, but it is in another.

Use with *Student Edition* pp. 466–471.

Lesson 2 (cont.)
p. RS 105

Name _____

4. **Sequence**

Use this space to complete the graphic organizer shown in the Reading Review of the Student Edition.

Sequence

Light strikes an object. → Some light bounces back, or A ___reflects___ .

Light travels through water. → When the light leaves the water, it bends, or B ___refracts___ .

An object blocks light. → A C ___shadow___ forms behind the object.

5. **Critical Thinking and Problem Solving**

Maggie stands between a wall and a light bulb. Her shadow is seen on the wall. Based on what you know about light, what exactly do you think happens to make her shadow?

Possible answer: Light travels in a straight line. When it hits something or someone such as Maggie, the light is blocked. Since the light does not pass through Maggie, a shadow is formed.

Lesson 3 Quick Study
p. RS 106

Name _____
Date _____

Lesson Quick Study

Lesson 3 - How Are Light and Color Related?

1. **Inquiry Skill Practice–Predict**

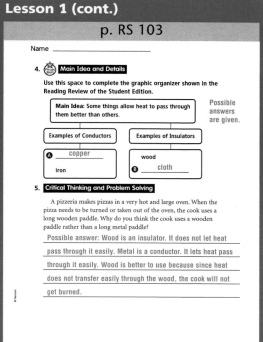

Imagine the three windows to the right belong to a room. Predict what will happen if you stand on the other side of each window and shine a flashlight to the inside. **Possible answer: When a flashlight is shined through window A, some light will go through. When a flashlight is shined through window B, all or most light will go through. When a flashlight is shined through window C, no light will go through.**

2. **Use Vocabulary**

Complete each sentence with the correct term from the box.

Julia used a ___translucent___ window covering to let some light into the room.

The water was so ___transparent___ that the fisherman could see the fish nibbling the worm.

| transparent |
| translucent |

3. **Reading Skill Practice–Cause and Effect**

Read the selection. Describe the cause and effect of light on the planets in the Solar System.

Why do planets appear bright in the sky? The sun shines on the planets just as it shines on Earth. However, not all the light from the sun is absorbed by the planets. Some of the light is reflected from the surface of the planet. This is why when the right telescope is used, the planets can be seen from Earth. **Possible answers: Cause: The sun shines on the planets. Effects: Some light is absorbed and some light is reflected. The planets can be seen from Earth.**

Lesson 3 (cont.)
p. RS 107

Name _____

4. **Cause and Effect**

Use this space to complete the graphic organizer shown in the Reading Review of the Student Edition.

Draw and complete this graphic organizer.

Cause → Effects

Light strikes an object. →
Object is A ___transparent___ when almost all light passes through.
Object is B ___translucent___ when some light passes through.
Object is opaque when C ___no___ light passes through.

Sunlight enters a prism. → The colors of light are D ___separated___ .

5. **Critical Thinking and Problem Solving**

You already know that light has many colors. When light hits an object, we do not see many colors. We see the color that the object reflects. All the other colors are absorbed. Explain what happens when light shines on a yellow banana.

Possible answer: When light shines on a yellow banana, all the colors from the light spectrum are absorbed by the banana. The only color that is reflected is yellow. This is why the banana appears yellow to us.

Use with *Student Edition* pp. 472–479.

Reading Support (cont.)

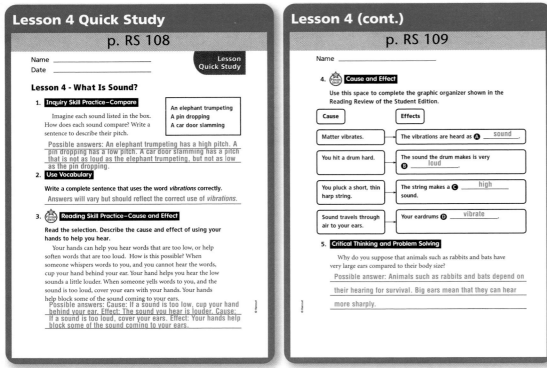

Lesson 4 Quick Study

p. RS 108

Name _____
Date _____

Lesson Quick Study

Lesson 4 - What Is Sound?

1. **Inquiry Skill Practice–Compare**

    Imagine each sound listed in the box. How does each sound compare? Write a sentence to describe their pitch.

    An elephant trumpeting
    A pin dropping
    A car door slamming

    Possible answers: An elephant trumpeting has a high pitch. A pin dropping has a low pitch. A car door slamming has a pitch that is not as loud as the elephant trumpeting, but not as low as the pin dropping.

2. **Use Vocabulary**

    Write a complete sentence that uses the word *vibrations* correctly.

    Answers will vary but should reflect the correct use of *vibrations*.

3. **Reading Skill Practice–Cause and Effect**

    Read the selection. Describe the cause and effect of using your hands to help you hear.

    Your hands can help you hear words that are too low, or help soften words that are too loud. How is this possible? When someone whispers words to you, and you cannot hear the words, cup your hand behind your ear. Your hand helps you hear the low sounds a little louder. When someone yells words to you, and the sound is too loud, cover your ears with your hands. Your hands help block some of the sound coming to your ears.

    Possible answers: Cause: If a sound is too low, cup your hand behind your ear. Effect: The sound you hear is louder. Cause: If a sound is too loud, cover your ears. Effect: Your hands help block some of the sound coming to your ears.

Lesson 4 (cont.)

p. RS 109

Name _____

4. **Cause and Effect**

    Use this space to complete the graphic organizer shown in the Reading Review of the Student Edition.

Cause		Effects
Matter vibrates.	→	The vibrations are heard as Ⓐ ___sound___.
You hit a drum hard.		The sound the drum makes is very Ⓑ ___loud___.
You pluck a short, thin harp string.		The string makes a Ⓒ ___high___ sound.
Sound travels through air to your ears.		Your eardrums Ⓓ ___vibrate___.

5. **Critical Thinking and Problem Solving**

    Why do you suppose that animals such as rabbits and bats have very large ears compared to their body size?

    Possible answer: Animals such as rabbits and bats depend on their hearing for survival. Big ears mean that they can hear more sharply.

Use with **Student Edition** pp. 480–485.

ASSESSMENT OPTIONS

Formal Assessment
- Chapter Review and Test Preparation SE pp. 490-491
- Chapter Test AG pp. 103-106

Standardized Test Preparation
- Reading Review and Test Preparations SE pp. 465, 471, 479, 485

Harcourt School Publishers Online Assessment
- Online chapter test taking and automatic scoring
- Banks of items from which to build tests

Ongoing Assessment
- Assess Prior Knowledge—Chapter Opener
- Daily Inquiry Transparencies
- Teacher Edition questions throughout
- Focus Skill questions throughout SE
- Reaching All Learners throughout TE
- Reading Review SE pp. 465, 471, 479, 485
- Observation Checklist AG

Performance Assessment
- Long-Option AG pp. 107-108
- Short-option TE p. 491

Student Self–Assessment
- Investigate Self-Assessment *Lab Manual*
- Self-Assessment AG

Portfolio Assessment
- Using Portfolio Assessment AG
- Suggested work samples TE p. 456

Chapter Test

p. AG 103

Name _____
Date _____

Chapter Assessment

Heat, Light, and Sound

Vocabulary 4 points each

Use the terms from the box to complete the sentences.

absorbed	conductor	insulator	opaque
reflection	pitch	thermal energy	shadow

1. When light strikes an object, some of it is taken in, or _____ absorbed

2. Objects that block light are _____ opaque

3. A dark area that forms when an object blocks the path of light is called a _____ shadow

4. The movement of heat between objects with different temperatures is _____ thermal energy

5. An object that doesn't conduct heat well is called an _____ insulator

6. How high or low a sound is is called _____ pitch

7. An object that heat can move through easily is _____ conductor

8. The bouncing of light off an object is _____ reflection

---

p. AG 104

Name _____

Science Concepts 4 points each

Write the letter of the best choice.

B 9. Which of the following is a good conductor?
   A. cloth   C. plastic
   B. copper   D.

G 10. Which of the following _____?
   F. aluminum
   G. cloth

A 11. When ca_____
   A. wh_____
   B.

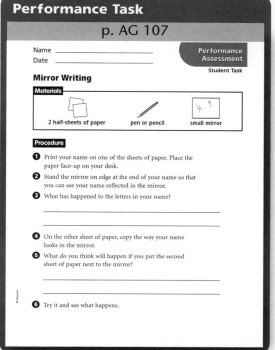

Name _____

H 16. W_____

17. _____ was _____ a rainb_____
   Possible _____
   the sun is ou_____
   though there are _____ not
   be a rainbow because _____ t to pass
   through the raindrops.

18. You are wearing a shirt that reads "TOM___ and you stand in front of a mirror. **Infer** what you will see in the mirror.
   Possible answer: Since the reflection in a mirror is reversed from left to right, the word will read "OTAMOT." (Since all of the letters in *tomato* are symmetrical, the letters themselves won't be reversed.)

---

p. AG 106

_____ points each

_____ ring a down jacket. The jacket has many air spaces. Will the _____ keep Jenna warm? Explain.
   _____ssible answer: The jacket will keep Jenna warm because _____ air is an insulator. The air keeps the heat from moving away from the body.

20. Look at the picture of the boats. Both people will hear the boat passing, but who will hear the sound more loudly? Why?

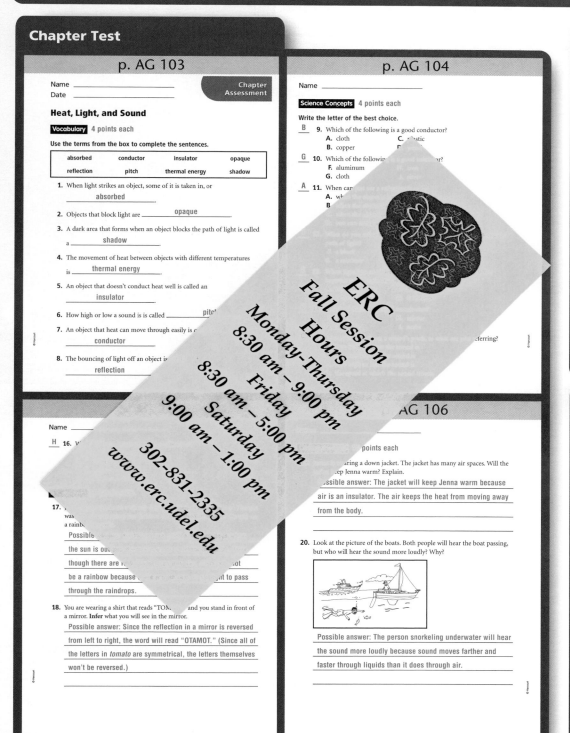

Possible answer: The person snorkeling underwater will hear the sound more loudly because sound moves farther and faster through liquids than it does through air.

Performance Task

p. AG 107

Name _____
Date _____

Performance Assessment
Student Task

Mirror Writing

Materials

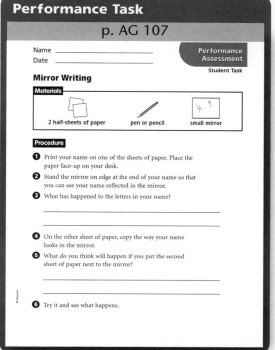

2 half-sheets of paper   pen or pencil   small mirror

Procedure

1. Print your name on one of the sheets of paper. Place the paper face-up on your desk.
2. Stand the mirror on edge at the end of your name so that you can see your name reflected in the mirror.
3. What has happened to the letters in your name?
   _____
   _____

4. On the other sheet of paper, copy the way your name looks in the mirror.
5. What do you think will happen if you put the second sheet of paper next to the mirror?
   _____
   _____

6. Try it and see what happens.

Rubric

p. AG 108

Mirror Writing

Performance Assessment
Teacher's Directions

Materials	Performance Task sheet, 2 half-sheets of paper, pen or pencil, small mirror
Time	20–30 minutes
Suggested Grouping	individuals
Inquiry Skills	observe, record, communicate, draw conclusions
Preparation Hints	none

Introduce the Task Begin the activity by asking students what happens to the writing on a T-shirt or a cap when you look at it in the mirror. Can you read it? Why or why not? Tell students that the great artist and inventor Leonardo da Vinci kept all of his notes in mirror writing. Ask students why they think he did that. Although no one knows for sure, many people think he did it so that people couldn't read his notebooks. Distribute the Performance Task sheets. Tell students they will make mirror writing.

Promote Discussion When students finish, have them meet in small groups to compare results. Tell students to put all of their mirror-writing sheets face down in a pile. Each student will take a sheet and will use a mirror to determine whose it is. Students can pass the names around so that everyone can view each name with a mirror. If time allows, let students write messages to each other using mirror writing.

Scoring Rubric

Performance Indicators

_____ Follows directions for setting up experiment.
_____ Writes name using mirror writing.
_____ Predicts that the backward name will appear correctly in the mirror.
_____ Communicates and shares results in a small group, and reads other students' names and messages by using a mirror.

Observations and Rubric Score

3	2	1	0

Chapter 14 Heat, Light, and Sound

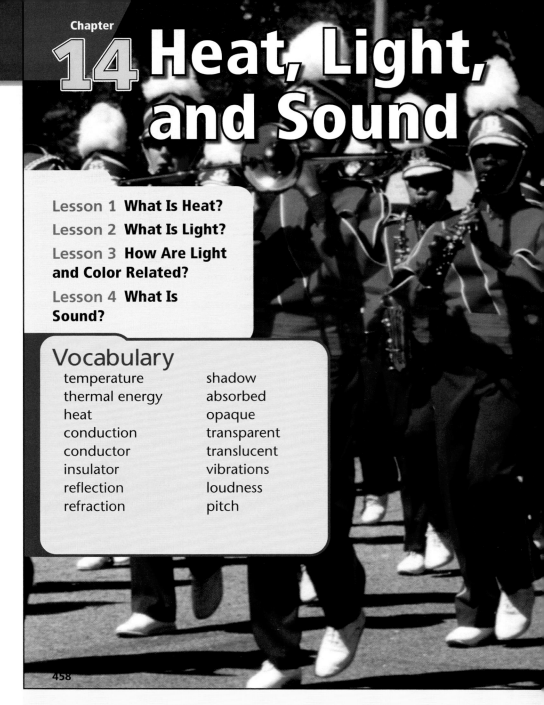

Vocabulary

temperature	shadow
thermal energy	absorbed
heat	opaque
conduction	transparent
conductor	translucent
insulator	vibrations
reflection	loudness
refraction	pitch

458

Assess Prior Knowledge

Use the photograph to get students interested in the chapter topic. Ask students to study the photograph carefully. Have students discuss their ideas about this question: **What examples of heat, light, and sound energy can you find in the picture?** Note their answers as a key to prior knowledge and misconceptions. Students may notice that the band members are carrying musical instruments, which make sound. They may also notice that the scene is sunny and that the sun is a source of heat and light.

Later, as students read about sound in Lesson 4, they will reevaluate the photograph. They should note that the musical instruments vibrate in different ways to create sound.

Generate Science Questions

Have students write down their questions about heat, light, and sound. Record these on the board or on chart paper. Encourage students to refer to the list as they complete the chapter. If questions remain unanswered, have students suggest and implement ways to find answers. In this chapter, students will learn about heat, light, and sound energy, and how these forms of energy move and interact with objects.

Professional Development

To prepare for effective instruction, you may wish to consult these resources:

The **Activity Video/DVD** provides previews of the activities, offers classroom-management techniques, and presents expected results.

The **Science eBook** provides chapter content online, with greater depth via additional content and activities.

The **Science Background** throughout this Teacher Edition provides content support.

Visit **www.hspscience.com** for additional Professional Development resources.

Science Background To Address Misconceptions

Heat vs. Temperature

Assess Prior Knowledge *Ask:* What is heat? What is temperature?

Students May Think that heat and temperature are the same scientific concept since the terms are often interchanged in everyday use.

Scientists Explain that temperature is a measure of the average speed of the particles in an object. The faster the particles move, the hotter the object is. Heat is a form of energy that moves between objects with different temperatures. Heat always transfers from hotter to colder objects.

What You Can Do Give students hot water in an uninsulated cup and direct them to measure the temperature with a thermometer. Have students wrap their hands around the cup and feel the heat transfer to their hands. After 3 minutes, they can measure the temperature again.

What do YOU wonder?

Heat, light, and sound are kinds of energy. What examples of these kinds of energy can you find in the picture?

Vocabulary

Opportunities for developing chapter vocabulary include:

- Develop Science Vocabulary strategies at point-of-use in the teaching plan
- Vocabulary questions in each Reading Review and the Chapter Review and Test
- Vocabulary sections on the Quick Study pages in *Reading Support and Homework*
- Vocabulary Cards and activities and Vocabulary Power worksheet in *Reading Support and Homework*

Reading Support and Homework

p. RS 101

Heat, Light, and Sound

A. Suffixes

Complete each sentence by adding a suffix to the word in parentheses. Choose one of the suffixes from the box below. Write the new word in the sentence.

–or	a thing or a person who does something
–tion	the act of doing something
–ness	the state of being something

1. Something that heat can move through easily is called a
   <u>conductor</u> (conduct)

2. <u>Reflection</u> is what happens when light bounces off of an object. (reflect)

3. The people covered their ears because of the <u>loudness</u> of the music. (loud)

B. Words in Context

Read the sentence and answer the question that follows based on clues from the sentence.

4. A light source is blocked in an area of <u>shadow</u>. What is a shadow?
   <u>Possible answer: a dark area formed when an object blocks the path of light</u>

5. The <u>pitch</u> of a sound goes up for higher notes, and it goes down for lower notes. What is pitch?
   <u>Possible answer: how high or low a sound is</u>

Reading Focus Skills

The content of each lesson is organized to focus on a key reading skill. The skill is reinforced by questions that appear at the end of each section and the graphic organizer at the end of the lesson. Additional practice is also provided in *Reading Support and Homework.*

The Reading Focus Skills for this chapter are:	
Lesson 1	Main Idea and Details
Lesson 2	Sequence
Lesson 3	Cause and Effect
Lesson 4	Cause and Effect
All Lessons	Draw Conclusions and Summarize

Strategies also appear in the Reading Mini-Lessons throughout the chapter.

ESL/ESOL Support

Spanish-speaking students may already be familiar with English words such as these cognates:

absorbed/absorbada

conduction/conducción

conductor/conductor

opaque/opaco

reflection/reflexión

refraction/refracción

temperature/temperatura

thermal energy/energía termal

translucent/translucente

transparent/transparente

vibrations/vibraciones

Objectives

■ Demonstrate that when a warm object is in contact with a cool one, the warm object loses heat and the cool one gains heat.

■ Define *heat* and *temperature*.

■ Compare conductors and insulators.

Transparency DI 44

Electronic Transparency DI 3018

Daily Inquiry

Measure and Check

 thermometer

Other Materials: water faucet

Review Skill: Measure, Predict

What to Do

■ Hold the bottom of the thermometer inside your fist. Record the results.

■ Next, hold your hands under cold running water for 20 seconds. Did the temperature of your fist change or stay the same?

■ What do you think would happen if you held your hands under hot water?

1 Introduce

Build on Prior Knowledge

Use the Fast Fact for a discussion starter about the lesson topic.

How does thermal energy move from the light bulb to the goo?

 When *Minutes* Count . . .

If time is short, consider these options.

Conduct the Investigate as a **whole-class demonstration**.

Use the Activity Video/DVD to model. After previewing, conduct the Investigate.

Lesson **1**

What Is Heat?

 Fast Fact

Up and Down Each lamp has a light bulb in its base. Heat from the bulb warms the goo, which rises. When the goo cools at the top, it falls. That's one way thermal energy moves from one place to another. In the Investigate, you will observe another way.

460

 Science Background

PROFESSIONAL DEVELOPMENT

Forms of Energy The original source of all energy on Earth is the sun. Sun energy can be converted to other natural sources such as wind, flowing rivers, fossil fuels, and nuclear fuels. Humans have learned to convert energy from these sources into an even more usable form called electricity. They use electricity to make heat and light and to power the electrical devices upon which modern life depends.

Every time energy is used or converted from one form to another, some of the usable energy is lost as heat. Heat energy is a very unusable form of energy. So although the sun provides a limitless supply of energy, the current supply of usable energy is limited and must be conserved.

Webliography
Keyword energy
www.hspscience.com

Getting Warmer?

Materials • safety goggles • wooden spoon • plastic spoon • metal spoon • 3 plastic foam cups • hot water • ceramic mug with handle • plastic mug with handle • metal mug with handle

Procedure

1. Put on safety goggles.

2. Touch the three spoons. Record your observations.

3. Caution: Be careful with hot water. Fill three plastic foam cups with hot water. Place one spoon in each cup. Wait 1 minute.

4. Gently touch each spoon. Record your observations.

5. Touch the three mugs. Record your observations.

6. Fill each mug with hot water. Carefully touch each handle every 30 seconds for 2 minutes. Record what you observe.

Step 2

Step 5

Draw Conclusions

1. **Compare** your observations of the spoons and the mugs before and after the water was used.

2. **Inquiry Skill** Draw a conclusion about the way heat travels through different substances. Write your conclusion down and compare it with a classmate's.

Investigate Further

Repeat the Investigate, using ice-cold water instead of hot water. Before you add the water, predict what will happen in each case.

461

Inquiry Skill Mini-Lesson

Draw Conclusions Explain to students that when they draw a conclusion, they use what they have observed in an experiment to decide what they have learned.

Display the Transparency. Point out that the block is at a very high temperature, but the person can hold it without getting burned. The block has special properties that allow only a small amount of heat to flow. Discuss the conclusion you can draw from this.

Inquiry Skill practice is provided in *Reading Support and Homework.*

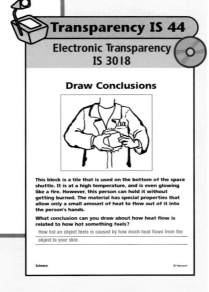

Transparency IS 44

Electronic Transparency
IS 3018

Draw Conclusions

This block is a tile that is used on the bottom of the space shuttle. It is at a high temperature, and is even glowing like a fire. However, this person can hold it without getting burned. The material has special properties that allow only a small amount of heat to flow out of it into the person's hands.

What conclusion can you draw about how heat flow is related to how hot something feels?

How hot an object feels is caused by how much heat flows from the object to your skin.

Science   © Harcourt

2 Teach

Time 30 minutes

Grouping groups of 3

Video Segment 3018

Lab Manual pages can be used to record results. Inquiry Skill Tips and Self-Assessment are also provided.

Tips and Guided Inquiry

Fill some pitchers with hot water before class. The metal items might feel cooler at room temperature than the other items because metal transfers heat away from the skin of the hand better than the other materials.

What is a conclusion? Students might comment that a conclusion is what you learn when you do an experiment.

How do you make a conclusion when you do an experiment? Students might comment that you use the results of your experiment.

Expected Results

All items will initially feel the same. The metal items will increase in temperature faster than the other items.

Draw Conclusions

1. Before hot water was added, all the spoons and mugs felt the same in temperature. After hot water was added, the metal spoon and mug got warm first.

2. Heat travels more quickly and easily through metal than it does through plastic, wood, or ceramic.

Investigate Further

Students can use this page in the *Lab Manual* for **Independent Inquiry**.

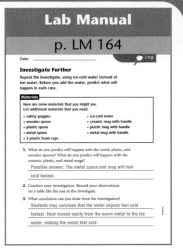

Lab Manual

p. LM 164

Date _____

Investigate Further

Repeat the Investigate, using ice-cold water instead of hot water. Before you add the water, predict what will happen in each case.

Materials

Here are some materials that you might use. List additional materials that you need.

• safety goggles   • ice-cold water
• wooden spoon   • ceramic mug with handle
• plastic spoon   • plastic mug with handle
• metal spoon   • metal mug with handle
• 3 plastic foam cups

1. What do you predict will happen with the metal, plastic, and wooden spoons? What do you predict will happen with the ceramic, plastic, and metal mugs?
    Possible answer: The metal spoon and mug will feel cold fastest.

2. Conduct your investigation. Record your observations on a table like the one in the Investigate.

3. What conclusion can you draw from the investigation?
    Students may conclude that the metal objects feel cold fastest. Heat moved easily from the warm metal to the ice water, making the metal feel cold.

2 Teach
continued

VOCABULARY For Vocabulary Cards and activities, see *Reading Support and Homework*.

SCIENCE CONCEPTS Have students write questions they may have about the science concept. List the questions on the board. Have students answer the questions as they go through the lesson.

READING FOCUS SKILL

MAIN IDEA AND DETAILS Tell students that the information in this lesson is organized to help them recognize a main idea and the details that support it.

1 Key Science Concepts

What makes you feel hot? heat coming from something that has a higher temperature than you

2 Develop Science Vocabulary

temperature Explain that *temperature* derives from the Latin *temperatura*, a term related to the meaning "to measure." Ask students to explain why temperature relates to measurement. Guide them to the understanding that temperature measures the hotness or coldness of an object or environment.

heat Have students use a dictionary to look up two alternative definitions of *heat* and relate them to the scientific meaning of "a form of energy."

thermal energy Explain that *thermal* derives from the Greek *thermos,* meaning "warm" or "hot." Ask students to suggest alternative names for thermal energy, such as heat energy or hot energy.

3 Interpret Data

Answer: 22°C

4 Main Idea and Details

Answer: Heat is a form of energy.

Reading in Science

VOCABULARY	SCIENCE CONCEPTS	READING FOCUS SKILL
temperature p. 462 thermal energy p. 462 heat p. 462 conduction p. 463 conductor p. 463 insulator p. 464	▶ how heat moves	**MAIN IDEA AND DETAILS** Look for details about the movement of heat.

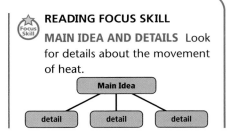

Producing Heat

1 Think about sitting by a campfire. If you sit too close, your skin temperature might go up. **Temperature** is the measure of how hot or cold something is. You feel hot when you are close to the fire because burning wood gives off heat. **Thermal energy** is a form of energy that moves between objects because of differences in temperature. This movement of thermal energy is **heat**. If you get too hot from the fire's heat, you can move away from it **2** or pour water on the fire to stop the heat.

Heat can be produced in other ways, too. When you rub your hands together, they get warm. If you use a heat pack, the chemicals mix in the pack and give off heat.

4 **MAIN IDEA AND DETAILS** What is heat?

462

Math in Science
Interpret Data

3 When you're outside, you can measure the temperature without using a thermometer. Count the number of cricket chirps you hear in one minute, and use this table. What is the temperature when you count 140 chirps?

Number of Chirps per Minute	Temperature in Celsius
10	4°
40	8°
80	14°
120	19°
160	25°
200	31°
240	36°

Reading Skill Mini-Lesson

USE SIGNAL WORDS

Remind students that when they read, they should look for words that are highlighted in the text. These words help them learn about the topic. Display the transparency. Have students reread *Producing Heat*. Ask them to write down the boldfaced words and their meanings. Then have them write an explanation of one form of moving energy. Review their results by writing answers on the transparency.

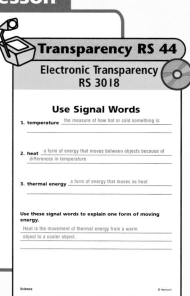

Transparency RS 44

Electronic Transparency
RS 3018

Use Signal Words

1. temperature _the measure of how hot or cold something is_

2. heat _a form of energy that moves between objects because of differences in temperature_

3. thermal energy _a form of energy that moves as heat_

Use these signal words to explain one form of moving energy.
Heat is the movement of thermal energy from a warm object to a cooler object.

Science

Conductors

To cook an egg, you put the egg in a pan and put it on the stove. The heat from the burner makes the pan hot. Soon the heat moves through the pan to the egg. This movement of heat between objects touching each other is **conduction**.

Cooking pans are made of metal, such as iron or aluminum. Heat moves easily through most metals. An object that heat can move through easily is called a **conductor**.

MAIN IDEA AND DETAILS What are two conductors?

Which of these items are good conductors?

Heat moves from warm objects— such as the burner—to cooler objects—such as the eggs.

463

Reaching All Learners

Below · On-Level · Advanced · ESL

Intervention · **Reteach**

Intervention Reader

Target: Struggling readers

Intervention Strategy: The Intervention Reader presents the essential lesson content at a reading level 1.5–2.0. A visual glossary and other text-style and comprehension aids increase student understanding of the content.

Assess: Use the strategies in the **Intervention Reader Teacher Guide** to assess learning, along with the guided questions in the reader.

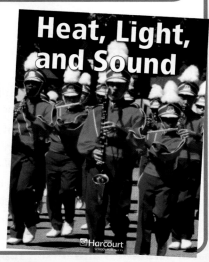

Heat, Light, and Sound

@Harcourt
SCHOOL PUBLISHERS

5 ▶ Key Science Concepts

What is conduction? the movement of heat between objects by touching

What can conduction be used for? Possible answer: cooking

Why are metal pans used for cooking? Heat moves easily through metal.

6 ▶ Develop Science Vocabulary

conduction, **conductor** Tell students that the root *conduct* is a verb that means "to lead, guide, direct, or control." Explain that the suffixes *-tion* and *-or* change the verb to a noun. Ask students to use this information to define *conduction* as the process of leading heat and a *conductor* as an object that guides heat from one object to another.

7 ▶ Interpret Visuals

Summarize what is happening in the picture. Use *conduct* or *conduction* in the answer. Possible answers: A person is cooking with heat. The frying pan conducts heat from the stove to the food. **What is the source of heat?** the stove **What does the pan do?** It conducts heat so the food will cook.

8 ▶ Inquiry Skills

Plan and Conduct Simple Investigations Which metal pots conduct heat best? Have students identify the material(s) in a variety of metal pots, such as copper or aluminum. Have them time how long it takes to boil 1 cup of water over the same flame in each pot. Students can conduct the investigation in class, if a heat source is available, or at home with adult supervision. **Which pot conducts heat best? How do you know?** Students should name the pot in which water boiled fastest.

9 ▶ Critical Thinking

Why are kitchen pans made of aluminum instead of silver? Possible answers: Silver costs too much; aluminum is lighter in weight.

10 ▶ Main Idea and Details

Possible answer: iron and copper

11 ▶ Develop Science Vocabulary

insulator Remind students that antonyms are words that have opposite meanings. Ask them to summarize the meanings of *conductor* and *insulator* and to explain why the terms are antonyms.

12 ▶ Interpret Visuals

What is the purpose of wrapping a pot in an insulator? The crockpot cooks food at low heat for a long time. The insulator keeps the heat inside the pot so the food cooks. **What is the source of heat that warms the water inside the wetsuit?** the surfer's body **What might happen to the surfer if he or she did not wear an insulating wetsuit?** His or her body heat would transfer to the cool ocean water and hypothermia might set in.

13 ▶ Critical Thinking

Why are cooking utensils, such as wooden spoons and potholders, made of insulators? They keep the heat from the food from conducting through the utensil and burning your hand.

14 ▶ Main Idea and Details

Possible answers: wood, cloth, plastic, air

 10 minutes

Feeling the Heat

Materials: butter, spoon, sponge, small piece of wood, metal jar lid

The butter on the metal jar lid melts quickly because metal is a good conductor of heat. The butter on the sponge and the wood may melt a little or not at all, because the sponge and the wood are good insulators.

Insulators

To pick up a hot pan, you use a potholder. It keeps the pan's heat from moving to your hand. **11 ▶** The potholder is an **insulator**—an object that doesn't conduct heat **13 ▶** well. Wood, cloth, and plastic are good insulators.

Air is an insulator, too. Some winter jackets have air spaces in their stuffing. The air keeps the heat from moving away from your body. When birds fluff up their feathers, they make air spaces. The air spaces help keep the birds warm.

14 ▶ MAIN IDEA AND DETAILS
What are two examples of good insulators?

Feeling the Heat
Place small pieces of butter on top of a sponge, a piece of wood, and a metal jar lid. Float each object in a shallow pan of hot water. What happens to the butter? Why?

Water seeps in between the wet suit and the surfer's skin. This water warms up and acts as an insulator along with the wet suit. ▼

12 ▶

The cover wrapped around this pot is an insulator.

464

Reaching All Learners — **ESL / ESOL Support**

Comprehensible Input

Some students might think that a *thermometer* measures length because of the root *-meter*.

Beginning Distribute a meterstick and a thermometer to students. Ask them to label each tool and to act out or demonstrate how to use each one.

Intermediate Have students measure the length of objects with a meterstick and temperature with a thermometer. Explain that *-meter* is Greek for *measure*. Ask students to explain why the root appears in both terms.

Advanced Have students use a dictionary to look up *thermometer* and *meter*. Ask them to use a meterstick and a thermometer to make a presentation to the class explaining the use of each tool and why *-meter* appears in each term.

For strategies and lesson support, see *ESL Support* pp. 190-193.

1. MAIN IDEA AND DETAILS Draw and complete this graphic organizer.

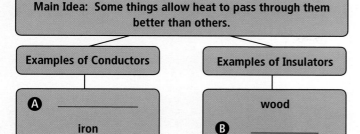

Main Idea: Some things allow heat to pass through them better than others.

Examples of Conductors

Ⓐ _____
iron

Examples of Insulators

wood
Ⓑ _____

2. SUMMARIZE Write two sentences that tell the most important ideas about heat.

3. DRAW CONCLUSIONS Tasha had a foam cup of hot cocoa. The cocoa stayed hot, and the cup didn't get too hot to hold. Explain why.

4. VOCABULARY Use the vocabulary words in this lesson to make a crossword puzzle.

Test Prep

5. Which of these is a good conductor?

A. air
B. cloth
C. copper
D. wood

Links

Writing

Descriptive
Write a **description** of what it feels like to sit by a campfire. Include adjectives to make your description exciting.

Health

Putting Out a Fire
Research some ways to put out a fire. Make a booklet to show your findings. Include pictures.

 For more links and activities, go to **www.hspscience.com**

465

Lesson Quick Study

The Lesson Quick Study in **Reading Support and Homework** provides the opportunity for students to practice inquiry skills, review lesson vocabulary, apply reading skills, and use critical thinking and problem solving. Students can use the second page of the Lesson Quick Study to complete the graphic organizer from the Reading Review. The graphic organizer is also available on overhead and electronic transparencies.

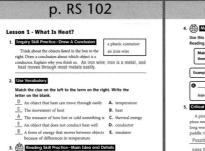

Reading Support and Homework

p. RS 102

Lesson 1 - What Is Heat?

1. Inquiry Skill Practice–Draw A Conclusion

Think about the objects listed in the box to the right. Draw a conclusion about which object is a conductor. Explain why you think so. An iron wire; iron is a metal, and heat moves through most metals easily.

a plastic container
an iron wire

2. Use Vocabulary

Match the clue on the left to the term on the right. Write the letter on the blank.

D An object that heat can move through easily — A. temperature
C The movement of heat — B. heat
A The measure of how hot or cold something is — C. thermal energy
E An object that does not conduct heat well — D. conductor
B A form of energy that moves between objects because of differences in temperature — E. insulator

3. Reading Skill Practice–Main Idea and Details

Read the selection. Underline the main idea. List at least three details about the main idea.
Maria uses a cooking pot to heat her food. A cooking pot is a conductor. Maria places the cooking pot on top of the stovetop. The stovetop is heated by a flame. The hot flame heats the cooking pot. The cooking pot heats Maria's food. Possible answers: The stovetop is heated by a flame. The hot flame heats the

p. RS 103

4. Main Idea and Details

Use this space to complete the graphic organizer shown in the Reading Review of the Student Edition.

Possible answers are given.

Main Idea: Some things allow heat to pass through them better than others.

Examples of Conductors
Ⓐ copper
iron

Examples of Insulators
wood
Ⓑ cloth

5. Critical Thinking and Problem Solving

A pizzeria makes pizzas in a very hot and large oven. When the pizza needs to be turned or taken out of the oven, the cook uses a long wooden paddle. Why do you think the cook uses a wooden paddle rather than a long metal paddle?
Possible answer: Wood is an insulator. It does not let heat pass through it easily. Metal is a conductor. It lets heat pass through it easily. Wood is better to use because since heat does not transfer easily through the wood, the cook will not get burned.

---

3 Assess and Extend

Transparency GO 44
Electronic Transparency GO 3018

Graphic Organizer

1. Ⓐ **Possible answer:** silver
   Ⓑ **Possible answer:** cloth

2. **Possible answer:** Heat is a form of energy, also called thermal energy. Heat moves between objects with different temperatures. Conductors conduct heat well, but insulators do not.

3. The foam cup is an insulator. Heat does not move through foam easily, so the heat stays in the cocoa and does not move through the cup to Tasha's hand.

4. Students should use all the terms in the lesson and include the appropriate number of boxes for the letters.

5. C, copper

Links

Writing If students need help getting started, have them make a list of synonyms for *warm*. Give them interesting examples, like *toasty*. Also have them make a list of things that would be around a campfire, such as *tents* and *trees*. Then have them write sentences that use these words.

 Students can consult the *Writing Models* in **Teaching Resources** as they complete the link. Rubrics are also provided.

Health Local fire stations may provide pamphlets or other information about fire safety. Encourage students to learn and practice the steps in the *Stop, Drop, and Roll* method of putting out fires.

Objectives

- Investigate the path of light.
- Define *reflection* and *refraction*.
- Understand shadows.

Transparency DI 45
Electronic Transparency DI 3019

Daily Inquiry

Me and My Shadow

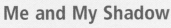

Tool Kit ruler

Other Materials: classroom objects, flashlight

Review Skill: Compare, Observe, Experiment

What to Do

- Shine the flashlight on an object, such as a pencil. Measure the length of the pencil. Then measure the length of the shadow it casts. How do they compare?
- Move the object around. Does that change the length of its shadow?

1 Introduce

Build on Prior Knowledge

Use the Fast Fact for a discussion starter about the lesson topic.

How would a lighthouse help a boat find its way back to shore?

What other uses does light have?

When *Minutes* Count . . .

If time is short, consider these options.

Conduct the Investigate as a **whole-class demonstration**. Perform the procedure in front of the class with the lights dimmed. Discuss the conclusions as a class.

Use the Activity Video/DVD to model the Investigate. After previewing, students can conduct the Investigate in small groups.

What Is Light?

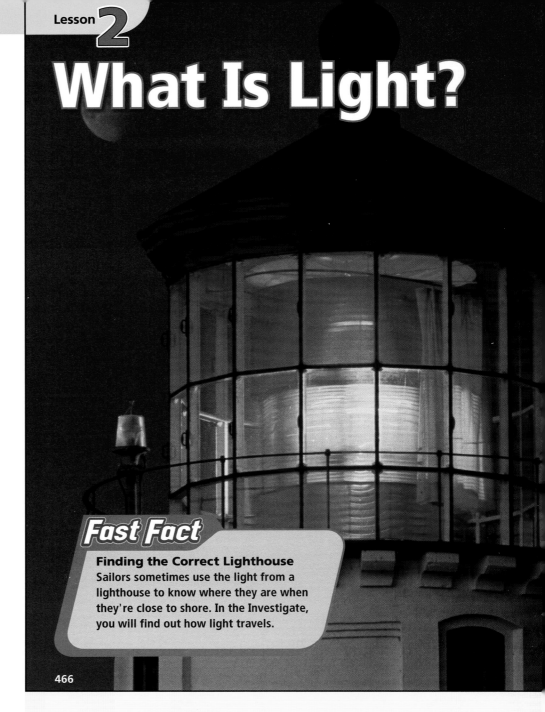

Fast Fact

Finding the Correct Lighthouse
Sailors sometimes use the light from a lighthouse to know where they are when they're close to shore. In the Investigate, you will find out how light travels.

466

PROFESSIONAL DEVELOPMENT   Science Background

Light Energy The sun generates energy through nuclear fusion deep in its core. Hydrogen atoms bond together to form helium, releasing energy as a result of that reaction. That energy escapes the sun in the form of light and heat. Light energy travels through empty space, where it provides energy to all of the planets and other objects in the solar system. Without energy from the sun, there would be no life on Earth.

Unlike heat, which is conducted through contact, light can radiate through a vacuum. This property enables it to travel through the vacuum of space. Light energy travels at the "speed of light," or about 300,000,000 meters per second in a vacuum. At these great speeds, it takes about 8 1/3 minutes for light leaving the surface of the sun to travel to Earth.

Webliography
Keyword light
www.hspscience.com

Where's the Light?

Materials • small object • flashlight • poster board

Procedure

1. Place a small object on the middle of your desk.

2. Place a flashlight on its side on your desk. Point the flashlight in the direction of the object.

3. Have your partner stand a piece of poster board on the desk. The poster board should be between the flashlight and the object.

4. Turn on the flashlight. Observe the object. Does the light shine on it?

5. Have your partner slide the poster board across your desk just until the light shines on the object. Observe and record the positions of the object, flashlight, and poster board.

Step 4

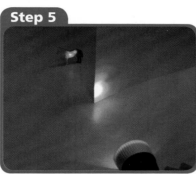

Step 5

Draw Conclusions

1. What kind of line would you draw to connect the object and the light?

2. **Inquiry Skill** Scientists infer, based on their observations. Infer what the path of light is like from the flashlight to the object.

Investigate Further

Does light always behave the same way? Write a hypothesis. Repeat the activity. Experiment with the angle of the flashlight as it points toward the object. Check your hypothesis.

467

Inquiry Skill Mini-Lesson

Infer Explain that an inference is an interpretation of data based upon known information.

Display the transparency. Explain that each drawing shows an arrangement of battery, bulb, and wires. Point out that only the bulb in diagram C is lit by electricity. Challenge students to infer, based on the knowledge that light can come from sources at high temperatures, what causes the bulb to light.

Inquiry Skill practice is provided in *Reading Support and Homework.*

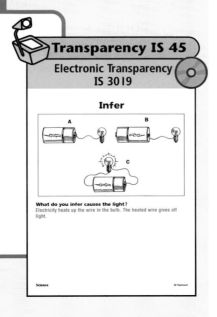

Transparency IS 45

Electronic Transparency
IS 3019

Infer

What do you infer causes the light?
Electricity heats up the wire in the bulb. The heated wire gives off light.

Science © Harcourt

---

2 Teach

Video Segment 3019

Time 10 minutes

Grouping pairs

Lab Manual pages can be used to record results. Inquiry Skill Tips and Self-Assessment are also provided.

Tips and Guided Inquiry

Students should use an object that is tall enough to be clearly seen when it is illuminated but avoid long, slender objects such as pencils. If the flashlights are not very bright, dim the classroom lights.

You can't see the path of the light directly, but you have seen paths of movement, such as those of a car or flowing water. What are some possible paths that light might move in? straight lines, curves, or zigzags

What observations might help you infer the direction of the path of light? Possible answer: The direction of a shadow suggests the path of light.

Expected Results

The object will be in shadow when the poster board is between it and the light. The light will shine on the object when the poster board is moved.

Draw Conclusions

1. Light from the flashlight shone on the object.

2. a straight line

3. The path of light is a straight line.

Investigate Further

Students can use this page in the *Lab Manual* for **Independent Inquiry**.

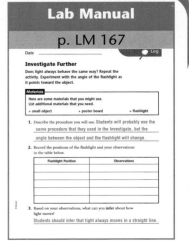

Lab Manual

p. LM 167

Date

Investigate Further
Does light always behave the same way? Repeat the activity. Experiment with the angle of the flashlight as it points toward the object.

Materials
Here are some materials that you might use. List additional materials that you need.
• small object   • poster board   • flashlight

1. Describe the procedure you will use. Students will probably use the same procedure that they used in the Investigate, but the angle between the object and the flashlight will change.

2. Record the positions of the flashlight and your observations in the table below.

Flashlight Position	Observations

3. Based on your observations, what can you infer about how light moves?
Students should infer that light always moves in a straight line.

LESSON 2 ■ 467

2 Teach
continued

VOCABULARY For Vocabulary Cards and activities, see *Reading Support and Homework.*

SCIENCE CONCEPTS Have students list questions they have about the science concept. Discuss how they might find answers. Have students write down answers to their own questions as they go through the lesson.

 READING FOCUS SKILL

SEQUENCE Tell students that the information in this lesson is organized to help them identify the sequence of events that causes a path of light to change direction. Use the Reading Mini-Lesson below to discuss a strategy that students can use to identify a sequence.

1 Key Science Concepts

What does light do when it reflects? It bounces off an object. **What is the path of light after it reflects?** Light always moves in a straight line, so the path is a straight line before and after reflection. **Identify some smooth and shiny objects that reflect light.** Possible answers: mirror, still water, some metals

2 Develop Science Vocabulary

reflection Remind students that when they look in a mirror, they are looking at their "reflection." Explain that *reflect* means "to bounce back." Bounce a ball against a wall to reinforce this meaning.

Interpret Visuals

3 Why does the lake reflect the trees, but the trees do not reflect the lake? The lake's surface is smooth and shiny, so it reflects light from the trees. The trees have a rough surface, so they do not reflect light from the lake. **How does a mirror change the perception of an object?** The object appears backward. Have students practice writing "secret" messages so that they read correctly in a mirror.

VOCABULARY reflection p. 468 refraction p. 469 shadow p. 470	**SCIENCE CONCEPTS** ▶ what the path of light is like and how it can be changed	**READING FOCUS SKILL** **SEQUENCE** See what happens next when light travels.

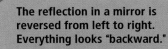

Ways Light Moves

1 In the Investigate activity, you saw that light moves in a straight line. When light strikes an object, some of the light bounces off the object. The bouncing of light off an object is called **reflection**. If
2 the object is smooth and shiny, the light reflects in a pattern that you can see.

The reflection in a mirror is reversed from left to right. Everything looks "backward."

3 You can see trees reflected in the lake.

468

Reading Skill Mini-Lesson

 SEQUENCE

Guide students to understand that a process is a series of steps that occur in an orderly fashion. Display the transparency. Point out that certain words are used to show a sequence of steps. Have students reread *Ways Light Moves* and write down sentences that use sequence cue words to explain reflection and refraction. Have students write a paragraph for each term using cue words to list the sequence of steps.

Transparency RS 45
Electronic Transparency RS 3019

Sequence

Sequence Words					
when	then	first	next	finally	later

Sentences from the reading that use cue words:
1. When light strikes an object, some of the light bounces off the object.
2. The light bends when it moves from the water to the air.
3. The light bends when it gets to the top of the water.

Explain reflection using cue words.
First, light approaches an object. Then light hits the object. Next, light bounces off the object. Finally, light moves away from the object.

Explain refraction using cue words.
First, light moves through the water. Then light hits the surface. Next, light changes directions. Finally, light moves away from the water into the air.

Science
© Harcourt

Refraction makes this piggy bank look broken.

The bank in the picture appears to be broken, but it isn't. Light bends when it moves from the water to the air. The bending of light as it moves from one material to another is **refraction**. Light from the top of the bank goes straight to your eyes. Light from the bottom of the bank goes through water first. The light bends when it gets to the top of the water. You see the bank in two parts.

 SEQUENCE What happens to light after it strikes a smooth object?

Insta-Lab

What Do You See?
Write the capital letters ABCD on a card. Hold the card in front of a mirror, and draw what you see in the mirror. Repeat, using BIRD and MOTH. How are these words different?

469

4 ▶ Key Science Concepts

What happens to light when it moves from one material to another, such as from water to air? The light bends and changes direction. Refraction occurs when light moves from one material to another and changes speed. Demonstrate this phenomenon by rolling roller skates at an angle from a hard, smooth surface to a carpet.

5 ▶ Develop Science Vocabulary

refraction Have students write *refraction* as a rebus so that the word bends in the middle. Display the rebuses for reference.

6 ▶ Inquiry Skills

Classify Have students classify ten classroom objects as reflectors, refractors, or neither. **What objects are reflectors?** Possible answers: mirror; window; metal door **What objects are refractors?** Possible answers: glass of water; fish tank **Do any objects act as both a reflector and a refractor?** Possible answer: A glass of water can bend light passing through it and reflect light bouncing off the surface.

7 ▶ Critical Thinking

What do you think happens to light that strikes an object that is neither a reflector nor a refractor? Possible answer: The object absorbs the light.

8 ▶ Sequence

Answer: The light bounces off the object, or reflects.

 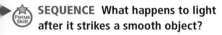
 **Insta-Lab**  10 minutes

What Do You See?

Materials: pencil, cards, mirror
ABCD looks like *DCBA*, with *D, C,* and *B* being backward. *MOTH* looks like *HTOM*. *BIRD* looks like *DRIB*, except the letters are all backward. *MOTH* is different from *BIRD* because it has all symmetrical letters, letters that look the same backward and forward.

⑨ Develop Science Vocabulary

shadow Tell students that *shadow* and *shade* come from the same term. Ask small groups of students to discuss what shade and shadow have in common and to explain why they have a common origin.

Science Up Close

ONLINE EXPERIENCE
For animations and activities, visit
www.hspscience.com

⑩ Interpret Visuals

How do you know that the photographs of the umbrella were taken at different times of the day? The shadows are at different places on the sand. **How could you use the shadow from the umbrella to tell time?** Sunlight moves around the umbrella throughout the day. As it moves, the direction of the shadow moves as well. Therefore, the position of the shadow would indicate the time of day.

⑪ Inquiry Skills

Identify and Control Variables Can an object make more than one shadow at the same time? Have small groups of students discuss this question; demonstrate how they might prove their prediction. Supply students with several flashlights so they can make multiple shadows. **What do you need to make more than one shadow?** more than one source of light

⑫ Critical Thinking

Why do most objects outside on a bright sunny day have only one shadow? The sun is so bright that you see only the shadow caused by sunlight. Any other shadows are too dim to see.

⑬ Sequence (Focus Skill)

Answer: A shadow forms behind the object.

Shadows

Think back to the Investigate. When the poster board was in front of the light, part of your desk was dark. The poster board blocked the light and ⑨ made a shadow. A **shadow** is a dark area that forms when an object blocks the path of light.

⑪ When an object moves, its shadow moves, too. After you moved the poster board, the shadow moved away from part of your desk.

⑬ 🌟 **SEQUENCE** An object blocks the path of light. What happens next?

⑫ Science Up Close

⑩ **SHADOWS THROUGHOUT THE DAY**
The size and position of shadows change during the day. Shadows are longer when the sun is low in the sky. In the morning, shadows point in one direction. Later in the day, they point in a different direction. Notice the position of the sun and the shadows of the umbrella and beach ball.

For more links and activities, go to
www.hspscience.com

470

Reaching All Learners

Enrichment

On-Level Reader

Target: Students who need reinforcement and enrichment of science concepts and vocabulary

Enrichment Strategy: The on-level reader reinforces and enriches lesson content and vocabulary using different visuals and examples. The reader also reinforces the Reading Focus Skills in each lesson.

Assess: Use strategies in the back of the reader to assess student understanding.

1. SEQUENCE Draw and complete this graphic organizer.

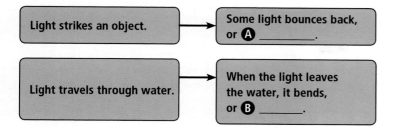

| Light strikes an object. | → | Some light bounces back, or **A** _____. |
| Light travels through water. | → | When the light leaves the water, it bends, or **B** _____. |

2. SUMMARIZE Write a summary of this lesson. Start with this sentence: Light travels in a straight line.

3. DRAW CONCLUSIONS Why can you see your reflection in a mirror but not on a brick wall?

4. VOCABULARY Draw a picture to illustrate each vocabulary word in the lesson. Exchange pictures with a classmate. Write captions for your classmate's pictures.

Test Prep

5. Critical Thinking Would the word WOW look the same in a mirror? Explain.

Writing

Narrative
Write a humorous **story** about a four-year-old who has just discovered his or her shadow. Include facts you have learned about shadows in your story.

Social Studies

Using Shadows to Tell Time
Research how people have used shadows and sundials to tell time. Write a report to share your research with your classmates.

 For more links and activities, go to www.hspscience.com

471

Lesson Quick Study

The Lesson Quick Study in **Reading Support and Homework** provides the opportunity for students to practice inquiry skills, review lesson vocabulary, apply reading skills, and use critical thinking and problem solving. Students can use the second page of the Lesson Quick Study to complete the graphic organizer from the Reading Review. The graphic organizer is also available on overhead and electronic transparencies.

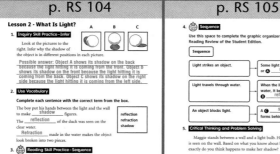

Reading Support and Homework

| p. RS 104 | p. RS 105 |

---

3 Assess and Extend

Graphic Organizer
Transparency GO 45
Electronic Transparency GO 3019

1. **A** reflects; **B** refracts

2. Light travels in a straight line. When it bounces off the object, it reflects. Light can bend as it passes from one material to another. This is refraction. A shadow forms when an object blocks the path of light.

3. The mirror is smooth and shiny, so it reflects light in a pattern that you can see. A brick wall is not smooth. Light does not reflect off it in a pattern, so you do not see your reflection.

4. Students should correctly identify each other's drawings.

5. Yes; each letter is symmetrical, meaning it looks the same forward and backward. The letters will look the same, even though the mirror shows the letters backward.

Writing If students need help getting started, have them make a list of silly things that kids do on the playground. Then have them list all of the facts they know about shadows.

 Students can consult the *Writing Models* in **Teaching Resources** as they complete the link. Rubrics are also provided.

Social Studies Encourage students to use the Internet or school library resources to find information on *sundials* or *timekeeping*. Have them write a report about one way that people have used shadows to tell time. If time allows, have small groups of students build sundials in a sunny part of the school grounds.

Objectives

- Investigate how white light can be split into colored light.
- Describe how objects absorb light in different amounts.
- Explain how colored lights combine to make other colors.

Transparency DI 46

Electronic Transparency DI 3020

Daily Inquiry

Making Colors

 dropper

Review Skill: Observe, Compare, Predict

What to Do

- Predict what will happen when two colors of water mix. What new color do you think will be made? Write your predictions for each combination of two colors.
- Test your prediction. Place a drop of red water and a drop of blue water in the bowl. What happens to the color?
- How can you make a darker or lighter shade of a color?

1 Introduce

Build on Prior Knowledge

Use the Fast Fact for a discussion starter about the lesson topic.

What do rainbows look like? When do you see them? How do they form?

When *Minutes* Count . . .

If time is short, consider these options.

Conduct the Investigate as a **whole-class demonstration**.

Use the Activity Video/DVD to model. After previewing, conduct the Investigate in small groups.

How Are Light and Color Related?

Fast Fact

All the Colors The colors of the rainbow are always in the same order. Red is on top and violet is on bottom. In the Investigate, you will use a prism to make a spectrum of colors.

472

 Science Background

PROFESSIONAL DEVELOPMENT

Dyes and Pigments George Washington Carver made the first crayons. He extracted dyes from different plants to create the various colors. Today, manufacturers heat paraffin wax inside large kettles and add coloring materials called pigments. The colored mixtures are then shaped and cooled.

When you draw with crayons, you leave trails of colored wax on the paper. The pigments reflect light of that color and absorb all others. The light that reflects from the wax to your eye is what gives the crayons their bright, subtle, shocking, or soothing colors.

 Webliography
Keyword light
www.hspscience.com

Making Rainbows

Materials
- prism
- sheet of red paper
- sheet of white paper
- crayons

Procedure

1. Cut a narrow slit in a piece of paper. Tape the paper to the bottom of a window. Pull down the blinds to make a narrow beam of sunlight.

2. Hold the prism in the beam of light over a sheet of white paper. Slowly turn the prism until it makes a rainbow on the paper.

3. Look closely at the paper. What do you see? Record your observations.

4. Repeat Steps 2 and 3, using a sheet of red paper.

Draw Conclusions

1. How does a prism change sunlight?

2. How was the light you saw on the white paper different from the light you saw on the red paper?

3. **Inquiry Skill** Scientists predict what might happen, based on patterns or experiences. What do you predict you would see if you used the prism to shine sunlight on a piece of blue paper?

Step 2

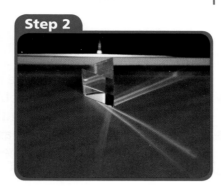

Step 3

Investigate Further

To find out if your prediction is correct, plan and conduct a simple investigation. Remember to use blue paper.

473

Inquiry Skill Mini-Lesson

Predict Remind students that a prediction is an educated guess about what will happen in the future based on past experience. Display the transparency. Ask students to predict what would happen if the plants switched places for a week. Have them justify their predictions based on prior experience and observations of the plants.

Inquiry Skill practice is provided in *Reading Support and Homework*.

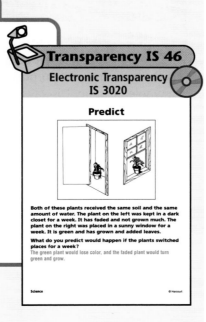

Transparency IS 46

Electronic Transparency IS 3020

Predict

Both of these plants received the same soil and the same amount of water. The plant on the left was kept in a dark closet for a week. It has faded and not grown much. The plant on the right was placed in a sunny window for a week. It is green and has grown and added leaves.

What do you predict would happen if the plants switched places for a week?
The green plant would lose color, and the faded plant would turn green and grow.

Science

---

2 Teach

Video Segment 3020

Time 10 minutes

Grouping pairs

Lab Manual pages can be used to record results. Inquiry Skill Tips and Self-Assessment are also provided.

Tips and Guided Inquiry

Students may need practice rotating a prism until the light catches it to create a rainbow. **What does a prism do? What does it demonstrate about sunlight (white light)?** A prism refracts and splits light into colored light. It shows that sunlight or white light actually combines all the colors of light in a rainbow. **Why did you see different colors on the white paper and the red paper?** White paper reflects all colors of light. Red paper reflects red light and absorbs all other colors, so you see only part of the rainbow.

Expected Results

Students should see all of the rainbow on the white paper. They will see mostly red on the red paper.

Draw Conclusions

1. A prism bends light and shows its different colors.

2. On white paper, all colors can be seen. On red paper, some colors cannot be seen; red is the brightest color.

3. Blue can be seen, but the other colors cannot be seen either at all or very well.

Investigate Further

Students can use this page in the *Lab Manual* for **Independent Inquiry**.

Lab Manual

p. LM 170

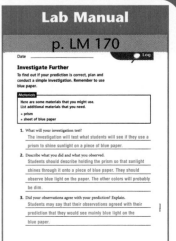

Date _____

Investigate Further
To find out if your prediction is correct, plan and conduct a simple investigation. Remember to use blue paper.

Materials
Here are some materials that you might use. List additional materials that you need.
- prism
- sheet of blue paper

1. What will your investigation test?
   The investigation will test what students will see if they use a prism to shine sunlight on a piece of blue paper.

2. Describe what you did and what you observed.
   Students should describe holding the prism so that sunlight shines through it onto a piece of blue paper. They should observe blue light on the paper. The other colors will probably be dim.

3. Did your observations agree with your prediction? Explain.
   Students may say that their observations agreed with their prediction that they would see mainly blue light on the blue paper.

2 Teach
continued

VOCABULARY For Vocabulary Cards and activities, see *Reading Support and Homework.*

SCIENCE CONCEPTS Have students turn the concept into two or three questions and then use their prior knowledge to suggest responses. List the responses on the board. Have students review and revise them as they discuss the lesson.

(Focus Skill) READING FOCUS SKILL

CAUSE AND EFFECT Tell students that the information in this lesson is organized to help them understand cause-and-effect relationships in science.

1 ▶ Key Science Concepts

What happens to light when it strikes a dull, dark object? Most of it is absorbed, or taken in. **Summarize three ways that light can react to an object.** It can be reflected, refracted, or absorbed.

2 ▶ Develop Science Vocabulary

absorbed Explain that objects can absorb light, just as a sponge or paper towel takes in water. Point out the term *absorb* or *absorbent* on paper towel or sponge packaging.

3 ▶ Critical Thinking

Does a mirror or a dark rock absorb more of the light that strikes it? Explain. A rock absorbs much light and reflects little. A mirror reflects a lot of the light that strikes it.

4 ▶ Inquiry Skills

Use Models Have students hold a folded paper towel at an angle underneath a slow trickle of water in a sink. **What happens to the paper towel?** It absorbs some of the water. **Does the paper towel absorb all of the water?** No, some of it bounces off and runs down the drain.

VOCABULARY	**SCIENCE CONCEPTS**	**READING FOCUS SKILL**
absorbed p. 474 opaque p. 475 transparent p. 475 translucent p. 475	▶ how light affects the way things look	(Focus Skill) **CAUSE AND EFFECT** Look for different ways that materials affect light.

cause → effect

How to Stop Light

1 ▶ When light strikes an object, some of the light is reflected. What happens to the rest of the light? It is
2 ▶ **absorbed**, or taken in by the object. Shiny objects, such as mirrors, reflect most of the light that strikes
3 ▶ them. Dull, dark objects, such as some rocks, absorb most of the light that strikes them. Most objects
4 ▶ reflect some light. They absorb the rest of the light.

The stones are opaque.

The frosted marbles are translucent.

474

Reading Skill Mini-Lesson

(Focus Skill) USE CONTEXT CLUES

Explain to students that context is the meaning and purpose of a whole passage. Display the transparency. Have students look at the title of the passage, *How to Stop Light.* Ask them what this means if they use the context clues *car* and *traffic light.* Then have students read the passage. Tell them to look for sentences with the context clues *light* and *object.* Discuss the meaning using the correct context.

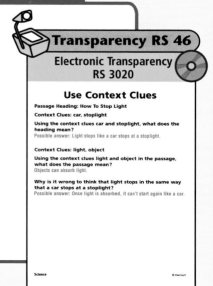

Transparency RS 46

Electronic Transparency RS 3020

Use Context Clues

Passage Heading: How To Stop Light
Context Clues: car, stoplight
Using the context clues car and stoplight, what does the heading mean?
Possible answer: Light stops like a car stops at a stoplight.

Context Clues: light, object
Using the context clues light and object in the passage, what does the passage mean?
Objects can absorb light.

Why is it wrong to think that light stops in the same way that a car stops at a stoplight?
Possible answer: Once light is absorbed, it can't start again like a car.

Science   © Harcourt

Objects that don't let light pass through them are ▶**opaque** (oh•PAYK). Mirrors, rocks, books, wooden desks, and people are opaque.

Some objects let most of the light that strikes them pass through. Objects that let most light pass through them are **transparent**. The clear glass in a window is transparent.

Objects that let some light pass through them, such as frosted light bulbs, are **translucent**. Light passes through the glass of the bulb. However, you can't see what is inside the bulb.

CAUSE AND EFFECT What effects does an opaque object have on light?

The clear marbles are transparent.

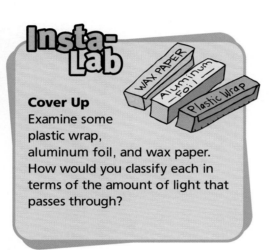

Cover Up
Examine some plastic wrap, aluminum foil, and wax paper. How would you classify each in terms of the amount of light that passes through?

5 ▶ Develop Science Vocabulary

opaque Tell students that *opaque* derives originally from Latin and later from the Old French *opaque,* meaning "shady." Ask them to explain how the meanings of *opaque* and *shady* are related.

transparent, translucent Have students identify the prefix common to both terms and use a dictionary to define it. When students define *trans-* as meaning "across" or "through," ask them to explain what passes through transparent and translucent objects (light). Tell students that *transparent* derives from words meaning "to show through," and *translucent* derives from words meaning "to shine light through."

6 ▶ Interpret Visuals

Which marbles and bowl are opaque? How do you know? The marbles and bowl on the left; they let very little light pass through. **Which marbles and bowl are translucent? Explain.** The marbles and bowl in the middle; they let some, but not all, of the light pass through. **Which marbles and bowl are transparent? How do you know?** The marbles and bowl on the right; they let most of the light pass through.

7 ▶ Cause and Effect

Answer: An opaque object reflects some of the light that hits it and absorbs the rest.

  5 minutes

Cover Up

Materials: plastic wrap, aluminum foil, wax paper

The plastic wrap is transparent, the wax paper is translucent, and the aluminum foil is opaque.

8 ▶ Key Science Concepts

What is white light? a mixture of different colors of light that makes white objects appear white

Give an example of white light. sunlight

9 ▶ Interpret Visuals

What is a prism? a pyramidal piece of glass that refracts light **What does a prism demonstrate about white light?** White light is really a mixture of different colors of light. **What colors of light make up white light?** red, orange, yellow, green, blue, violet

10 ▶ Inquiry Skills

Observe and Infer Have students observe that a beam of white light enters the prism as a single beam moving in a straight line. Ask them to describe the light that exits the prism. They should observe that light exits in bands of color and that the bands have been refracted. **Describe how the bands of color differ from each other.** Possible answers: Each band is a different color. The bands are different widths. Each band has been refracted, or bent, a different amount. **What can you infer about the relationship between the color of light and refraction?** The amount of refraction is related to the color of the light. Red light bends the least and violet bends the most.

11 ▶ Critical Thinking

Do you think the amount of energy in the orange band of light is greater than, less than, or equal to the energy in the white light that entered the prism? Why? Possible answer: Less than; the prism splits the white light into different colors, so it probably also splits the energy among the colors.

Light and Color

8 What do you see when you hold white paper in white light, such as sunlight? Since the light that hits the paper is reflected, the paper looks white.

In the Investigate, when sunlight went into the prism, colored light came out. Where did the colors come from? The white light of sunlight is a mixture of colors. In the activity, did you notice that light doesn't go straight through the prism? The light bends as it passes through the prism. This bending separates light into its different colors.

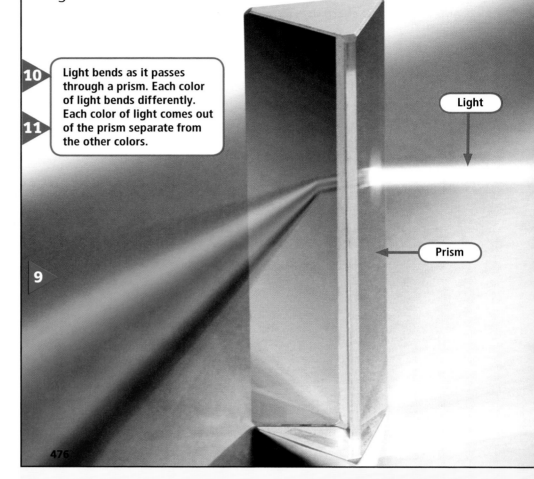

10 11 Light bends as it passes through a prism. Each color of light bends differently. Each color of light comes out of the prism separate from the other colors.

9

Light

Prism

476

Reaching All Learners

Challenge

More Inquiry

Target: Students who finish early, enjoy the content, and want to work more with the concepts of the chapter

Challenge Strategy: Have students hold a prism near a sunny window and a sheet of white paper so that the spectrum shows on the paper. Have them trace a triangle on the paper and draw a white light beam going in from the left. Then have them use crayons or markers to draw the six beams exiting to the right, ordered correctly from top to bottom—red, orange, yellow, green, blue, violet. Allow time for students to work in small groups to write a mnemonic to help them identify and remember the order of the colors.

Assess: Groups present their drawings and mnemonics to the class.

▶ You need sunlight and rain to see a rainbow outside. These two things don't often happen at the same time. That's why you don't often see rainbows. When it rains and then the sun comes out, drops of water in the air act like tiny prisms. They break up white light into its colors.

CAUSE AND EFFECT What effects does a prism have on white light?

How Rainbows Form

A drop of water is like a tiny prism.

White light from the sun strikes drops of water in the air. Light enters each water drop, refracts, and then it's reflected inside the drop. When the light leaves the drop, it separates into many colors.

14 ◀ The colors that most people see in a rainbow are red, orange, yellow, green, blue, and violet.

477

12 Key Science Concepts

What two things do you need to see a rainbow? sunlight and raindrops **Why are rainbows so unusual?** You do not often have the right conditions to see a rainbow.

13 Interpret Visuals

Summarize what you see in the picture. Possible answer: a rainbow with dark clouds behind it and sun shining on the clouds **The arrows show the direction that light travels. Explain the path that light travels in the formation of a rainbow.** White sunlight passes through raindrops. Each raindrop acts like a tiny prism and bends the light into its many colors. **How does a rainbow form?** When raindrops refract sunlight into its many colors, observers see the effect as a rainbow in the sky.

14 Critical Thinking

How is a raindrop like a prism? They are both transparent. They both refract white light into its many colors.

15 Cause and Effect

Answer: It refracts the light that enters it, causing it to separate into its many colors.

Reaching All Learners

Challenge

Below · On-Level · Advanced · ESL

Above-Level Reader

Target: Students who want to go further with the chapter content

Challenge Strategy: The reader enriches and extends learning by presenting high-interest science concepts and ideas related to the key science concepts in the chapter. The reader can be used with early finishers and students requiring additional challenge.

Assess: Use the strategies at the end of the reader to assess student understanding.

Heat, Light, and Sound

Harcourt

Interpret Visuals

What color do you see when only red light hits the white paper? red **Why?** The white paper will reflect any color that strikes it, but only red light is hitting it. **What color do you see when red light mixes with blue? When red mixes with green? What does this show about different colors of light?** They can mix to form new colors. **What color do you see when red, blue, and green mix together?** white **How is this possible?** White light is a mixture of different colors of light.

Inquiry Skills

Plan and Conduct Simple Investigations In what other ways do colored lights combine? Allow time for students to experiment with flashlights and red, blue, green, and yellow filters. Have them organize a chart that shows the results of combining each color with one other color, all the combinations of three filters, and then all four colors together. **Do any other combinations besides red, blue, and green make white light?** Check that students' answers correspond to their results.

18

Cause and Effect

Answer: The light appears white.

Separating Different Colors

17 Do you know that you can make white light? You can do this by shining lights together onto one surface. The picture shows three lights shining on a white surface. Each flashlight has a different-colored filter the light shines through. Find the place where all three colors shine on the same spot. Red, green, and blue light together make white light.

18 **CAUSE AND EFFECT** What effects do red light, blue light, and green light have when you shine them together onto a white surface?

The filters on these flashlights each let only one color pass through. These three colors can combine to make white light. ▼

16

478

Art Link

Mixing Colors

Materials: red, green, and blue paint; paintbrushes; cardboard

Explain that mixing colors of paint gives different results than mixing colors of light. Have students refer to page 478 to make a table summarizing the results of mixing red and blue; red and green; green and blue; and red, green, and blue light. Have them mix equal amounts of paint in the same combinations and record the results in the chart. How are the results of mixing paint different from mixing light? Students should describe the differences in the colors that they created with paint.

1. **CAUSE AND EFFECT** Draw and complete this graphic organizer.

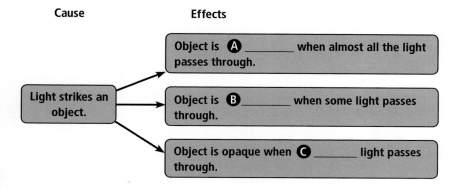

Cause

Effects

Light strikes an object.

Object is **Ⓐ** _____ when almost all the light passes through.

Object is **Ⓑ** _____ when some light passes through.

Object is opaque when **Ⓒ** _____ light passes through.

2. **SUMMARIZE** Write two sentences that tell what this lesson is about.
3. **DRAW CONCLUSIONS** Katie is watering her garden. She is using a hose with a fine spray. She sees a rainbow over her garden. Explain why.
4. **VOCABULARY** Write two sentences that use the vocabulary terms from this lesson.

Test Prep
5. What color will you see if you shine red, green, and blue lights on the same spot on a sheet of white paper?
   A. black
   B. purple
   C. white
   D. yellow

Links

Writing

Expository
Write an **explanation** of how a rainbow forms.

Math

Graph Favorite Colors
Using the six main colors of the rainbow, ask 10 classmates which color is their favorite. Place your findings in a bar graph. Color the bars to match the colors chosen.

For more links and activities, go to
www.hspscience.com

479

Lesson Quick Study

The Lesson Quick Study in **Reading Support and Homework** provides the opportunity for students to practice inquiry skills, review lesson vocabulary, apply reading skills, and use critical thinking and problem solving. Students can use the second page of the Lesson Quick Study to complete the graphic organizer. The graphic organizer is also available on overhead and electronic transparencies.

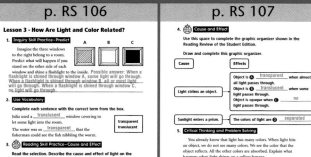

Reading Support and Homework

p. RS 106 | p. RS 107

3 Assess and Extend

Graphic Organizer

Transparency GO 46
Electronic Transparency GO 3020

1. **Ⓐ** transparent; **Ⓑ** translucent; **Ⓒ** very little

2. Objects can be opaque, transparent, or translucent, depending on how much light goes through them. White light is made up of colors that can be separated and put back together again.

3. The fine drops of water she sprays into the air separate light into colors and reflect it back toward Katie.

4. Possible answer: Light is absorbed by objects that are opaque. More light passes through transparent objects than through translucent objects.

5. C, white

Links

Writing Students can refer to the illustration of the rainbow in "Light and Color."

 Students can consult the *Writing Models* in **Teaching Resources** as they complete the link. Rubrics are also provided.

Math If students need help getting started, draw a blank graph for them. Label the vertical axis "Number of Students" and the horizontal axis "Favorite Color."

LESSON 3 ▪ 479

Objectives

- Investigate how a maraca makes sound.
- Identify vibrations as the source of sound, and define *loudness* and *pitch*.
- Explain how hearing works.

Transparency DI 47

Electronic Transparency DI 3021

Daily Inquiry

What's that Tune?

Tool Kit measuring cups, forceps

Other Materials: 5 identical glass jars, water

Review Skill: Measure, Draw Conclusions

What to Do
- Fill the five containers with the following amounts of water: 50 mL, 100 mL, 150 mL, 150 mL, and 200 mL. Use the forceps to lightly tap on the side of each glass.
- Tap out a familiar tune for a partner to identify.
- Was it hard to play a tune on these musical bottles?

1 Introduce

Build on Prior Knowledge

Use the Fast Fact for a discussion starter about the lesson topic.

Describe any experiences you have had playing a percussion instrument. How do percussion instruments make sound?

When *Minutes* Count . . .

If time is short, consider these options.

Conduct the Investigate as a **whole-class demonstration**. .

Use the Activity Video/DVD to model. After previewing, conduct the Investigate.

Lesson 4

What Is Sound?

Fast Fact

Percussion Section Percussion instruments include maracas, drums, and tambourines. They keep the beat of the music. In the Investigate, you will make a model of a maraca.

PROFESSIONAL DEVELOPMENT **Science Background**

Sound Energy Sound is energy that is transmitted through vibrations, or waves. Unlike light, which can travel in a vacuum, sound requires a medium of a gas, liquid, or solid for transmission. Sounds are described by pitch and loudness. Pitch is how high or low a tone is and depends on how fast the wave vibrates up and down (frequency). Loudness depends on the amount of energy in the waves. Sound travels faster and farther through solids than liquids and better through liquids than gases. This explains why sea mammals can communicate successfully over great distances. Humans hear sound when the inner ear vibrates and transmits messages for the brain to decode. Most humans can hear sounds with frequencies between 20 and 20,000 Hertz, or cycles ,per second.

Webliography
Key Word sound
www.hspscience.com

Make a Maraca

Materials
- empty paper-towel roll
- dried beans
- dried rice
- masking tape
- stapler

Procedure

1. Flatten one end of a paper-towel roll. Fold it over and staple it closed. Put tape over the staples to protect your hands.

2. Put a handful of dried rice and dried beans into the roll.

3. Flatten the open end of the roll. Don't let the rice and beans leak out. Fold over the end of the roll and staple it closed. Tape over the staples. You have made a maraca!

4. Shake the maraca gently a few times. If it leaks beans or rice, check the ends and tape them again. Observe the sound it makes.

5. Shake the maraca with more force. Observe the sound it makes now.

Step 2

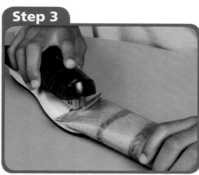

Step 3

Draw Conclusions

1. How does a maraca make sound?

2. **Inquiry Skill** Scientists compare to learn how things are alike or different. How did the sounds compare in Step 4 and Step 5?

Investigate Further

How could you change the maraca's sound? Write a hypothesis. Then plan and conduct a simple investigation to find out.

481

Inquiry Skill Mini-Lesson

Compare Remind students that when they compare things, they are looking for similarities and differences. Display the transparency; then discuss the questions.

Play musical recordings loudly and then softly. Have students compare the music with the pictures on the transparency. Point out that music played softly relates to the picture of the shorter ripples and loud music relates to the picture of the taller ripples.

Inquiry Skill practice is provided in *Reading Support and Homework*.

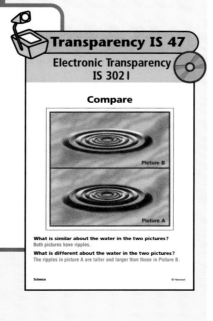

Transparency IS 47

Electronic Transparency
IS 3021

Compare

Picture B

Picture A

What is similar about the water in the two pictures?
Both pictures have ripples.

What is different about the water in the two pictures?
The ripples in picture A are taller and larger than those in Picture B.

Science   © Harcourt

---

2 Teach

Video Segment 3021

Time 15 minutes

Grouping individuals

Lab Manual pages can be used to record results. Inquiry Skill Tips and Self-Assessment are also provided.

Tips and Guided Inquiry

Students may have difficulty hearing the different sounds generated by the maraca if many maracas are being shaken at the same time. If possible, separate students into different parts of the room or the hallway to provide acoustic privacy.

Explain how the rice, beans, and paper towel roll interact when you shake the maraca. The rice, beans, and paper towel roll bang into each other and make noise.

How does shaking the maraca with more force affect the way the beans, rice, and paper towel interact? The objects strike each other with more force, too.

Expected Results

Shaking the maraca with more force generates louder sounds.

Draw Conclusions

1. The things inside it move back and forth and hit against each other.

2. Student responses should indicate that the sound was louder when the maraca was shaken with more force.

Investigate Further

Students can use this page in the *Lab Manual* for **Independent Inquiry**.

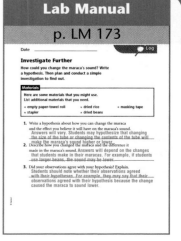

Lab Manual

p. LM 173

Date _____

Investigate Further
How could you change the maraca's sound? Write a hypothesis. Then plan and conduct a simple investigation to find out.

Materials
Here are some materials that you might use. List additional materials that you need.

- empty paper-towel roll
- stapler
- dried rice
- dried beans
- masking tape

1. Write a hypothesis about how you can change the maraca and the effect you believe it will have on the maraca's sound. Answers will vary. Students may hypothesize that changing the size of the tube or changing the contents of the tube will make the maraca's sound higher or lower.

2. Describe how you changed the maraca and the difference it made in the maraca's sound. Answers will depend on the changes that students make in their maracas. For example, if students use larger beans, the sound may be lower.

3. Did your observations agree with your hypothesis? Explain. Students should note whether their observations agreed with their hypothesis. For example, they may say that their observations agreed with their hypothesis because the change caused the maraca to sound lower.

2 Teach
continued

VOCABULARY For Vocabulary Cards and activities, see *Reading Support and Homework.*

SCIENCE CONCEPTS Have students list what they know about the science concept. Ask partners to exchange lists and summarize the information together. Have students look and listen for the ideas on the list as you go through the lesson.

READING FOCUS SKILL

CAUSE AND EFFECT Tell students that the information in this lesson is organized to help them understand cause-and-effect relationships in science.

Key Science Concepts

What is sound? a kind of energy that results from vibrations

Develop Science Vocabulary

vibrations Review the meaning of *vibrations* as "back-and-forth movements." Then have students draw and label a picture or pantomime an action to model vibrations.

loudness Remind students that the adjective *loud* describes something that is noisy or has volume. Then explain that the suffix *-ness* turns adjectives into nouns and means "being in a condition or state of." Therefore, *loudness* is a noun meaning "being loud." Ask volunteers to identify the part of speech and to define *brightness, sadness,* and *happiness.*

Interpret Visuals

How does a harp make sound? the strings vibrate **Demonstrate the pitch that the short, thin strings would make.** Students should create soft, high-pitched sounds. **Demonstrate the pitch that the long, thick strings would make.** Check that students create soft, low-pitched sounds.

VOCABULARY	**SCIENCE CONCEPTS**	**READING FOCUS SKILL**
vibrations p. 482	▶ how sounds are made and how they move	**CAUSE AND EFFECT** Look for different ways to cause sound.
loudness p. 482		
pitch p. 483		

cause ⟶ effect

Sound

1 When you shake a maraca, you can feel back-and-forth movements called **vibrations**. The maraca makes the air vibrate, too. You hear the **2** vibrations as sound.

3 When you shake the maraca harder, the vibrations have more energy. The sound is louder. **Loudness** is a measure of how much energy sound has.

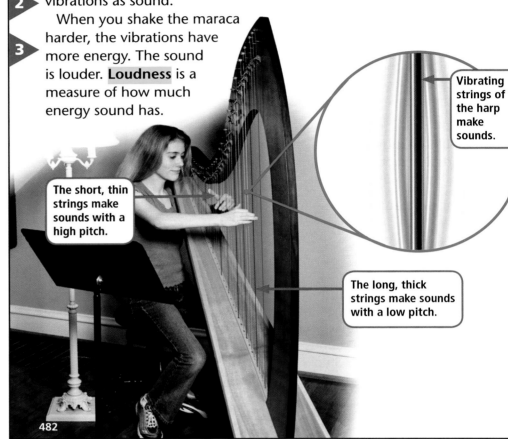

Vibrating strings of the harp make sounds.

The short, thin strings make sounds with a high pitch.

The long, thick strings make sounds with a low pitch.

482

Reading Skill Mini-Lesson

 USE PARAGRAPH STRUCTURE

Explain that the last sentence of a paragraph is often a summary that recaps the main idea. Display the transparency and have students copy it onto their papers. Then have students reread *Sound* and copy the last sentence of each paragraph. Explain that when students take notes from a textbook, they can sometimes look to the last sentence of a paragraph for the key information.

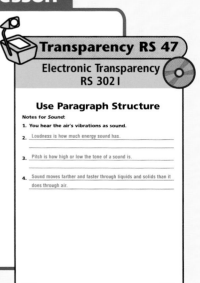

Transparency RS 47

Electronic Transparency RS 3021

Use Paragraph Structure

Notes for *Sound*:
1. You hear the air's vibrations as sound.
2. Loudness is how much energy sound has.
3. Pitch is how high or low the tone of a sound is.
4. Sound moves farther and faster through liquids and solids than it does through air.

Science

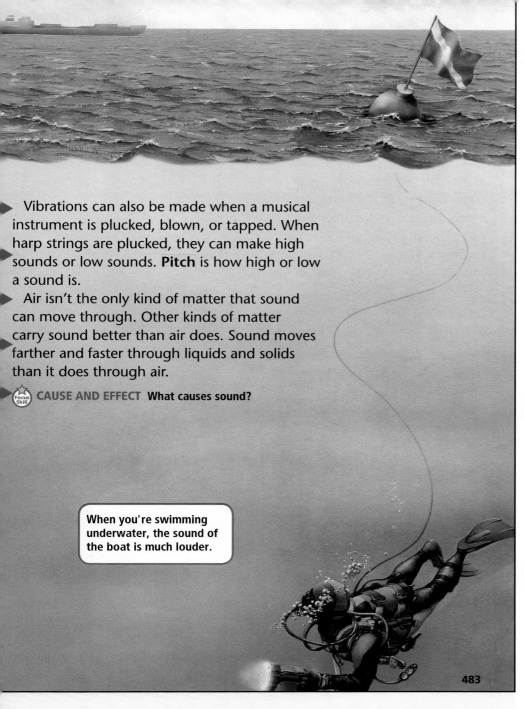

Vibrations can also be made when a musical instrument is plucked, blown, or tapped. When harp strings are plucked, they can make high sounds or low sounds. **Pitch** is how high or low a sound is.

Air isn't the only kind of matter that sound can move through. Other kinds of matter carry sound better than air does. Sound moves farther and faster through liquids and solids than it does through air.

CAUSE AND EFFECT What causes sound?

> When you're swimming underwater, the sound of the boat is much louder.

483

Below   On-Level   Advanced   ESL

Reaching All Learners

Intervention   Reteach

Pitch

Target: Struggling readers
Intervention Strategy: Hands-On Activity

■ Have partners make a "tin can phone" using two empty cans and a 15-foot string. They may need help punching holes in the cans.

■ Have students talk to each other through the "phone" in soft voices so that the sound does not travel through the air. Ask them to identify what object vibrates to transmit their voices (string) and its state of matter (solid).

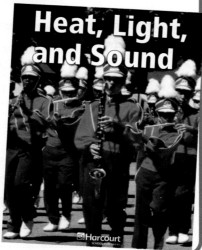

Heat, Light, and Sound

@Harcourt

---

4 ▶ Key Science Concepts

What does pitch describe about a sound? Give examples of sounds with high and low pitch. Pitch describes how high or low a sound is. High pitch: whistles, squeaky brakes; low pitch: foghorns, large dog's bark

What do YOU wonder?

Have students look back at the chapter opener photo. **How do the instruments in the marching band make sound?** When it is hit, plucked, blown, or tapped, the instrument generates vibrations that travel through the air. Those vibrations are sound.

5 ▶ Develop Science Vocabulary

pitch Tell students that pitch is described as "high" or "low." Have them sing as high a note as they can and as low a note as they can. Point out that they probably stretched their necks high to sing the high note and lowered their chins to sing the low note.

6 ▶ Inquiry Skills

Infer Have students recall a time they had their heads underwater. **Could you hear underwater?** Yes; students may recall hearing someone call to them or the sounds of a boat above. **Infer how whales and other sea mammals communicate with each other.** The animals generate sounds such as squeaks, which travel far and fast through the water.

7 ▶ Critical Thinking

If sound goes through the air by causing the air to vibrate, how do you think it goes through a solid or liquid? by making the solid or liquid vibrate

8 ▶ Cause and Effect

Answer: vibrations

9 ▸ Inquiry Skills

Use Models Borrow a drum or tambourine. Have students model the eardrum by singing a long tone in front of the drumhead. **What happens to the drumhead when sound hits it?** It vibrates. **How does this model relate to the eardrum?** The eardrum acts just like the drum when sound hits it.

10 ▸ Interpret Visuals

Why do humans hear sounds, such as a bird chirping? The chirping causes the air to vibrate. When those vibrations reach your ears, your ears vibrate too. When your eardrums vibrate, you hear sound.

11 ▸ Cause and Effect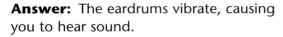

Answer: The eardrums vibrate, causing you to hear sound.

 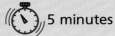 5 minutes

Big Ears

Materials: paper

Students should say that they can hear better when they use the paper cone. This is because the paper cone helps channel vibrating air directly into the ear.

Hearing Sounds

9 You have read how sounds come from objects that vibrate. Sounds can also make objects vibrate. You may have heard windows rattle from a loud boom of thunder. The sound made the

10 windows vibrate. It might have made you vibrate, too.

You hear sounds when vibrations move through the air to your ears. The vibrating air makes your eardrums vibrate, and you hear sound.

11 CAUSE AND EFFECT What effect does vibrating air have when it reaches your ears?

Big Ears
Stand about 3 meters (10 ft) from a partner. Whisper to each other. Can you hear the soft sound? Now roll up a piece of paper to make a cone. Hold the cone close to but not directly in your ear. Listen again while your partner whispers. Can you hear better now? Explain any difference that you hear.

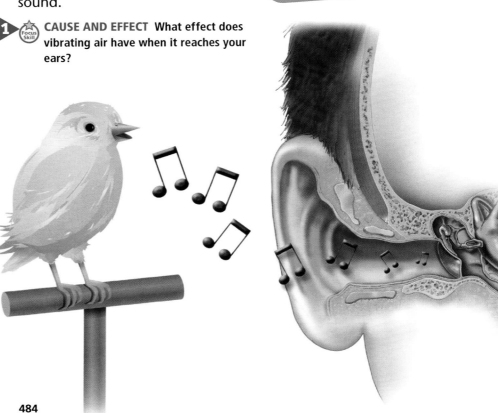

484

1. CAUSE AND EFFECT Draw and complete this graphic organizer.

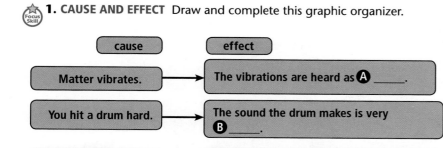

cause		effect
Matter vibrates.	→	The vibrations are heard as **Ⓐ** _____.
You hit a drum hard.	→	The sound the drum makes is very **Ⓑ** _____.
You pluck a short, thin harp string.	→	The string makes a **Ⓒ** _____ sound.
Sound travels through air to your ears.	→	Your eardrums **Ⓓ** _____.

2. SUMMARIZE Use your completed graphic organizer to write a lesson summary.

3. DRAW CONCLUSIONS If a 20-cm tightly held piece of string is plucked, would it have a higher or lower pitch than a 50-cm tightly held piece of string?

4. VOCABULARY For each vocabulary term, list three examples that help explain what the term means.

Test Prep

5. Which of these would not produce vibrations?
- **A.** blowing into a trumpet
- **B.** listening to an orchestra
- **C.** plucking a guitar
- **D.** tapping a piano key

Links

Writing

Expository
Write a **letter** to a friend, telling about a piece of music that you like. Use some of the vocabulary words you learned in this lesson.

For more links and activities, go to www.hspscience.com

Music

Make Your Own Musical Instrument
Using an empty tissue box and rubber bands of different thicknesses, make a musical instrument. Pluck the "strings" of your instrument, and record your observations.

485

Lesson Quick Study

The Lesson Quick Study in **Reading Support and Homework** provides the opportunity for students to practice inquiry skills, review lesson vocabulary, apply reading skills, and use critical thinking and problem solving. Students can use the second page of the Lesson Quick Study to complete the graphic organizer. The graphic organizer is also available on overhead and electronic transparencies.

Reading Support and Homework

p. RS 108

Lesson 4 - What Is Sound?

1. **Inquiry Skill Practice–Compare**

Imagine each sound listed in the box. How does each sound compare? Write a sentence to describe their pitch.

> An elephant trumpeting
> A pin dropping
> A car door slamming

Possible answers: An elephant trumpeting has a high pitch. A pin dropping has a low pitch. A car door slamming has a pitch that is not as loud as the elephant trumpeting, but not as low as the pin dropping.

2. **Use Vocabulary**

Write a complete sentence that uses the word vibrations correctly.
Answers will vary but should reflect the correct use of *vibrations*.

3. **Reading Skill Practice–Cause and Effect**

Read the selection. Describe the cause and effect of using your hands to help you hear.

Your hands can help you hear words that are too low, or help soften words that are too loud. How is this possible? When someone whispers words to you, and you cannot hear the words, cup your hand behind your ear. Your hand helps you hear the low sounds a little louder. When someone yells words to you, and the sound is too loud, cover your ears with your hands. Your hands help block some of the sound coming to your ears.
Possible answers: Cause: If a sound is too low, cup your hand behind your ear. Effect: The sound you hear is louder. Cause: If a sound is too loud, cover your ears. Effect: Your hands help block some of the sound coming to your ears.

p. RS 109

4. **Cause and Effect**

Use this space to complete the graphic organizer shown in the Reading Review of the Student Edition.

Cause		Effects
Matter vibrates.	→	The vibrations are heard as Ⓐ _sound_
You hit a drum hard.	→	The sound the drum makes is very Ⓑ _loud_
You pluck a short, thin harp string.	→	The string makes a Ⓒ _high_ sound.
Sound travels through air to your ears.	→	Your eardrums Ⓓ _vibrate_

5. **Critical Thinking and Problem Solving**

Why do you suppose that animals such as rabbits and bats have very large ears compared to their body size?
Possible answer: Animals such as rabbits and bats depend on their hearing for survival. Big ears mean that they can hear more sharply.

---

3 Assess and Extend

Graphic Organizer

Transparency GO 47
Electronic Transparency GO 3021

1. Ⓐ sound; Ⓑ loud; Ⓒ high; Ⓓ vibrate

2. Possible answer: Matter vibrates, which causes sound. Sounds can be loud or soft. Sounds can be high or low. When your eardrum vibrates, you hear sounds.

3. higher

4. Possible answers: Vibration: beating a drum, humming, plucking a rubber band. Loudness: jackhammer, jet plane, motorcycle for loud sounds; babbling brook, rustling leaves, rubbing hands together for soft sounds. Pitch: flute, duckling, baby laughing for high sounds; bass drum, thunder, bullfrog for low sounds.

5. B, listening to an orchestra

Links

Writing Students might write about playing or singing a special piece of music, noting such things as how hard it is to hit the high notes or how the piece has an exciting part where the sound becomes very loud.

 Students can consult the *Writing Models* in **Teaching Resources** as they complete the link. Rubrics are also provided.

Music Have students use rubber bands of different thicknesses and observe the differences in pitch.

Technology

- Explain how schools are using traffic light technology to make cafeterias quieter.
- Describe how the *Talk Light* works.

1 Introduce

Preview/Set a Purpose

Have students preview the article by reading the title and looking at the pictures. Ask a volunteer to identify the purpose of the article based on the title and pictures.

2 Teach

Chapter Concepts

Knowing how sound energy reacts with matter will lead to a better understand about noise in cafeterias and how *Talk Lights* work.

How does the *Talk Light* **act in ways similar and different to the ear?** Like the ear, the *Talk Light* receives sounds. But the *Talk Light* uses the sounds only to determine loudness.

What kinds of materials could be used in cafeterias to help reduce the loudness? Students may answer that cafeterias could use materials that absorb sound, such as rugs, acoustical tiles, and wall hangings.

Inquiry Skills

Compare Ask students to discuss how using the *Talk Light* in the cafeteria compares with having teachers or aides quieting students down when they get too noisy. Discuss which method students prefer and why they prefer it. Upon completion of the discussion, take a class vote to decide which method is more popular with the class. Encourage students to share their findings with the principal and the people in charge of the cafeteria.

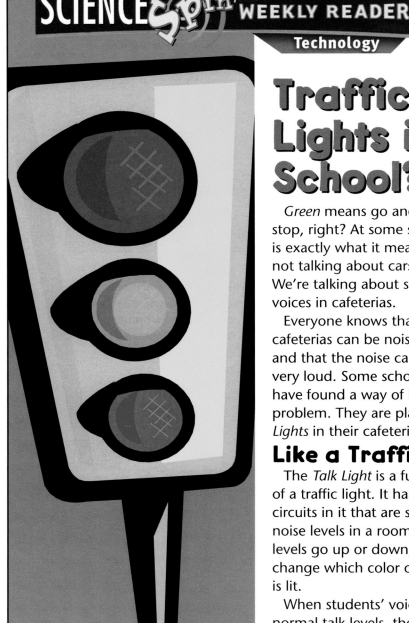

SCIENCE Spin from WEEKLY READER

Technology

Traffic Lights in School?

Green means go and *red* means stop, right? At some schools, that is exactly what it means, but we're not talking about cars in traffic. We're talking about students' voices in cafeterias.

Everyone knows that school cafeterias can be noisy places and that the noise can become very loud. Some school principals have found a way of handling the problem. They are placing *Talk Lights* in their cafeterias.

Like a Traffic Light

The *Talk Light* is a full-size model of a traffic light. It has computer circuits in it that are sensitive to noise levels in a room. As noise levels go up or down, the circuits change which color on the light is lit.

When students' voices are at normal talk levels, the green light

486

Science Background

Cafeteria Noise Parent Teacher Associations and other concerned people have asked scientists to study noise in school cafeterias. You may want to share some of their findings with students:

- Cafeterias are often loud because of their design. They are usually filled with hard surfaces like chairs, tables, and walls that bounce sound instead of softer surfaces that absorb sound.
- Sound bouncing off surfaces makes the cafeteria even louder. Students trying to talk to each other (even if they are near each other) have to raise their voices to be heard.
- These louder voices also bounce off the hard surfaces, making the cafeteria even louder! This causes everyone to speak louder.
- Some schools are looking into solutions to make cafeterias quieter, but for now technology like the *Talk Light* will help keep the noise level down.

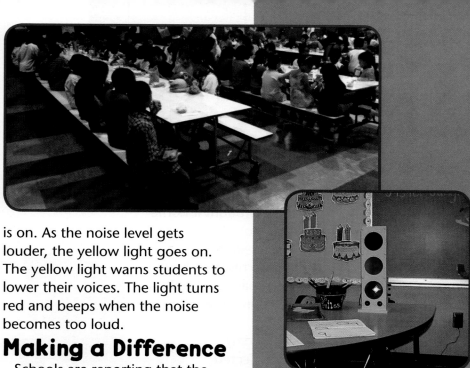

is on. As the noise level gets louder, the yellow light goes on. The yellow light warns students to lower their voices. The light turns red and beeps when the noise becomes too loud.

Making a Difference

Schools are reporting that the *Talk Light* has made a big difference in their students' lunchtime behavior. *Talk Lights* allow students to monitor themselves.

When the yellow light goes on, they know they have one minute until it turns red. In some schools, no one can leave the cafeteria while the light is red—and that can cut down on recess time.

THINK ABOUT IT

1. How are sound and light connected in a *Talk Light*?

2. What do the three colors mean?

▲ Traffic lights can even be used in the classroom.

Find out more! Log on to **www.hspscience.com**

487

Think About It

1. Sound and light are connected in a *Talk Light* because a difference in the loudness of sound makes the light change colors.

2. Green means that students are talking at normal levels. Yellow indicates that students are getting louder. Red shows that the noise has become too loud.

Writing Link

Narrative Writing Have students consider what it would be like to have a *Talk Light* in the school cafeteria. Have them write a letter to a friend describing how the *Talk Light* works and how it has affected life in the cafeteria.

Inspire Inquiry

Inquiry starts with wonder and with asking questions. Sometimes the questions are just about things people want to know. Sometimes they are problems that people want to solve.

■ Have students suggest the reasons why school officials might be interested in using the *Talk Light* in schools.

■ Ask students to suggest other ways they think the *Talk Light* could be used both in schools and in other areas.

■ Invite students to research how the technology used in the *Talk Light* has been used in other ways. Prior to beginning their research, help students develop a research plan. Ask students to share their findings with the class.

People

1 Introduce

Preview/Set a Purpose

Invite students to identify the parts of a stereo or CD player and what each part does. Ask, **Where does sound come from on a stereo?**

2 Teach

The Work of Scientists

Have students infer that scientists think of ways to improve how technology works.

Why did Amar Gopal Bose want to make a new kind of speaker? He did not like the way his stereo sounded. He wanted a sound more like live music.

What did he need to learn before he could design a better speaker? He researched how speakers made sound and how that was different from live sound.

How is music heard through Bose's speakers similar to live music? It reflects off the ceiling and walls, instead of coming from one direction.

3 Wrap Up and Assess

Think About It

Have students conclude that sound travels in waves that can reflect off surfaces.

How are Bose's speakers different from regular speakers? Regular speakers direct the sound waves in one direction. Bose's speakers direct the sound waves at the walls and ceilings as well.

Why does music reflect off walls and ceilings? Music is sound, which travels in waves. Sound waves can reflect off surfaces.

People

Bouncing Off the Walls

When Amar Gopal Bose was in college, he decided to buy a new stereo system. When he brought it home, Bose did not like the way the system sounded. So he decided to research how speakers make sound. Bose wanted to make a speaker that sounded as close to live music as possible.

As a result, Bose came up with a new kind of speaker. Bose's speakers reflected sound off walls and the ceiling, just as music reflects off the walls of a concert hall. Bose went on to start the Bose Corporation in 1964.

Career Sound Technician

When you're at the movies, you see the pictures. But do you ever think about the sound? Sound technicians are the ones who bring the explosions and screams to the screen. These technicians use special equipment to record music, voices, or sound effects. They can work in many different places, including studios, arenas, or even a jungle.

Find out more! Log on to **www.hspscience.com**

488

PROFESSIONAL DEVELOPMENT Science Background

A foley artist is a sound technician who creates special sounds for movies.
- A foley artist watches the film and supplies sound effects such as rustling clothing, breaking bones, or a squeaky door.
- Many times, the noise you hear when watching a film is not made by what you see on the screen. The sound of footsteps on snow, for example, is made by walking on Kosher Sea Salt covered in cornstarch.
- Several foley artists work as a team to make and record the sounds.
- A foley stage is a studio equipped with objects needed to make different noises. It usually has cans, pie tins, metal pipes, silverware, paper, fabric, and lots of other "junk." It also has various kinds of floors so that any kind of footsteps can be recorded.

SCIENCE Projects
for Home or School

You Can Do It!

Quick and Easy Project
Melt Down

Procedure

1. Choose three different places to leave an ice cube. Predict which ice cube will melt the most in 10 minutes.
2. Label three cups with the locations you will use. Place one ice cube in each cup.
3. Place the cups in their locations. A half hour later, observe the ice cubes.

Materials
- 3 ice cubes of equal size
- 3 foam cups

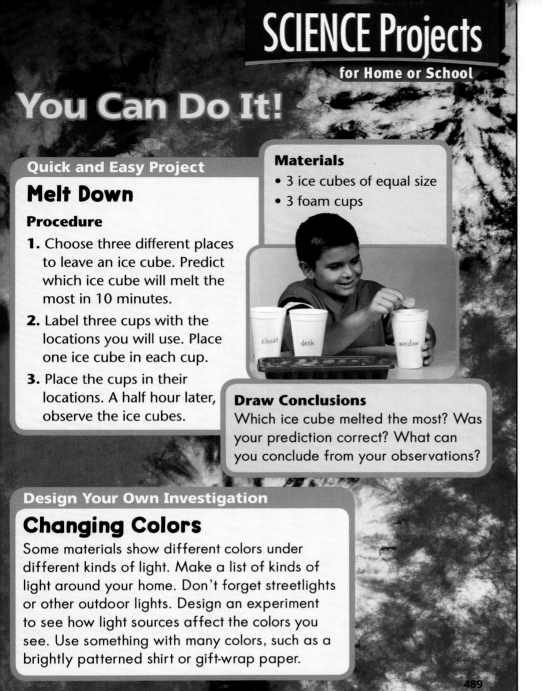

Draw Conclusions
Which ice cube melted the most? Was your prediction correct? What can you conclude from your observations?

Design Your Own Investigation
Changing Colors
Some materials show different colors under different kinds of light. Make a list of kinds of light around your home. Don't forget streetlights or other outdoor lights. Design an experiment to see how light sources affect the colors you see. Use something with many colors, such as a brightly patterned shirt or gift-wrap paper.

489

A reproducible copy of this page is provided in *Teaching Resources*.

You Can Do It!

Quick and Easy Project
Melt Down

Objectives
- Predict how fast ice will melt in different locations.

- **Tips and Hints**

  Start the activity early enough that students have time to set up the cups, wait a half hour, and then observe the ice cubes. Have students choose locations that have different air temperatures and amounts of sunlight. Make sure each cup is labeled with the name of its location.

- **Draw Conclusions**

  Possible answer: The ice cube in the warmest place melted the most. Check that students correctly compare their predictions with the results. Students should conclude that heat causes ice cubes to melt.

- **Extend the Activity**

  Students repeat this activity but predict how fast water evaporates in different locations.

Design Your Own Investigation

Changing Colors

Objectives
- Observe how different kinds of light change the way we see the colors of objects.

Inspire Inquiry
Use this activity as an at-home investigation or as a suggestion for a science fair project. Have students use the investigation as a starting point for developing their own questions and ideas for research. Ask students to share their plans and ideas with you and the class and to work together to help make the investigation procedure better.

Vocabulary Review (5 pts. each)

1. reflection
2. absorbed
3. insulator
4. translucent
5. vibrations
6. shadow
7. pitch
8. loudness
9. opaque
10. conductor

Check Understanding (5 pts. each)

11. C, refraction
12. H, the direction of the shadows
13. A, air
14. H, [pair of clear eyeglasses]
15. B, cloth
16. J, a rainbow

Vocabulary Review

Use the terms below to complete the sentences. The page numbers tell where to look in the chapter if you need help.

> conductor p. 463
> insulator p. 464
> reflection p. 468
> shadow p. 470
> absorbed p. 474
> opaque p. 475
> translucent p. 475
> vibrations p. 482
> loudness p. 482
> pitch p. 483

1. The bouncing of light off an object is _____.

2. Light is taken in by some objects, or _____.

3. An object that doesn't conduct heat well is an _____.

4. An object that lets some light pass through it is _____.

5. Back-and-forth movements of matter are _____.

6. A dark area that forms when an object blocks light is a _____.

7. A sound can have a high or a low _____.

8. The amount of energy that a sound has is its _____.

9. An object that doesn't let light pass through it is _____.

10. A material that lets heat move through it easily is a _____.

Check Understanding

Write the letter of the best choice.

11. What does this picture show?
    A. conduction
    B. reflection
    C. refraction
    D. vibration

12. Tamika has two pictures of a tree, taken on different days. By comparing the pictures, what can she look at to tell if they were taken at the same time of day?
    F. the brighness of the reflections
    G. the size of the reflections
    H. the direction of the shadows
    J. the darkness of the shadows

Harcourt School Publishers Online Assessment provides even more options. For a preview, go to:
www.hspscience.com

Portfolio Assessment

Have students select their best work from the following suggestions:
- **Reading Skill Mini-Lesson,** pp. 462, 468
- **Writing Links,** pp. 465, 471, 479, 485
- **Social Studies Link,** p. 471
- **Investigate,** p. 473

See **Assessment Guide** pp. xx–xxiv.

13. In which of these materials does sound travel most slowly ?
A. air C. steel
B. glass D. water

14. Which of these is transparent?

F.

G.

H.

J.

15. MAIN IDEA AND DETAILS Which of these is a good insulator?
A. aluminum C. copper
B. cloth D. steel

16. CAUSE AND EFFECT When light passes through drops of water in the air, what appears next in the sky?
F. lightning
G. a shadow
H. a rainstorm
J. a rainbow

Inquiry Skills

17. Jason was watching a play. He saw an actor's white shirt change color from white to red to green. What can you infer about the stage lights?

18. You stand in front of a mirror and wave your right hand. Predict what you will see in the mirror.

Critical Thinking

19. Maria is holding an ice cube. Is heat moving from her hand to the ice cube or from the ice cube to her hand? Explain.

20. Most pots and pans are made of some type of metal. Explain why they are made of metal and not wood or plastic.

491

Inquiry Skills (5 pts. each)

17. The lights were changed from white lights to red lights and then to green lights. The shirt reflected the light that was shining on it.

18. It looks like your left hand is waving.

Critical Thinking (5 pts. each)

19. Heat is moving from her hand to the ice cube. Heat moves from warmer objects to cooler objects.

20. Accept all reasonable answers. Possible answers: Metal is a better conductor of heat than wood or plastic; plastic melts and wood burns.

Chapter Test

See *Assessment Guide* pp. AG 103–108 for a Chapter Test and Performance Task, with rubric. Assessment options appear on page 458J.

Performance Assessment

Sound Vibrations

Have students strike a tuning fork and observe the results. Students should then explain how the tuning fork makes sound and how humans are able to hear that sound. Have students place the base of the tuning fork on a large table while it is ringing. Ask them to observe changes in the loudness and pitch of the sound.

Rubric for Performance Assessment

Preparation Each student will need a tuning fork.

Scoring Rubric—Performance Indicators

_____ Notes that the tuning fork vibrates to make sound.

_____ Explains that tuning forks make sound by vibrating. May explain that the air vibrates to transmit the sound.

_____ Explains that humans hear sound when the vibrations vibrate their eardrums.

_____ Observes that touching the tuning fork to the table increases loudness. Students may or may not observe changes in pitch; check that their conclusions are consistent with their observations.

Observations and Rubric Scores

3   2   1   0

Teaching Notes

Unit F

Exploring Forces and Motion

UNIT **F**

Energy in Motion

UNIT OVERVIEW

Unit Theme

The interaction of forces causes a change in the motion of objects. Simple machines can be thought of as systems for changing forces in order to do work.

Curriculum Integration

Use these topics to integrate science into your daily planning.

 Reading
Compare and Contrast–pp. 498, 546
Use Sentence Structure–p. 498
Main Idea and Details–pp. 506, 515, 528, 536
Make Generalizations–p. 506
Use Titles and Headings–p. 536
Use Context Clues–p. 546
Reading in Science Handbook–pp. R16–R27

 Math
Interpret Data–pp. 450, 537
Solve Problems–p. 503
Measure Wavelength–p. 517
Math in Science Handbook–pp. R28–R35

 Writing
Expository Writing–pp. 503, 533, 543
Narrative Writing–pp. 512, 517, 551

  Art Link and Music
Working Art–p. 533

 Social Studies
Egyptian Pyramids–p. 551

 Health and Physical Education
Losing Mass–p. 511
Experiment with Forces–p. 512
Body Levers–p. 543
Health Handbook, pp. R1–R15

 Literature
See pages 494C and 524C for Chapter Readers and trade books suggestions.

Technology Resources

Use a variety of technology resources for interactive tools and experiences. www.hspscience.com

For the Teacher

ePlanner
This online resource allows you to:
▶ Customize planning and pacing,
▶ Select resources for daily instruction,
▶ Reorder content to meet your state, district, or local needs.

Activity Video/DVD
This DVD provides previews of the activities, offers classroom-management techniques, and presents expected results.

Harcourt School Publishers Online Assessment
This online program provides:
▶ Online chapter and unit test taking and automatic scoring,
▶ Banks of items from which to build tests.

Teacher Resources CD-ROM
Electronic versions of all your teaching tools and resources.

Electronic Transparencies
Can be used to display transparencies with an LCD projector or monitor.

For the Student

eBook
An online version of the student edition, plus interactive explorations and investigations. Accessible for those with special needs.

Science Up Close CD-ROM
Activities that enhance and expand key chapter concepts through simulations and investigations.

For the Family

The Harcourt Learning Site
Family members can visit the Science section of The Learning Site for a variety of interactive learning experiences.
www.hspscience.com

UNIT F Materials List

Quantities are indicated for a class of 30 students working individually or in groups of 5, depending on the nature of the activity. Where shared equipment is suggested, a smaller number of items is specified. Quantities are also listed for those materials included in the Materials Kit.

Nonconsumable Materials

Materials	Class Quantity	Kit Quantity	Activity Page
block, wood (3" x 1.5" x 1.5")	6	pkg/6	505
board, wood	6		545
book	several		493A
car, toy (pull-back action)	6	6	545
chair	6		545
checker	6	pkg/24	527
checkerboard	6		527
coin	6		505
cookie sheet	6		505
forceps	6	pkg/6	535
goggles, safety	30		527, 545
jump rope	6	6	513
marble	6	6	493A
ruler, metric	6	6	505
scissors	6 pairs		493A
slinky, plastic	6	6	513
spoon, measuring	6 sets	6	535
spring scale	6	6	545
stopwatch	6	6	493A
tape measure	6	pkg/6	545

Consumable Materials

Materials	Class Quantity	Kit Quantity	Activity Page
cardboard, thin	6 sheets		493A
clay, modeling (4 colors)	1 set	1 set	497
eraser, flat	6		505
glue, white	6 bottles		493A
lid	6	6	535
rice, brown	1 bag	1 bag	535
rice, white	1 bag	1 bag	535
shoe box lid	6		493A
straw, plastic	12	pkg/50	497, 527
string (200')	1 ball	1 ball	497, 545
tape, transparent	1 roll		493A

A complete grade-level materials list and lists for all life, earth, or physical science chapters are provided on page R67.

Unit F

UNIT F

PHYSICAL SCIENCE

Exploring Forces and Motion

Chapter 15 Forces and Motion

Chapter 16 Work and Machines

Cape May Lighthouse

TO: sarah@hspscience.com

FROM: jason@hspscience.com

RE: Cape May, New Jersey

Dear Sarah,
My family went to see the Cape May Lighthouse. The strong seas damaged the first two lighthouses built here. A third lighthouse was built in 1859. It still stands today. Its light flashes once every fifteen seconds. It uses a 1,000-watt bulb. This is equal to the light of 350,000 candles. That's some nightlight!
Jason

492

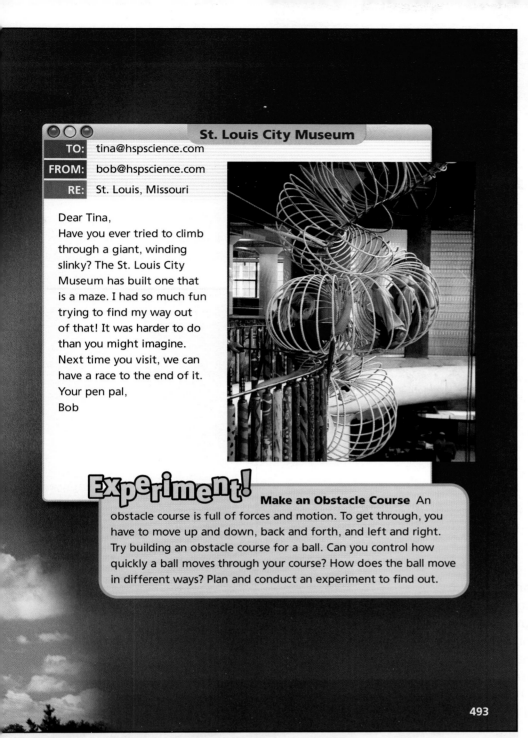

St. Louis City Museum

TO:	tina@hspscience.com
FROM:	bob@hspscience.com
RE:	St. Louis, Missouri

Dear Tina,

Have you ever tried to climb through a giant, winding slinky? The St. Louis City Museum has built one that is a maze. I had so much fun trying to find my way out of that! It was harder to do than you might imagine. Next time you visit, we can have a race to the end of it.

Your pen pal,

Bob

Experiment!

Make an Obstacle Course An obstacle course is full of forces and motion. To get through, you have to move up and down, back and forth, and left and right. Try building an obstacle course for a ball. Can you control how quickly a ball moves through your course? How does the ball move in different ways? Plan and conduct an experiment to find out.

493

More About the Cape May Lighthouse

The first lighthouse built on this site was constructed in 1821. The lighthouse was 70 feet high and had a revolving light of 15 lamps. The light flashed instead of being fixed to help distinguish it from the lighthouse across the bay at Cape Henlopen, Delaware. The sea eroded this lighthouse. In 1847, a second lighthouse was built. This time, the light was 14 feet higher than the first light and was made from 15 concave reflectors mounted to make a full light every minute. It met the same fate as the first lighthouse. The third lighthouse, which still stands today, is 157.5 feet tall. It now has a 250-watt electric bulb shining a light that can be seen up to 19 miles away.

More About the St. Louis City Museum

The unique aspect of the City Museum rests in the material used in the works of art. All of the materials are recycled, recovered and reshaped treasures. The slinkies were made by a team, which included both welders and artists. The exhibit consists of wired tunnels that resemble giant slinkies. The path takes you five stories high and twists and turns through "MonstroCity".

Writing Link

Have students generate their own e-mail message describing a personal experience or observation about an event or phenomena related to the unit topics.

A unit writing prompt and prewriting activity is provided in *Reading Support and Homework*, p. RS 117.

Experiment!

Turn the page to see options for helping students complete the experiment.

Unit F

Modern Rocket Stages

Objectives

- Promote scientific inquiry.
- Use a scientific method to plan and conduct a long-term investigation.
- Design an experiment to study how speed, distance, and time are related.

OPTIONS FOR INQUIRY

Option 1: Independent Inquiry Assign the experiment for students to complete independently. Students should use the prompt as a springboard for writing their own questions and designing their own experiment. They can write a hypothesis, design a procedure, select materials, and conduct the experiment. Students can refer to pages 174–177 in the **Lab Manual** for guidance.

Option 2: Guided Inquiry Suggest that students use the prompt and the experiment log (**Lab Manual** pages LM 174–177) to help them plan their experiment The Experiment Log pages shown below appear in the **Lab Manual**, but without answers. Use the lesson plan to guide students as they design the experiment.

Option 3: Structured Inquiry Have students complete the experiment by testing the hypothesis and using the procedure that has been provided for them. Display the overhead transparencies show below (or provide photocopies from the transparency package), and have students copy the hypothesis, variables, and procedure into the Experiment Log (**Lab Manual** pages LM 174–177). Students then should conduct the experiment and gather and record their data. Use the Lesson Plan to guide students as they complete the experiment.

Science Background

Moving Around Born in England in 1642, Sir Isaac Newton was a physicist and mathematician. Newton's laws of motion describe the relationship between forces and motion. The first law states that an object's motion will not change unless a force acts upon the object. So, an object that is not moving will remain at rest until a force causes it to move. A moving object will continue to move until another force, such as friction, causes it to stop. A force causes an object to move in a straight line until another force, such as gravity, causes the direction of the object to change.

Webliography
Keyword motion
www.hspscience.com

Experiment! LESSON PLAN

Resources

Experiment Log, *Lab Manual* pp. LM 174–177

Experiment Transparencies, Unit F

Time 30–45 minutes for students to build an obstacle course; 15–30 minutes for students to test their obstacle course and obtain data

Expected Results Students will determine that a ball traveling quickly will not take as long to travel a certain distance as a ball moving more slowly.

Suggested Materials

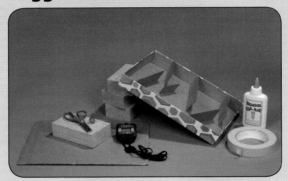

- ▶ shoebox lid
- ▶ cardboard
- ▶ scissors
- ▶ tape and glue
- ▶ marble
- ▶ books or blocks
- ▶ stopwatch

Preparation A model obstacle course can be made before the experiment to demonstrate the concept to students. The cardboard can be cut into thin stips before the experiment to save time.

Transparency EX 174

Lab Manual p. LM 174

Make A Maze

1. **Observe and Ask Questions**

   How are motion, speed, time, and distance related? Design an experiment using a marble and an inclined plane. Make a list of questions you have about motion. Then circle a question you want to investigate.

   Does increasing the distance a marble travels always increase the time it takes the marble to get to the finish?

2. **Form a Hypothesis**

   Write a hypothesis. A hypothesis is a suggested answer to the question you are testing.

   Increasing the speed of a marble will decrease the amount of time it takes the marble to get from one point to another.

3. **Plan an Experiment**

   Identify and Control Variables

   To plan your experiment, you must first identify the important variables. Complete the statements below.

   The variable I will change is

   the speed of a marble

   The variables I will observe or measure are

   how long it takes the marble to travel through the maze

   The variables I will keep the same, or *control*, are

   the shape of the maze, the starting point, the finishing point

❶ Observe and Ask Questions

Have students discuss the prompt and then brainstorm a list of other questions they may have about the topic. Students can record their questions in the Experiment Log, and then circle the question they are going to test.

Find Out More A first step in answering questions in science is to find out what is already known. Suggest that students use their textbooks and media resources to find out more about motion and speed. The research may lead them to investigate other questions or to vary their experiments as a result of any interesting facts they may uncover.

❷ Form a Hypothesis

Guided Inquiry Guide students in forming a testable hypothesis.

- **Look at the question you have chosen to investigate.** What is the relationship between speed and time? **What do you predict will be an answer to this question?** Possible answer: Speed is based on the distance an object travels and the time it takes to travel that distance.

- **Use your answer to form a statement. Your statement should include all the things you are testing. This statement will be your hypothesis.** Possible hypothesis: Increasing the speed of a marble will decrease the amount of time it takes the marble to get from one point to another.

❸ Plan an Experiment

Identify and Control Variables Remind students that an experiment is a fair test of a hypothesis. Identifying and controlling the variables will ensure that the test is conducted fairly. Have students complete the statements in the Experiment Log.

Develop a Procedure and Gather Materials Have students write a detailed procedure or have them use the procedure that appears on the transparency.

❹ Conduct the Experiment

Gather and Record Data Students can record their data in the Experiment Log.

Common Error Alert Students are making an obstacle course for the marble. The obstacle course must allow the ball to fall freely from one end of the course to the other, relying only on gravity. Guide students to keep them from building a dead-end spot in their course that would trap the ball.

Interpret Data Students should make a bar or line graph using their data. The graph should show that the ball took less time to reach the end of the obstacle course when the course was propped up higher by the books or blocks, causing the marble to have a greater speed.

❺ Draw Conclusions and Communicate Results

Have students answer the questions in the Experiment Log.

Using Inquiry Skills Emphasize that there is no "right" answer for an experiment. Hypotheses may not be supported by the data. If so, the hypothesis needs to be changed, not the data. Consider experimental results honestly and objectively.

Independent Inquiry Encourage students to build upon this experiment to develop further investigations.

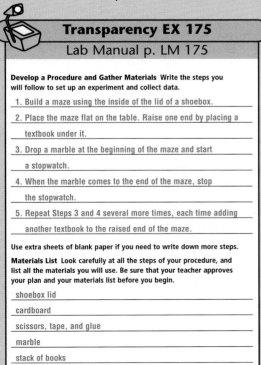

Transparency EX 175
Lab Manual p. LM 175

Develop a Procedure and Gather Materials Write the steps you will follow to set up an experiment and collect data.

1. Build a maze using the inside of the lid of a shoebox.
2. Place the maze flat on the table. Raise one end by placing a textbook under it.
3. Drop a marble at the beginning of the maze and start a stopwatch.
4. When the marble comes to the end of the maze, stop the stopwatch.
5. Repeat Steps 3 and 4 several more times, each time adding another textbook to the raised end of the maze.

Use extra sheets of blank paper if you need to write down more steps.

Materials List Look carefully at all the steps of your procedure, and list all the materials you will use. Be sure that your teacher approves your plan and your materials list before you begin.

shoebox lid
cardboard
scissors, tape, and glue
marble
stack of books

Transparency EX 176
Lab Manual p. LM 176

4. Conduct the Experiment

Gather and Record Data Follow your plan and collect data. Use the table below or a table you design to record your data. **Observe** carefully. **Record** your observations and be sure to note anything unusual or unexpected.

Maze Length (cm)	Time (sec)	Speed (cm/sec)

Transparency EX 177
Lab Manual p. LM 177

Interpret Data Make a graph of the data you have collected. Plot the data on a sheet of graph paper or use a software program.

5. Draw Conclusions and Communicate Results

Compare the **hypothesis** with the data and the graph. Then answer these questions.

1. Given the results of the experiment, do you think the hypothesis was correct? Explain.

2. How would you revise the hypothesis? Explain.

3. What else did you **observe** during the experiment?

Prepare a presentation for your classmates to **communicate** what you have learned. Display your data tables and graphs.

Investigate Further

Write another hypothesis that you might investigate.

CHAPTER 15 LESSON PLANNER

Lesson	Pacing	Vocabulary	Objectives & Reading Focus	Resources & Technology
1 What Is Motion? pp. 496–503	2 days	motion distance speed	■ Investigate different kinds of motion. ■ Identify and describe types of motion. ■ Define *speed*. *(Focus Skill)* **COMPARE AND CONTRAST** Look for different ways to describe how objects move. [alike]——[different]	■ Lab Manual pp. LM178–180 ■ Transparencies DID48, IS48, RS48, GO 48 ◉ Electronic Transparencies ■ Activity Video/DVD 3009 ◉ ESL Support pp. 46–49 ■ Reading Support and Homework pp. RS112–113
2 What Are Forces? pp. 504–511	2 days	force gravity weight	■ Investigate the motion of an object sliding down a ramp. ■ Define *force*, and describe how forces affect motion. ■ Define *weight*. *(Focus Skill)* **MAIN IDEA AND DETAILS** Look for details that describe forces. [Main Idea] [detail] [detail] [detail]	■ Lab Manual pp. LM181–183 ■ Transparencies DI49, IS49, RS49, GO 49 ◉ Electronic Transparencies ■ Activity Video/DVD 3010 ◉ ESL Support pp. 212–215 ■ Reading Support and Homework pp. RS114–115
3 How Do Waves Move? pp. 511–517	2 days	wave crest trough wavelength	■ Observe the motion of different kinds of waves. ■ Define *waves*, and describe their motion. ■ Identify the parts of a wave. *(Focus Skill)* **MAIN IDEA AND DETAILS** Look for kinds of waves and the parts of a wave. [Main Idea] [detail] [detail] [detail]	■ Lab Manual pp. LM184–186 ■ Transparencies DI50, IS50, RS50, GO 50 ◉ Electronic Transparencies ■ Activity Video/DVD 3011 ◉ ESL Support pp. 216–219 ■ Reading Support and Homework pp. RS116–117
End of Chapter pp. 518–523	3 days		■ Evaluate relationships of science, technology, and society ■ Review chapter concepts	■ Intervention, On-Level, and Above-Level Readers ■ Assessment Guide pp. AG19–24

Plan Ahead for Activities

Investigate

Make It Move p. 497

Materials: clay, string (about 25cm long), straw

Time: 20 minutes

Inquiry Focus: Interpret data

Prep Tip: This activity will work best when students make small clay balls and a ring about 1 inch in diameter.

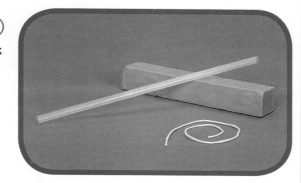

Speed Ramp p. 505

Materials: books, cookie sheet, block, metric ruler, penny, block, rubber eraser

Time: 25 minutes

Inquiry Focus: Infer

Prep Tip: To ensure that the objects are released at the same time, have three students in each group hold them at the top of the ramp while the fourth student says "three, two, one, go." This will involve all students.

Two Kinds of Waves p. 512

Materials: rope about 2 meters long, coiled-spring toy

Time: 20 minutes

Inquiry Focus: Compare

Prep Tip: Ensure that the ropes do not touch the ground between the students. If the rope hangs too loosely and the waves do not form well, have students move apart to make the rope a little tighter.

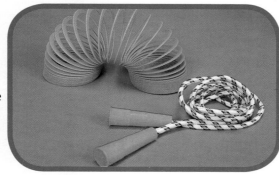

Insta-Lab

Getting There Fast
p. 502

10 minutes

Materials: meterstick, tape, stopwatch

Tip: Use chalk or tape to mark the stopping point at 10m. If the surface is too hard to crawl on, use a blanket or a piece of carpet for cushioning.

The Amazing Paper Clip
p. 507

5 minutes

Materials: water, cup, paper clip

Tip: Make sure the cup is on a sturdy, broad, flat surface to avoid spills. Clean up any spills that do occur quickly to avoid falls.

Move It!
p. 407

5 minutes

Materials: foil pie plate, bread crumbs, wooden spoon, cookie sheet

Tip: Consider covering work surfaces with paper towels or a table cloth for a quick cleanup.

REACHING ALL LEARNERS

Reading Support

Page R51 provides additional information

Below-Level/Intervention

Forces and Motion

When used along with the hands-on experiences from the *Student Edition*, the Intervention Reader promotes science success for all students.
Reading Level 1.5–2.0

The Intervention Reader presents identical chapter content and vocabulary at a below-grade reading level. The reader uses a visual glossary, simplified language, and comprehension aids especially designed for struggling readers. The *Intervention Readers Teacher Guide* provides additional strategies and support.

On-Level/Enrichment

What Makes It Move?

This reader promotes success on state science tests by reinforcing test content objectives, chapter vocabulary, and reading skills.
Reading Level 2.5–3.5

Advanced/Challenge

Thinking About Motion

This interesting nonfiction reader enriches and extends chapter concepts.
Reading Level 4.0–5.5

Trade Books for Students

These books provide in-depth information on chapter content. For more information about each selection, see the Bibliography beginning on page R48.

Easy
Albert Einstein by Lola M. Schaefer and Wyatt S. Schaefer, Pebble Books, 2004

Average
Forces: Science All Around Me by Karen Bryant-Mole, Heinemann, 1997

Challenge
Forces by Robert Snedden, Heinemann, 1999, Award-Winning Author

Alternative Teaching Strategies

This guide provides additional support for the strategies and activities that appear throughout this chapter.

 **Intervention and Reteaching**

Strategies for reteaching key lesson concepts provide options for addressing a variety of learning styles.

Intervention Reader p. 499

Greater Speeds p. 502

Magnetic Force p. 507

 **Using the E-Book**

This chapter is also available online and has provisions for children with special needs. Adjustable text size and audio text can be used with children who have vision impairments or learning difficulties.

www.hspscience.com

Science Concepts Across the Grades

Grade 2	Grade 3	Grade 4
Related Chapters		
Chapter 13 Motion **Lesson 1** What Are Ways Things Move? **Lesson 2** What Makes Things Move? **Lesson 3** How Do Magnets Move Things?	**Chapter 15 Forces and Motion** **Lesson 1** What Is Motion? **Lesson 2** What Are Forces? **Lesson 3** How Do Waves Move?	**Chapter 15 Forces and Motion** **Lesson 1** How Is Motion Measured and Described? **Lesson 2** What Is Acceleration? **Lesson 3** Why Is the Force of Gravity Important?
Learning Goals		
▶ Understand that things move at different speeds and in different paths (straight, circular, back and forth). ▶ Classify moves as pushes or pulls and know that pushing or pulling something changes the way it is moving.	▶ Know that objects may be moved by being pushed and pulled with magnets. ▶ Identify different types of motion. ▶ Describe how forces affect motion.	▶ Identify the parts of a wave. ▶ Explain how to measure motion. ▶ Describe how velocity and acceleration are related. ▶ Explain how force and mass affect acceleration. ▶ Identify several natural forces including gravity and friction.

RESOURCES FOR INQUIRY

Daily Practice

Daily Inquiry pp. 496, 504, 512
   Teaching Transparencies DI 48–50
   Electronic Transparencies DI 3009–3011

Inquiry Tool Kit

Harcourt Investigations

Harcourt School Publishers offers an alternative program that provides more opportunities for inquiry-based science experiences. The program provides a series of investigations that promote guided, structured, and independent inquiry using student journals, lab manuals, science readers and other materials.

Visit **www.hspscience.com** for more information.

Guided Inquiry

Investigate pp. 497, 505, 513; *Lab Manual* pp. LM 178–180, 181–183, 184–186

Inquiry Skill Mini Lesson pp. 497, 505, 513; *Teaching Transparencies* IS 48–50; *Electronic Transparencies* IS 3009–3011

Insta-Lab pp. 502, 507, 407

Unit Experiment pp. 493A–B; *Lab Manual* pp. LM 174–177

Independent Inquiry

Investigate Further *Lab Manual* pp. LM 498, 506, 514

Lab Manual

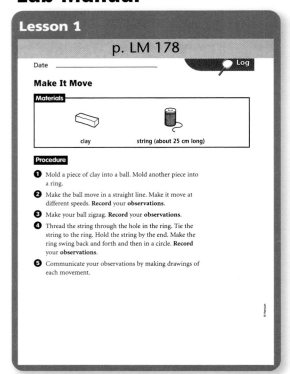

Use with *Student Edition* p. 497.

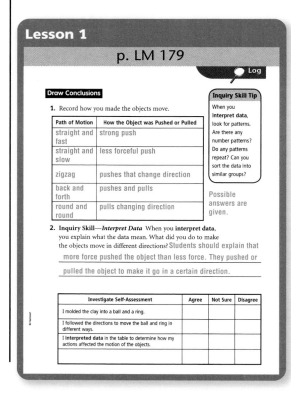

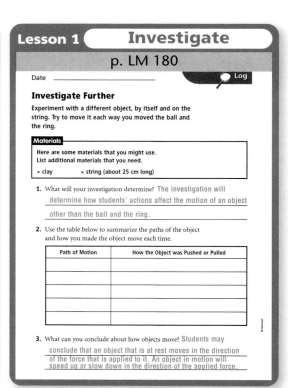

Independent Inquiry (continued)

Science Projects for Home or School
p. 521 *Teaching Resources* p. TR 25

Unit Experiment pp. 493A-B; *Lab Manual* pp. LM 9–11 and *Science Fair Projects Lab Manual* LM 196–201

Lab Manual (cont.)

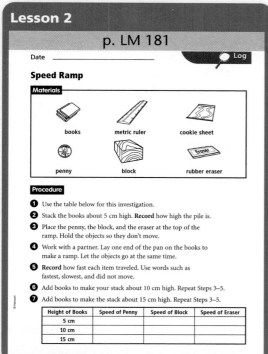

Lesson 2 — p. LM 181

Date _____

Speed Ramp

Materials
- books
- metric ruler
- cookie sheet
- penny
- block
- rubber eraser

Procedure
1. Use the table below for this investigation.
2. Stack the books about 5 cm high. **Record** how high the pile is.
3. Place the penny, the block, and the eraser at the top of the ramp. Hold the objects so they don't move.
4. Work with a partner. Lay one end of the pan on the books to make a ramp. Let the objects go at the same time.
5. **Record** how fast each item traveled. Use words such as fastest, slowest, and did not move.
6. Add books to make your stack about 10 cm high. Repeat Steps 3–5.
7. Add books to make the stack about 15 cm high. Repeat Steps 3–5.

Height of Books	Speed of Penny	Speed of Block	Speed of Eraser
5 cm			
10 cm			
15 cm			

Use with **Student Edition** p. 505.

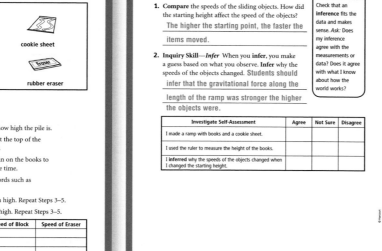

Lesson 2 — p. LM 182

Draw Conclusions

1. **Compare** the speeds of the sliding objects. How did the starting height affect the speed of the objects? The higher the starting point, the faster the items moved.

2. **Inquiry Skill—*Infer*** When you **infer**, you make a guess based on what you observe. **Infer** why the speeds of the objects changed. Students should infer that the gravitational force along the length of the ramp was stronger the higher the objects were.

Inquiry Skill Tip
Check that an **inference** fits the data and makes sense. *Ask:* Does my inference agree with the measurements or data? Does it agree with what I know about how the world works?

Investigate Self-Assessment	Agree	Not Sure	Disagree
I made a ramp with books and a cookie sheet.			
I used the ruler to measure the height of the books.			
I inferred why the speeds of the objects changed when I changed the starting height.			

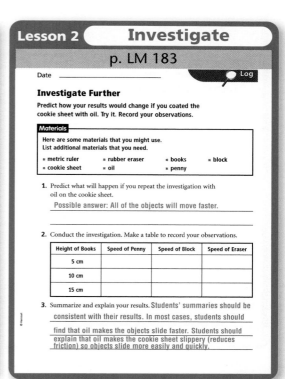

Lesson 2 — **Investigate** — p. LM 183

Date _____

Investigate Further

Predict how your results would change if you coated the cookie sheet with oil. Try it. Record your observations.

Materials
Here are some materials that you might use. List additional materials that you need.
- metric ruler
- rubber eraser
- books
- block
- cookie sheet
- oil
- penny

1. Predict what will happen if you repeat the investigation with oil on the cookie sheet.
   Possible answer: All of the objects will move faster.

2. Conduct the investigation. Make a table to record your observations.

Height of Books	Speed of Penny	Speed of Block	Speed of Eraser
5 cm			
10 cm			
15 cm			

3. Summarize and explain your results. Students' summaries should be consistent with their results. In most cases, students should find that oil makes the objects slide faster. Students should explain that oil makes the cookie sheet slippery (reduces friction) so objects slide more easily and quickly.

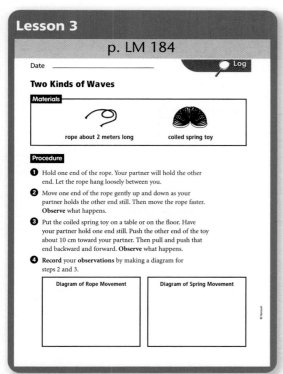

Lesson 3 — p. LM 184

Date _____

Two Kinds of Waves

Materials
- rope about 2 meters long
- coiled spring toy

Procedure
1. Hold one end of the rope. Your partner will hold the other end. Let the rope hang loosely between you.
2. Move one end of the rope gently up and down as your partner holds the other end still. Then move the rope faster. **Observe** what happens.
3. Put the coiled spring toy on a table or on the floor. Have your partner hold one end still. Push the other end of the toy about 10 cm toward your partner. Then pull and push that end backward and forward. **Observe** what happens.
4. **Record** your **observations** by making a diagram for steps 2 and 3.

Diagram of Rope Movement	Diagram of Spring Movement

Use with **Student Edition** p. 513.

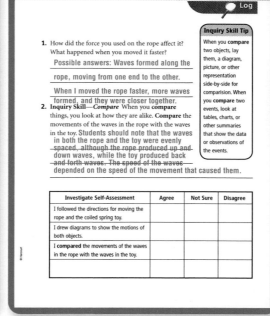

Lesson 3 — p. LM 185

1. How did the force you used on the rope affect it? What happened when you moved it faster?
   Possible answers: Waves formed along the rope, moving from one end to the other. When I moved the rope faster, more waves formed, and they were closer together.

2. **Inquiry Skill—*Compare*** When you **compare** things, you look at how they are alike. **Compare** the movements of the waves in the rope with the waves in the toy. Students should note that the waves in both the rope and the toy were evenly spaced, although the rope produced up-and-down waves, while the toy produced back-and-forth waves. The speed of the waves depended on the speed of the movement that caused them.

Inquiry Skill Tip
When you **compare** two objects, lay them, a diagram, picture, or other representation side-by-side for comparision. When you **compare** two events, look at tables, charts, or other summaries that show the data or observations of the events.

Investigate Self-Assessment	Agree	Not Sure	Disagree
I followed the directions for moving the rope and the coiled spring toy.			
I drew diagrams to show the motions of both objects.			
I compared the movements of the waves in the rope with the waves in the toy.			

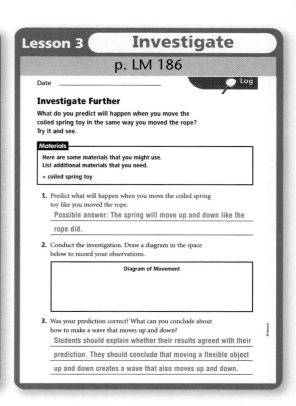

Lesson 3 — **Investigate** — p. LM 186

Date _____

Investigate Further

What do you predict will happen when you move the coiled spring toy in the same way you moved the rope? Try it and see.

Materials
Here are some materials that you might use. List additional materials that you need.
- coiled spring toy

1. Predict what will happen when you move the coiled spring toy like you moved the rope.
   Possible answer: The spring will move up and down like the rope did.

2. Conduct the investigation. Draw a diagram in the space below to record your observations.

Diagram of Movement

3. Was your prediction correct? What can you conclude about how to make a wave that moves up and down? Students should explain whether their results agreed with their prediction. They should conclude that moving a flexible object up and down creates a wave that also moves up and down.

CHAPTER PLANNER ▪ 494F

READING SUPPORT AND HOMEWORK

Lesson 1

p. RS 112

Name _____
Date _____

Lesson Quick Study

Lesson 1 - What Is Motion?

1. **Inquiry Skill Practice–Interpret Data**

Mia used a slingshot to throw a pebble, a golf ball, and a marble at the same speed. She recorded the distance each traveled in the chart. Interpret the data. What can you tell about each object and the distance each traveled?

Object	Distance Each Traveled
pebble	3.0 yards
golf ball	1.5 yards
marble	2.2 yards

Possible answer: The larger the object, the less distance it traveled.

2. **Use Vocabulary**

Write a complete sentence that uses the word *distance* correctly.

Answers will vary but should reflect the correct use of *distance*.

Write a complete sentence that uses the word *speed* correctly.

Answers will vary but should reflect the correct use of *speed*.

3. **Reading Skill Practice–Compare and Contrast**

Read the selection. Compare and contrast how the rabbit and the turtle move.

A rabbit and a turtle are traveling to a cave. The cave is four miles away from their starting point. The turtle walks in slow motion. Its body moves slowly making small zigzags. The rabbit moves fast. Its hops are long as he moves up and down. Possible answers: Alike: They both have to travel four miles. away. Different: The turtle walks in slow motion. Its body moves slowly making small zigzags. The rabbit moves fast. Its hops are long as he moves up and down.

Use with *Student Edition* pp. 495–503.

Lesson 1

p. RS 113

Name _____

4. **Compare and Contrast**

Use this space to complete the graphic organizer shown in the Reading Review of the Student Edition.

Give examples of different kinds of motion. Answers will vary.

Types of Motion	Straight-line	Zig Zag	Round and Round	Back and Forth
Example	Ⓐ	Ⓑ	Ⓒ	Ⓓ

5. **Critical Thinking and Problem Solving**

Rita and Lauren run 2 miles. It takes Rita 1 hour to finish. It takes Lauren 1.5 hours to finish. Who has the greater speed? How do you know?

Possible answer: Rita has the greater speed because it takes her less time to travel the same distance as Lauren.

Lesson 2

p. RS 114

Name _____
Date _____

Lesson Quick Study

Lesson 2 - What Are Forces?

1. **Inquiry Skill Practice–Infer**

Suppose you have a soccer ball. Infer what you think will happen if you kick the ball, throw it with your hands, and roll it on the floor. Possible answer: If the soccer ball is kicked, it will go far. If the ball is thrown, it will also go far, but not as far as if it is kicked. If the ball is rolled, it will not go as far as if the ball is kicked, or thrown.

2. **Use Vocabulary**

Complete each sentence with the correct term from the box.

The _____weight_____ of the box made it difficult to lift.

_____Gravity_____ caused the ball to come down after Jim threw it up.

gravity
weight

3. **Reading Skill Practice–Main Idea and Details**

Read the selection. Underline the main idea. List at least two details about the main idea.

The weight of an object affects the force needed to carry it. Suppose you are carrying your empty backpack. The weight of the backpack is very light. You can move easily without having to apply much force. What if you filled your backpack with books? The weight of your backpack is now heavy. You will have to apply more force than before. Possible answer: To carry a light backpack or object, you do not have to apply a lot of force. To carry a heavy backpack or object, you have to apply a lot of force.

Use with *Student Edition* pp. 504–512.

Lesson 2

p. RS 115

Name _____

4. **Main Idea and Details**

Use this space to complete the graphic organizer shown in the Reading Review of the Student Edition.

Things that affect the motion of an object
- The strength of the force
- The Ⓐ _____direction_____ of the force
- The Ⓑ _____mass_____ of the object

5. **Critical Thinking and Problem Solving**

Suppose you threw a baseball and a basketball using the same force. Both balls move forward in a straight line. You notice that the baseball landed further than the basketball. What affected the motion of the balls?

Possible answer: The motion of the balls was affected by their mass. They were both thrown with the same force. They both traveled in the same direction, but both balls do not weigh the same. The baseball is lighter that the basketball.

Lesson 3

p. RS 116

Name _____
Date _____

Lesson Quick Study

Lesson 3 - How Do Waves Move?

1. **Inquiry Skill Practice–Compare**

Compare the drawings of the waves. Based on what you learned, which of the two drawings shows the waves that have more energy? Explain your reasoning.

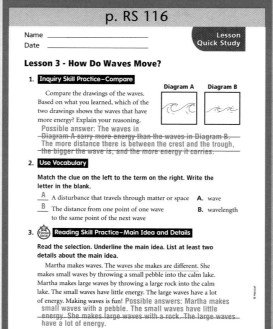

Diagram A   Diagram B

Possible answer: The waves in Diagram A carry more energy than the waves in Diagram B. The more distance there is between the crest and the trough, the bigger the wave is, and the more energy it carries.

2. **Use Vocabulary**

Match the clue on the left to the term on the right. Write the letter in the blank.

__A__ A disturbance that travels through matter or space

__B__ The distance from one point of one wave to the same point of the next wave

A. wave
B. wavelength

3. **Reading Skill Practice–Main Idea and Details**

Read the selection. Underline the main idea. List at least two details about the main idea.

Martha makes waves. The waves she makes are different. She makes small waves by throwing a small pebble into the calm lake. Martha makes large waves by throwing a large rock into the calm lake. The small waves have little energy. The large waves have a lot of energy. Making waves is fun! Possible answers: Martha makes small waves with a pebble. The small waves have little energy. She makes large waves with a rock. The large waves have a lot of energy.

Lesson 3

p. RS 117

Name _____

4. **Main Idea and Details**

Use this space to complete the graphic organizer shown in the Reading Review of the Student Edition.

Types of Waves
- up-and-down
  - Ⓐ Possible answer: lightwaves
- Ⓑ back-and-forth
  - soundwaves

5. **Critical Thinking and Problem Solving**

Suppose you are measuring waves. One of the waves measures 3 cm from the highest point to the lowest point. Another wave measures 5.5 cm from the highest point to the lowest point. Which of the two waves carries more energy? How do you know?

Possible answer: The wave that measures 5.5 cm from the highest point, or crest, to the lowest point, or trough, carries more energy. The larger the distance between these two points, the larger the wave, and the more energy it carries.

Use with *Student Edition* pp. 513–517.

ASSESSMENT OPTIONS

Chapter Test

p. AG 115

Name _____
Date _____

Chapter Assessment

Forces and Motion

Vocabulary 4 points each

Match each term in Column B with its meaning in Column A.

	Column A		Column B
D	1. Force that pulls two objects toward each other	A.	distance
H	2. Change of position	B.	trough
E	3. Disturbance that travels through matter or space	C.	force
A	4. How far it is from one place to another	D.	gravity
G	5. Highest point of a wave	E.	wave
B	6. Lowest part of a wave	F.	speed
F	7. Distance an object moves in a certain period of time	G.	crest
C	8. Any kind of push or pull	H.	motion

Science Concepts 4 points each

Write the letter of the best choice.

A 9. What does a ruler measure?
   A. distance   C. speed
   B. motion   D. weight

G 10. Which surface would cause the **least** friction?
   F. dirt   H. grass
   G. ice   J. rocks

p. AG 116

Name _____

B 11. The strength of a force and the direction of a force affect the motion of an object. What is the third thing that affects the object's motion?
   A. color   C. texture
   B. mass   D. volume

H 12. Which object would be most affected by magnetic force?
   F. a marble   H. a paper clip
   G. a pillow   J. a wooden fence

C 13. Which object would take the least amount of force to move?
   A. a book   C. a pencil
   B. a car   D. a table

H 14. Look at the picture. What part of the wave is the arrow pointing to?
   F. crest
   G. disturbance
   H. trough
   J. wavelength

B 15. There is a book on the table. You push the book to the left. At the same time, your friend pushes the book to the right. What is the net force on the book?
   A. your friend's push
   B. your push plus your friend's push
   C. your push
   D. the weight of the book

H 16. How do scientists figure out the speed of a wave?
   F. by measuring its height
   G. by measuring its depth
   H. by measuring its wavelength
   J. by measuring the water's temperature

p. AG 117

Name _____

Inquiry Skills 8 points each

17. Look at the data below. **Interpret the data** to determine how far Runner 1 ran and how long it took her. Which runner ran the farthest?

	Distance	Direction	Time
Runner 1	1 mile	Northeast	7 min 10 sec
Runner 2	1.5 miles	South	9 min 23 sec
Runner 3	2 miles	Southwest	15 min 14 sec

Runner 1 ran 1 mile in 7 minutes and 10 seconds. Runner 3 ran the farthest.

18. Michael is going to conduct an investigation to **compare** the speed of a turtle with the speed of a rabbit. What should he use to measure their speeds? How should he conduct the investigation?

Possible answer: Michael could use a stopwatch to measure time and a meterstick to measure distance. Speed is the measure of an object's change in position during a unit of time, so in the investigation, he would have to measure both distance and time.

p. AG 118

Name _____

Critical Thinking 10 points each

19. If friction did not exist, could you ride a bicycle? Why or why not?

No. Without friction, the tires would just slide around and you couldn't get the bike to move forward. Also, the brakes would not work.

20. Jeremy and his friend are playing basketball. Describe two forces that are involved when Jeremy shoots a basketball through the net.

Possible answers (any two): Shooting is a push. Gravity pulls the ball through the net. Friction between his shoes and the floor allows Jeremy to stand still while shooting.

Performance Task

p. AG 119

Name _____
Date _____

Performance Assessment

Student Task

Bobsled Races

Materials

oil   petroleum jelly   water in spray bottle

heavy bolt   stack of books   tape measure or ruler

Procedure

Using the heavy bolt for a bobsled, compare three surfaces to find out which one allows the bolt to travel the farthest. Your teacher will provide each team with three tracks that are lined with aluminum foil.

1. Lightly cover each of the tracks with a different material (oil, petroleum jelly, or water).
2. Predict which surface will allow the bobsled to travel the farthest.
3. Test your prediction. Prop up the tracks, one at a time, on the stack of books. Give the same push to the bobsled on each track.
4. Record the distances in the data table. Was your prediction correct?

Track	Distance Traveled from Top of Ramp
Track with oil	
Track with petroleum jelly	
Track with water	

Rubric

p. AG 120

Performance Assessment

Teacher's Directions

Bobsled Races

Materials   Performance Task sheet, oil, petroleum jelly, water in spray bottle, heavy bolt, stack of books, tape measure or ruler

Time   30 minutes

Suggested Grouping   groups of three or four

Inquiry Skills   predict, experiment, observe, record

Preparation Hints   Make three tracks for each group of students. First, cut identical strips of poster board; the strips should be about 8 cm wide and 60–90 cm long. Cover each strip with aluminum foil, folding the foil around the edges. Fold up the long sides of each strip about 2 cm to keep the bobsled from falling off. Alternatively, you may have students construct the tracked tracks. Make sure there is enough space in the room for students to conduct their trials.

Introduce the Task   Begin the activity by asking students what kinds of things help reduce friction (oil, smooth ice). Then have students name things that create more friction (bumpy ice, other rough surfaces). Tell students that they will conduct an investigation to see what kind of surface allows a small, heavy object—their bolt "bobsled"—to travel the farthest.

Promote Discussion   When students finish, have the groups compare results. Are they the same or different? If different, can students explain why? Were their predictions correct?

Scoring Rubric

Performance Indicators

_____ Coats each track surface with one material: oil, petroleum jelly, or water.
_____ Measures distance accurately with a tape measure or ruler.
_____ Records data in the table.
_____ Compares results to prediction.

Observations and Rubric Score

3   2   1   0

Chapter 15 Forces and Motion

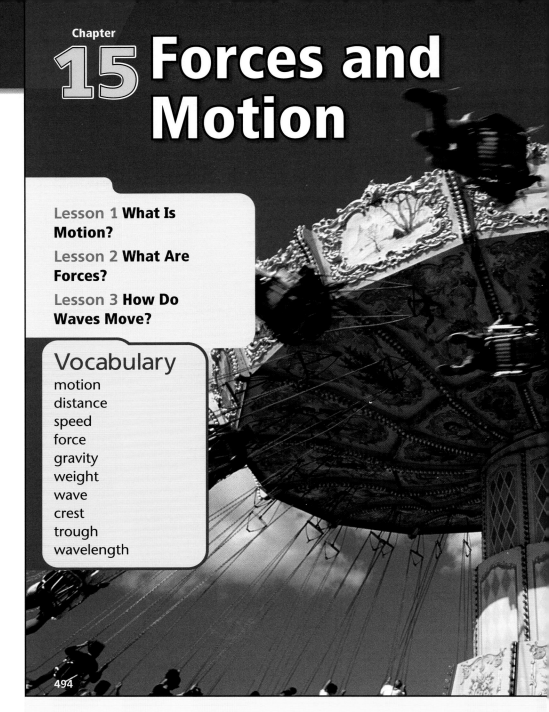

Lesson 1 **What Is Motion?**

Lesson 2 **What Are Forces?**

Lesson 3 **How Do Waves Move?**

Vocabulary

motion
distance
speed
force
gravity
weight
wave
crest
trough
wavelength

494

Assess Prior Knowledge

Use the photograph to get students interested in the chapter topic. Ask students to study it carefully. Students will probably realize that the photograph shows an amusement park ride with people sitting in swings.

Have students discuss their ideas about this question: **What makes the swings spin around?** Note their answers as a key to prior knowledge and misconceptions. (See also Science Background.) Students may notice that the swings are hanging from chains or cables and may speculate that some kind of force is passing through the cables to make them move.

Later, as students read in Lesson 2 about how forces change motion, they will be able to reevaluate the photograph. They should then note that the spinning ride exerts a pulling force on the swings that causes them to move in a circle.

Generate Science Questions

Have students write questions they have about forces and motion. Record the questions on the board or chart paper. Ask students to refer to the list as they complete the chapter. If questions remain unanswered, have students suggest ways to find answers. In this chapter, students will learn about motion, forces, and waves.

Professional Development

To prepare for effective instruction, you may wish to consult these resources:

The *Activity Video/DVD* provides previews of the activities, offers classroom-management techniques, and presents expected results.

The *Science eBook* provides chapter content online, with greater depth via additional content and activities.

The *Science Background* throughout this Teacher Edition provides content support.

Visit **www.hspscience.com** for additional Professional Development resources.

Science Background To Address Misconceptions

When do objects curve?

Assess Prior Knowledge *Ask:* What path will a rolling ball follow when it exits a curved track?

Students May Think that the ball will continue on a curved path.

Scientists Explain that objects move in a straight line unless an outside force affects them. A curved track forces a ball to move along in a curved path. When the ball exits, however, the ball will roll in a straight line.

What You Can Do Use poster board to create a curved track on the ground. Ask students to predict the path of a ball when it exits the track. Allow time for students to roll the ball in the track. Have them draw diagrams to summarize the motion of the ball in and out of the track.

What do YOU wonder?

To build a ride like this one, you need to understand forces and motion. What causes the swings to move farther from the center pole? What brings them back to the center pole?

Vocabulary

Opportunities for developing chapter vocabulary include:

■ Develop Science Vocabulary strategies at point-of-use in the teaching plan

■ Vocabulary questions in each Reading Review and the Chapter Review and Test

■ Vocabulary sections on the Quick Study pages in **Reading Support and Homework**

■ Vocabulary Cards and activities in **Reading Support and Homework**

Students can use the **Vocabulary Power** worksheet below to preview and explore more about the chapter vocabulary.

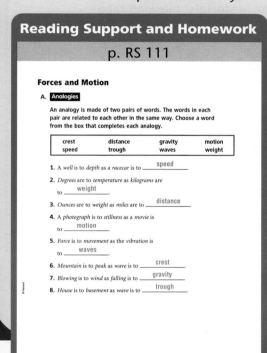

Reading Support and Homework

p. RS 111

Forces and Motion

A. Analogies

An analogy is made of two pairs of words. The words in each pair are related to each other in the same way. Choose a word from the box that completes each analogy.

crest	distance	gravity	motion
speed	trough	waves	weight

1. A *well* is to *depth* as a *racecar* is to ____speed____

2. *Degrees* are to *temperature* as *kilograms* are to ____weight____

3. *Ounces* are to *weight* as *miles* are to ____distance____

4. A *photograph* is to *stillness* as a *movie* is to ____motion____

5. *Force* is to *movement* as the *vibration* is to ____waves____

6. *Mountain* is to *peak* as *wave* is to ____crest____

7. *Blowing* is to *wind* as *falling* is to ____gravity____

8. *House* is to *basement* as *wave* is to ____trough____

Reading Focus Skills

The content of each lesson is organized to focus on a key reading skill. The skill is reinforced by questions that appear at the end of each section and the graphic organizer at the end of the lesson. Additional practice is also provided in Reading Support and Homework.

The Reading Focus Skills for this chapter are:	
Lesson 1	Compare and Contrast
Lesson 2	Main Idea and Details
Lesson 3	Main Idea and Details
All Lessons	Draw Conclusions and Summarize

Strategies also appear in the Reading Mini-Lessons throughout the chapter.

ESL/ESOL Support

Spanish-speaking students may already be familiar with English words such as these cognates:

crest/cresta

distance/distancia

force/fuerza

gravity/gravedad

speed/velocidad

Objectives

■ Investigate different kinds of motion.

■ Identify and describe types of motion.

■ Define *speed*.

Transparency DI 48

Electronic Transparency DI 3009

Daily Inquiry

What a Jump!

 tape measure

Other Materials: masking tape

Review Skill: Compare, Measure

What to Do

■ Use masking tape to mark a starting line on the floor in your classroom. Stand at the starting line. Jump as far as you can without taking a running start. Mark the distance and measure it. Record the measurement. Repeat the activity two more times.

■ Did your jumps get longer or shorter as you completed the three jumps?

1 Introduce

Build on Prior Knowledge

Use the Fast Fact for a discussion starter about the lesson topic.

Have you ever played a pinball machine? How does it work?

What are some ways the ball moves inside the machine? What makes the ball move and change direction?

When *Minutes* Count . . .

If time is short, consider these options.

Conduct the Investigate as a **whole-class demonstration.**

Use the Activity Video/DVD to model the Investigate. After previewing, students can conduct the Investigate in small groups.

What Is Motion?

Fast Fact

Speedy Pinball In the game of pinball, a ball can reach a speed of 145 kilometers (90 mi) per hour! The ball moves in many directions. In the Investigate, you will experiment with several kinds of motion.

496

PROFESSIONAL DEVELOPMENT **Science Background**

How Fast Do Things Move?

How fast do other things move compared to a ball in a pinball machine? The pinball moves at a top speed of around 145 kilometers per hour.

■ A jogger can run about 10 kilometers per hour.

■ At normal highway speeds, a car travels about 100 kilometers per hour.

■ Sound moves through air at around 1200 kilometers per hour.

■ The space shuttle orbits Earth at around 27,800 kilometers per hour.

■ Light moves through space at over 1 billion kilometers per hour. That's a 1 with nine zeros after it.

Webliography
Keyword motion
www.hspscience.com

1. COMPARE AND CONTRAST Draw and complete this chart. Give examples of different kinds of motion.

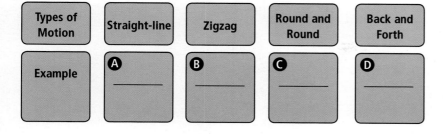

Types of Motion	Straight-line	Zigzag	Round and Round	Back and Forth
Example	**A** ___	**B** ___	**C** ___	**D** ___

2. SUMMARIZE Use the vocabulary words to write a summary of the lesson.

3. DRAW CONCLUSIONS Would it be faster to zigzag or to walk in a straight line from one location to another? Why?

4. VOCABULARY Write a quiz question that uses all the vocabulary terms.

Test Prep

5. What changes when an object moves?
  A. its direction
  B. its height
  C. its position
  D. its shape

Links

Writing

Expository

Write a paragraph that **describes** the kinds of motion you see when you go outside at recess. Describe the speeds and distances of the people and things you observe.

Math

Solve Problems

Use a meterstick to measure the distance from one side of your classroom to the other. If you cross the classroom four times, how far will you walk?

> **For more links and activities, go to www.hspscience.com**

503

Lesson Quick Study

The Lesson Quick Study in *Reading Support and Homework* provides the opportunity for students to practice inquiry skills, review lesson vocabulary, apply reading skills, and use critical thinking and problem solving. Students can use the second page of the Lesson Quick Study to complete the graphic organizer from the Reading Review. The graphic organizer is also available on overhead and electronic transparencies.

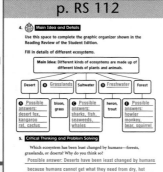

Reading Support and Homework

p. RS 112 | p. RS 113

3 Assess and Extend

Graphic Organizer

Transparency GO 48
Electronic Transparency IS 3009

1. Students should give examples of different kinds of motion.

2. Possible answer: When an object is in motion, it changes position. Distance is how far it is from one place to another. Speed tells the distance an object moves in a certain amount of time. A slow object takes longer to move a certain distance than a fast object.

3. It would be faster to walk in a straight line. When you zigzag, you have to walk a greater distance, which takes a longer time.

4. Possible answer: Does an animal with a motion that takes a long time to go a short distance move at a fast or slow speed?

5. C, its position

Links

Writing Have students review their observations of objects in motion from the outdoor activity. They can start their writing with the sentence "I observed many kinds of motion today." Better responses will describe different kinds of motion.

 Students can consult *Writing Models* in **Teaching Resources** as they complete the link. Rubrics are also provided.

Math Possible answer: 8.6 meters; 4 X 8.6 meters = 34.4 meters

Objectives

- Investigate the motion of an object sliding down a ramp.
- Define *force* and describe how forces affect motion.
- Define *weight*.

Transparency DI 49

Electronic Transparency DI 3010

Daily Inquiry

Give Me a Hand!

 spring scale

Review Skill: Observe, Predict

What to Do

- Predict which finger on your hand is the strongest. Hold the spring scale with one hand. With the fingers on the other hand outstretched, pull the hook of the spring scale down by curling each finger down until it touches your palm.
- How did you make sure the test was a fair one?

1 Introduce

Build on Prior Knowledge

Use the Fast Fact for a discussion starter about the lesson topic.

Have you ever slid down a hill or a slide? What happened? How did it feel?

What causes a sled to slide down a hill?

When *Minutes* Count . . .

If time is short, consider these options.

Conduct the Investigate as a **whole-class demonstration.**

Use the Activity Video/DVD to model the Investigate. After previewing, students can conduct the Investigate in small groups.

Lesson **2**

What Are Forces?

 Fast Fact

Super Sledding Olympic bobsledders zoom down the track at speeds of up to 145 kilometers (90 mi) per hour! These children aren't going quite so fast, but they're having lots of fun! In the Investigate, you will see how the height of a starting point affects speed.

504

 Science Background

PROFESSIONAL DEVELOPMENT

Sliding Faster A sled moves down a hill because of gravity. The steeper the hill, the faster a sled will go. Friction between the rails of the sled and the surface of the hill as well as air resistance slow down the sled. Reducing friction and air resistance increase the speed of the sled. Waxing the rails or shaving them to make them smoother reduces friction and makes the sled go faster.

A sled with longer rails or more rails distributes the weight of the sled better and reduces pressure between any one part of the rail and the hill. This change reduces friction and increases speed. Reducing air resistance by lying down, rather than sitting up, on the sled increases speed.

Webliography
Keyword gravity
www.hspscience.com

Speed Ramp

Materials • books • cookie sheet • block • metric ruler
• penny • rubber eraser

Procedure

1 Make a table like the one shown.

2 Stack the books about 5 cm high. **Record** how high the pile is.

3 Work with a partner. Lay one end of the pan on the books to make a ramp.

4 Place the penny, the block, and the eraser at the top of the ramp. Hold the objects so they don't move. Let the objects go at the same time.

5 **Record** how fast each item traveled. Use words such as *fastest*, *slowest*, and *did not move*.

6 Add books to make the stack about 10 cm high. Repeat Steps 2–5.

7 Add books to make the stack about 15 cm high. Repeat Steps 2–5.

	Height of Books	Speed
Penny		
Block		
Eraser		

Step 3

Draw Conclusions

1. **Compare** the speeds of the sliding objects. **Record** your **observations**.

2. **Inquiry Skill** When you **infer**, you make a guess based on what you **observe**. **Infer** why the speeds of the objects changed.

Investigate Further

Predict how your results would change if you coated the cookie sheet with oil. Try it. **Record** your observations.

505

Inquiry Skill Mini-Lesson

Infer Explain that *infer* means to interpret data based on things you already know.

Display the Transparency. Discuss how the first drawing shows that all three dropped objects hit the ground at the same time. Encourage students to work with partners to complete the questions on the Transparency. Remind them to consider their experiences in the Investigate and in sliding or rolling objects down hills.

Inquiry Skill practice is provided in *Reading Support and Homework*.

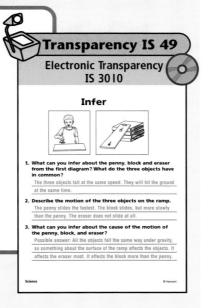

Transparency IS 49

Electronic Transparency
IS 3010

Infer

1. What can you infer about the penny, block and eraser from the first diagram? What do the three objects have in common?
The three objects fall at the same speed. They will hit the ground at the same time.

2. Describe the motion of the three objects on the ramp.
The penny slides the fastest. The block slides, but more slowly than the penny. The eraser does not slide at all.

3. What can you infer about the cause of the motion of the penny, block, and eraser?
Possible answer: All the objects fall the same way under gravity, so something about the surface of the ramp affects the objects. It affects the eraser most. It affects the block more than the penny.

Science   © Harcourt

---

2 Teach

Video Segment 3010

Time 25 minutes

Grouping groups of 4

Lab Manual pages can be used to record results. Inquiry Skill Tips and Self-Assessment are also provided.

Tips and Guided Inquiry

Three students in each group should each hold one object at the top of a ramp while the fourth says, "three, two, one, go." **Would you want to slide down a very steep hill? Why or why not?** Students might answer in the positive or negative but should recognize that they would be moving very fast. **If an object reaches the bottom of a ramp first, how does its speed compare to the speeds of other objects on the ramp?** Students should say that the object that reaches the bottom first moves fastest.

Expected Results

Every object should move faster down a higher ramp than on a shallower one. The penny will likely slide faster than the block, which will likely slide faster than the eraser. Some objects may not slide at all or go only partway on shallow ramps.

Draw Conclusions

1. The higher the starting point, the faster the items moved.

2. They were rolled from different heights. The higher the objects were, the stronger was the force of gravity.

Investigate Further

Students can use this page in the *Lab Manual* for **Independent Inquiry.**

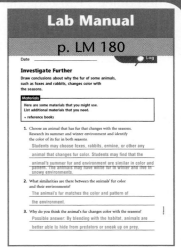

Lab Manual

p. LM 180

Date _____

Investigate Further
Draw conclusions about why the fur of some animals, such as foxes and rabbits, changes color with the seasons.

Materials
Here are some materials that you might use.
List additional materials that you need.
• reference books

1. Choose an animal that has fur that changes with the seasons. Research its summer and winter environment and identify the color of its fur in both seasons.
Students may choose foxes, rabbits, ermine, or other any animal that changes fur color. Students may find that the animal's summer fur and environment are similar in color and pattern. The animals may have white fur in winter and live in snowy environments.

2. What similarities are there between the animals' fur color and their environments?
The animal's fur matches the color and pattern of the environment.

3. Why do you think the animal's fur changes color with the seasons?
Possible answer: By blending with the habitat, animals are better able to hide from predators or sneak up on prey.

2 Teach
continued

VOCABULARY For Vocabulary Cards and activities, see *Reading Support and Homework.*

SCIENCE CONCEPTS Have students list questions they might have about the science concepts and discuss in small groups how they might find answers. Have students write down their answers as they go through the lesson.

 READING FOCUS SKILL

MAIN IDEA AND DETAILS Tell students that the information in this lesson is organized to help them recognize a main idea and the details that support it.

1 Develop Science Vocabulary

force Tell students that a push is a force that moves toward the object, and a pull is a force that moves away from the object. Have students pair up and clasp arms. Have them push toward each other and say, "push," and then pull as they say "pull." Ask them to describe how pushes and pulls feel. Summarize that they are moving toward each other when they push and are moving away when they pull.

2 Key Science Concepts

What is a force? a push or a pull

For how long will an object keep moving? until another force stops it

What is friction? a force that happens when objects rub together

If a box is sliding on a street, how does friction change its motion? Friction slows down objects in motion. The box will slow down until it stops.

3 Interpret Visuals

Summarize the two main kinds of forces. Give an example of each. Forces can push or pull. Opening a drawer is a pull; a rocket engine propels a rocket with a push.

VOCABULARY	SCIENCE CONCEPTS	READING FOCUS SKILL
force p. 506 gravity p. 510 weight p. 510	▶ what the kinds of forces are ▶ what forces do	**MAIN IDEA AND DETAILS** Look for details that describe forces.

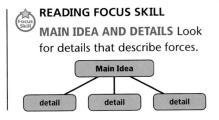

Types of Forces

1 To move a ball, you can throw it, kick it, or hit it with a bat. Any kind of push or pull is a **force**. You must apply a force to make an object move. An object will keep moving until another force stops it.
2 When you catch a moving ball, the force from your hand stops the ball.

Friction is one force that stops things or slows them down. When two objects rub together, there is friction between them. Most rough surfaces make more friction than smooth surfaces. You can slide farther on ice than you can on dirt or grass.

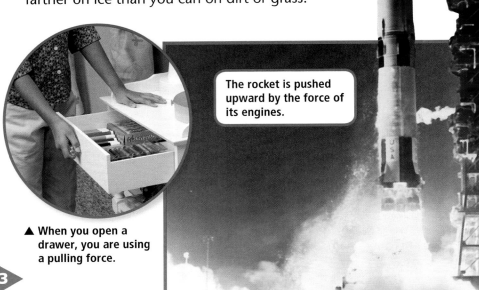

The rocket is pushed upward by the force of its engines.

▲ When you open a drawer, you are using a pulling force.

3

506

Reading Skill Mini-Lesson

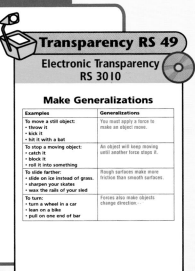

MAKE GENERALIZATIONS

Tell students that a generalization is a "general" or overall statement about a passage of information. A generalization can summarize the main point of a passage or section.

Display the Transparency and ask students to copy it. Have them read the examples in the chart and reread *Types of Forces*. Ask them to write a generalization for each group of examples.

Transparency RS 49

Electronic Transparency RS 3010

Make Generalizations

Examples	Generalizations
To move a still object: • throw it • kick it • hit it with a bat	You must apply a force to make an object move.
To stop a moving object: • catch it • block it • roll it into something	An object will keep moving until another force stops it.
To slide farther: • slide on ice instead of grass. • sharpen your skates • wax the rails of your sled	Rough surfaces make more friction than smooth surfaces.
To turn: • turn a wheel in a car • lean on a bike • pull on one end of bar	Forces also make objects change direction.

Science   © Harcourt

Forces at Work   When the basilisk lizard runs fast across the water, it looks as if it is running above the water. If the forward force were stopped, the lizard would start to sink into the water.

For more links and activities, go to www.hspscience.com

Forces also make objects change directions. You apply a force to the handlebar to turn your bike. When you push one end of a seesaw down, the other end comes up.

Some forces do not even have to touch the object. A magnet can be used to push or pull objects made of iron or steel. This is called magnetic force. A magnet can pull a nail.

 MAIN IDEA AND DETAILS A magnet picks up paper clips. What force is at work?

Insta-Lab

Amazing Paper Clips Put some water in a cup. Carefully lay a paper clip on the water's surface. Observe. What force causes the paper clip to stay on top of the water? Why doesn't the paper clip sink?

507

---

4 ▶ Key Science Concepts

How can forces affect the motion of an object? Forces can make objects start moving, stop moving, speed up, slow down, or change direction.

How is the magnetic force that moves an iron nail different from the kicking force that moves a soccer ball? The magnet itself does not have to touch the nail to make it move.

5 ▶ Main Idea and Details

Answer: magnetic force

6 ▶ Interpret Visuals

How does the basilisk's feet help it take advantage of surface tension? The feet are wide and flat to distribute weight across the "skin" of the water.

If a basilisk were 6 feet tall and weighed 200 pounds, would it be able to walk on water? No, it would sink through the "skin" of the surface tension on the water.

  5 minutes

The Amazing Paper Clip

Materials: water, cup, paper clip
Surface tension acts like a skin on which the paper clip can rest.

---

7 ▶ **Key Science Concepts**

What three things affect the motion of an object? the strength of the force, the direction of the force, and the mass of the object

What is the relationship between the direction of a force and the direction an object moves because of the force? An object moves in the same direction as the force.

8 ▶ **Interpret Visuals**

What makes the stroller move? the force of the jogger pushing on it **In what direction is the jogger running?** to the right **In what direction is the stroller moving? Why?** The stroller moves to the right because that is the direction of the force that pushes it.

What do YOU wonder?

Have students look back at the photo on the chapter opener. **Why do the swings spin in circles?** The ride turns in a circle. The chains pull on the swings and exert a force. That force also makes the swings turn in circles.

9 ▶ **Critical Thinking**

Once the stroller in the picture is moving, how could the jogger slow it down? Possible answers: pull on it; let go and let friction slow it down

Why is it harder to hit a home run in baseball than a fly ball or a pop-up? You apply a force to the ball when you hit it. To make it fly fast and far enough to hit a home run requires a lot of force. Less force is needed to hit fly balls or pop-ups, which don't go as far.

Ways That Forces Change Motion

7 ▶ Three things affect the motion of an object.

- the strength of the force
- the direction of the force
- the mass of the object

The stronger the force is, the greater the change in motion. If you toss a ball gently, it doesn't move fast or far. If you throw a ball hard, the ball moves faster and farther. You use more force on the ball when you throw it as hard as you can.

9 ▶ An object moves in the same direction as the force pushing or pulling it. When you pull up on an object, it comes up. When you push an object to the right, it moves to the right.

The smaller the mass of an object is, the easier it is to move. It takes less force to pick up a pencil than to pick up a book. The pencil has less mass than the book.

The jogger pushes the stroller in the direction in which he wants it to go. The direction in which an object moves is the direction of the force used to move it.

8

508

▲ Each of these people is using force to push the boat. When forces act in the same direction, they add up to make a greater force. The sum of all the forces is called the net force.

▶ You can add all the forces that push or pull on an object. The sum is called the net force. Suppose you and a friend push the same way on a door. The net force on the door equals your push plus your friend's push.

▶ **MAIN IDEA AND DETAILS** Name three things that affect the motion of an object, and tell what each one does.

When equal forces act in opposite directions, they cancel each other out. The net force is zero.

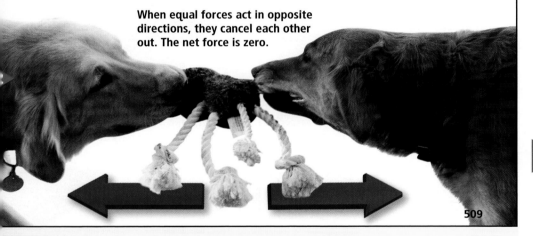

509

10 Key Science Concepts

How does mass affect motion? Give an example. Objects with less mass need less force to speed them up. It is easier to push a book quickly than to push a car.

What is net force? the sum of all the forces acting on an object

How do you find the net force acting on an object? add all of the forces that push or pull on it

11 Interpret Visuals

Summarize the forces acting on the boat. How many are there? In what direction are they moving? There are two forces, each pushing the boat into the water. **Do the forces work together or cancel each other out? Explain.** They work together to make a greater force because they are pushing in the same direction. **Summarize the forces acting on the rope toy. How many are there? In what direction are they moving?** There are two forces acting in opposite directions. **Do the forces work together or cancel each other out? Explain.** If the dogs apply the same force, they cancel each other out because they act in opposite directions.

12 Inquiry Skills

Predict Have students consider the photo of the two dogs pulling on the rope toy. **What would happen if the dog on the left pulled harder than the dog on the right, but the dog on the right kept holding on to the rope?** The rope toy and the dogs would move to the left. **What would happen if the dog on the right let go?** The dog on the left would move quickly backward.

13 Main Idea and Details

Answer: The strength of the force affects how far or fast an object moves. The direction of the force affects the direction in which an object moves. The mass of the object affects the amount of force needed to speed it up.

14 Develop Science Vocabulary

gravity Tell students that gravity comes from the Latin *gravitas*, meaning "heavy." Explain that objects seem heavy because they fall to the ground. Remind students that gravity acts on all objects, whether they are heavy or light.

weight Have students explain the difference between mass and weight. They should understand that mass tells the amount of matter in an object. Weight is a measure of force. It depends on mass and on the gravity in a particular place.

15 Key Science Concepts

What is gravitation? Gravitation is a force that pulls all objects toward each other.

Why do objects fall back to Earth? Gravity pulls the object and Earth toward each other. Earth has a lot of mass, so it has a lot of force of gravity. That force pulls objects back toward Earth.

16 Inquiry Skills

Use Numbers Tell students that the force of gravity on Jupiter is about two times stronger than on Earth. Have them find the weight on Jupiter of a book that weighs 5 pounds on Earth: 5 pounds + 5 pounds = 10 pounds, or 5 pounds × 2 = 10 pounds

17 Main Idea and Details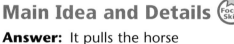

Answer: It pulls the horse harder. You can tell because the horse weighs more.

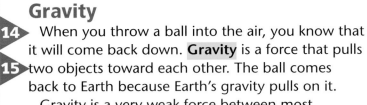

Gravity

14 When you throw a ball into the air, you know that it will come back down. **Gravity** is a force that pulls
15 two objects toward each other. The ball comes back to Earth because Earth's gravity pulls on it.

Gravity is a very weak force between most objects. You don't feel the force of gravity between you and your desk. But Earth's gravity pulls very strongly. This is because Earth is so large.

The force of gravity depends on how much mass an object has.
16 **Weight** is a measure of the force of gravity on an object. Objects with a large mass weigh more.

17 **MAIN IDEA AND DETAILS** Does gravity pull a horse or a puppy harder? How do you know?

Why does the water fall back down to Earth after shooting up from the fountain?

510

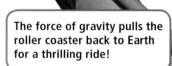

The force of gravity pulls the roller coaster back to Earth for a thrilling ride!

🌿 Health Link

Losing Mass

A person who wants to lose "weight" really wants to lose mass. Eating fewer calories or burning more calories through exercise causes the body to lose stored fat. Losing stored fat can reduce overall body mass or change body mass by building muscle. Have students research the Activity Pyramid and plan a weekly exercise schedule.

1. MAIN IDEA AND DETAILS Copy and complete this concept map. Use the terms *pulls, weight, gravity, turn,* and *net force.*

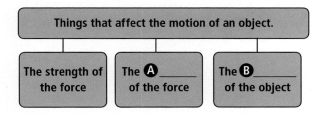

Things that affect the motion of an object.

The strength of the force

The **A**_____ of the force

The **B**_____ of the object

2. SUMMARIZE Write a summary of this lesson. Begin with the sentence *An object's motion changes because a force pushes or pulls it.*

3. DRAW CONCLUSIONS Why is it easier to ride a bike downhill than to ride it uphill?

4. VOCABULARY Use the terms *force, gravity,* and *weight* in sentences.

Test Prep
5. Critical Thinking Suppose you kick a ball sideways. In which direction will it move? Explain.

Links

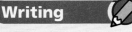
Writing

Narrative
The moon is smaller than Earth, so the moon's gravity is weaker than Earth's. Write a **short story** about a day on the moon. How would the weaker gravity affect your motion?

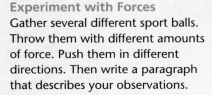
Physical Education

Experiment with Forces
Gather several different sport balls. Throw them with different amounts of force. Push them in different directions. Then write a paragraph that describes your observations.

For more links and activities, go to www.hspscience.com

511

3 Assess and Extend

Graphic Organizer

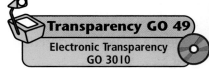
Transparency GO 49
Electronic Transparency GO 3010

1. **A** direction [B] Mass

2. An object's motion changes because a force pushes or pulls on it. The strength and direction of the force as well as the mass of the object determine the motion of an object after a force acts on it. The sum of the forces acting on an object is called the net force. Gravity is a force that pulls objects toward each other. Weight is the measure of the force of gravity between two objects.

3. Possible answer: The force of gravity pulls against you when you go uphill, but it pulls with you when you go downhill.

4. Possible answer: Weight is a measure of the force of gravity on an object.

5. The ball will move sideways because an object that is not moving will move in the direction of the force applied to it.

Links

Writing If students have trouble getting started, have them focus on games and sports-related activities such as jumping and hitting balls. Explain that playing in a location with weaker gravity would make them seem extra-strong. They would, for example, be able to kick a soccer ball farther.

 Students can consult the *Writing Models* in **Teaching Resources** as they complete the link. Rubrics are also provided.

Physical Education Students should see that the ball moves in the same direction as the applied force. They should see that the ball's speed and distance depend on the strength of the applied force.

Lesson Quick Study

The Lesson Quick Study in **Reading Support and Homework** provides the opportunity for students to practice inquiry skills, review lesson vocabulary, apply reading skills, and use critical thinking and problem solving. Students can use the second page of the Lesson Quick Study to complete the graphic organizer from the Reading Review. The graphic organizer is available on overhead and electronic transparencies.

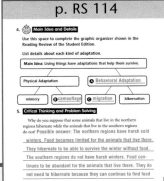

Reading Support and Homework

p. RS 114

4. Main Idea and Details
Use this space to complete the graphic organizer shown in the Reading Review of the Student Edition.

List details about each kind of adaptation.

Main Idea: Living things have adaptations that help them survive.

Physical Adaptation | **A** Behavioral Adaptation

mimicry | **B** camouflage | **C** migration | hibernation

5. Critical Thinking and Problem Solving

Why do you suppose that some animals that live in the northern regions hibernate while the animals that live in the southern regions do not? Possible answer: The northern regions have harsh cold winters. Food becomes limited for the animals that live there. They hibernate to be able to survive the winter without food. The southern regions do not have harsh winters. Food continues to be abundant for the animals that live there. They do not need to hibernate because they can continue to find food to eat.

p. RS 115

Lesson 4 - How Do Ecosystems Change?

1. Inquiry Skill Practice–Predict
Predict how the ecosystem in your area would change if the garbage started getting dumped in the lake and glass, plastic, and paper did not get recycled. Possible answers: The animals that live in the lake would die. The animals that use the lake to get their food and water would not be able to. Air quality would get bad and would not allow the people and animals that live in the area to breathe clean air. More trees would have to be cut to produce more paper.

2. Use Vocabulary
Write a complete sentence that uses the word *resource* correctly.
Answers will vary but should reflect the correct use of *resource*.

3. Reading Skill Practice–Cause and Effect
Read the selection. Underline the cause of the lake clean-up project. List at least two effects of the project.

The people that lived near Mendota Lake in Madison, Wisconsin realized that the lake water had a bad smell. They decided to clean it up. The trash from the lake shores was cleaned up. An effort was made to stop dumping waste into the lake. Factories were told to dump their trash someplace else. Today, the lake does not smell. There are even some fish living in Mendota Lake.

Effects: The lake does not smell. Some fish live in the lake.

Objectives

- Observe the motion of different kinds of waves.
- Define *waves* and describe their motion.
- Identify the parts of a wave.

Transparency DI 50

Electronic Transparency DI 3011

Daily Inquiry

How Far Will It Roll?

tape measure

Other Materials: ball, books, measuring tape

Review Skill: Measure, Experiment

- Set up a ramp using a stack of books. Mark a start line on the ramp with masking tape.
- Rest the ball at the starting line. Let go of the ball without pushing it. Measure how far it traveled. Record your measurement. Repeat the activity three times.
- Did the ball travel the same distance with each trial? Would it matter if you gave the ball a push for one of the trials? Why?

1 Introduce

Build on Prior Knowledge

Use the Fast Fact for a discussion starter about the lesson topic.

What do you see in this picture? What do you think caused the ripples in the pond?

Where else have you seen waves? What kinds of waves are there?

When *Minutes* Count . . .

If time is short, consider these options.

Conduct the Investigate as a **whole-class demonstration.**

Use the Activity Video/DVD to model the Investigate. After previewing, students can conduct the Investigate in small groups.

512 ■ CHAPTER 15

How Do Waves Move?

Fast Fact

Waves! Water waves can be tiny, like these ripples in a pond. Waves in the ocean are much larger. The largest wave measured was 520 meters (1,700 ft) high. In the Investigate, you will see how two different kinds of waves move.

512

Science Background

Springs The coiled spring toy in the Investigate is one example of a spring. A spring is coiled wire or other elastic material that returns to its original shape after being stretched or compressed. In 1676, English scientist Robert Hooke discovered that springs stretch by an amount related to the force that pulls on them. To stretch a spring two inches takes twice as much force as to stretch the same spring one inch. The spring stores energy when it is stretched. When released, it converts the stored potential energy to kinetic energy, moving the object back and forth. A spring can also carry energy along it by wave motion.

Webliography
Keyword forces
www.hspscience.com

Two Kinds of Waves

Materials   • rope about 2 meters long   • coiled spring toy

Procedure

1. Hold one end of the rope. Your partner will hold the other end. Let the rope hang loosely between you.

2. Move one end of the rope gently up and down as your partner holds the other end still. Then move the rope faster. **Observe** what happens.

3. Put the coiled spring toy on a table or on the floor. Have your partner hold one end still. Push the other end of the toy about 10 cm toward your partner. Then pull and push that end backward and forward. **Observe** what happens.

4. **Record** your **observations** by making diagrams for steps 2 and 3.

Step 1

Step 2

Draw Conclusions

1. How did the force you used on the rope affect it? What happened when you moved it faster?

2. **Inquiry Skill** When you **compare** things, you look at how they are alike. **Compare** the movements of the waves in the rope with the waves in the toy.

Investigate Further

What do you **predict** will happen when you move the coiled spring toy in the same way you moved the rope? Try it and see.

513

Inquiry Skill Mini-Lesson

Compare Explain to students that *compare* means to tell how things are alike. *Contrast* means to tell how they are different.

Display the Transparency. Have students compare and contrast the first pair of waves. Repeat for the second pair of waves. Students can complete the Transparency in small groups or as a class.

Inquiry Skill practice is provided in *Reading Support and Homework*.

Transparency IS 50

Electronic Transparency IS 3011

Compare

1. **How are the waves alike?**
   Possible answer: Both wave sets are up-and-down waves. Both show the same number of peaks and valleys.

2. **How are the waves different?**
   Possible answer: Wave set A has taller peaks and deeper valleys than wave set B.

3. **How are the waves alike?**
   Possible answer: Both wave sets are up-and-down waves. Both show the same height of the peaks and depth of the valleys.

4. **How are the waves different?**
   Possible answer: Wave set A has more peaks and valleys in the same space as wave set B.

Science   © Harcourt

---

2 Teach

Time 20 minutes

Grouping pairs

Video Segment 3011

Lab Manual pages can be used to record results. Inquiry Skill Tips and Self-Assessment are also provided.

Tips and Guided Inquiry

Ensure that the ropes touch the ground when they hang between the students. If the rope hangs too loosely and the waves do not form well, have the students move apart to make the rope a little tighter.

What do you do when you compare things? You look for how things are the same and different.

What are you trying to compare in this Investigate? Students might comment that they are comparing the movements in the rope and spring.

Expected Results

The rope moves up and down in S-shaped waves. Waves move down the coiled spring from one end to the other. Moving the rope or coil faster forms more waves and presses them closer together.

Draw Conclusions

1. **Possible answer:** Waves formed along the rope, moving from one end to another. When I moved it faster, more waves formed and they were closer together.

2. **Possible answer:** The waves move down the rope and spring.

Investigate Further

Students can use this page in the *Lab Manual* for **Independent Inquiry**.

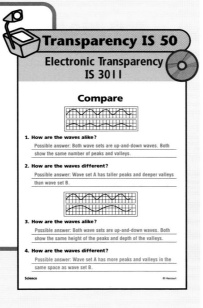

Lab Manual

p. LM 186

Date _____

Investigate Further
What do you predict will happen when you move the coiled spring toy in the same way you moved the rope? Try it and see.

Materials
Here are some materials that you might use. List additional materials that you need.
• coiled spring toy

1. Predict what will happen when you move the coiled spring toy like you moved the rope.
   Possible answer: The spring will move up and down like the rope did.

2. Conduct the investigation. Draw a diagram in the space below to record your observations.

   Diagram of Movement

3. Was your prediction correct? What can you conclude about how to make a wave that moves up and down!
   Students should explain whether their results agreed with their prediction. They should conclude that moving a flexible object up and down creates a wave that also moves up and down.

2 Teach
continued

VOCABULARY For Vocabulary Cards and activities, see *Reading Support and Homework.*

SCIENCE CONCEPTS Have students list what they know about the science concepts. Have them be alert to the ideas on the list as you go through the lesson. Ask them to check off the information on the list as they find it in the lesson or to modify the ideas to reflect what they learn.

 READING FOCUS SKILL

MAIN IDEA AND DETAILS Tell students that the information in this lesson is organized to help them recognize a main idea and the details that support it. Use the Reading Mini-Lesson below to discuss a strategy that students can use to find the main idea and identify supporting details.

1 Key Science Concepts

What is a wave? a disturbance in space or matter

What do waves carry? energy

What materials will carry a wave? Waves can travel through solids, liquids, and gases. Some waves can travel through empty space.

2 Develop Science Vocabulary

wave Relate the motion of waving a hand to the scientific meaning of *wave*. Have students wave to each other and observe the motion of each other's hand or fingers. Ask them to compare that motion to wave motion. Guide them to understand that to wave hello, you move your hand or fingers back and forth or up and down. A wave on a spring or a rope also moves back and forth or up and down.

3 Interpret Visuals

Something floating on the ocean, like a boat or seaweed, moves when waves go by. Why? Waves carry energy, so they disturb the water and move things that float on it.

VOCABULARY
wave p. 514
crest p. 516
trough p. 516
wavelength p. 516

SCIENCE CONCEPTS
▶ what the types of waves are
▶ how to measure waves

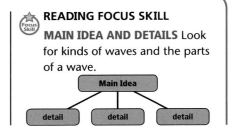 **READING FOCUS SKILL**
MAIN IDEA AND DETAILS Look for kinds of waves and the parts of a wave.

Types of Waves

1 Even if you live far from the ocean, waves are all around you. There are many kinds of waves. Light travels in waves, and so does sound. Microwaves cook your food. A doctor uses X-ray waves to take pictures of the inside of your body.

2 A **wave** is a disturbance that travels through matter or space. Waves disturb matter by causing it to move. This is because waves carry energy. Waves can travel through solids, liquids, and gases. Some waves can travel through empty space.

3 **Waves disturb the water particles.** ▼

514

Reading Skill Mini-Lesson

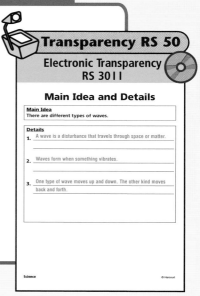

MAIN IDEA AND DETAILS

Tell students they will better recall what they read in a section if they summarize the main idea and the details that support it.

Display the Transparency. Show students that the main idea of *Types of Waves* —that there are different types of waves—can be found in the first paragraph. Have students identify one supporting detail from each of the second, third, and fourth paragraphs.

Transparency RS 50

Electronic Transparency RS 3011

Main Idea and Details

Main Idea
There are different types of waves.

Details
1. A wave is a disturbance that travels through space or matter.
2. Waves form when something vibrates.
3. One type of wave moves up and down. The other kind moves back and forth.

Science   © Harcourt

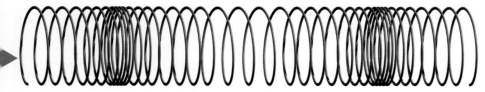

▲ A spring toy that is moved in and out makes a back-and-forth wave.

Sound waves from this xylophone (ZY•luh•fohn) bring sound energy to your ears. Sounds waves are back-and-forth waves. ▶

Waves are made when something vibrates. Things that vibrate move back and forth. When you speak, your vocal cords vibrate quickly to make sound waves.

There are two types of waves. Some waves move up and down. Examples are radio waves and light waves. Some waves, like sound waves, move back and forth.

MAIN IDEA AND DETAILS
What is a wave?

Insta-Lab

Move It!
Sprinkle some tiny bread crumbs on top of a cookie sheet. Bang a large wooden spoon against the cookie sheet. Observe the crumbs. What makes them move?

515

4 ▶ Key Science Concepts

How do waves form? Waves form when something vibrates, or moves back and forth. **What two ways can waves move?** up and down or back and forth

Have students place their fingers over their vocal cords and hum a long note to feel the vibration. If one is available, have students feel the vibrations in a turning fork.

  5 minutes

Move It!

Materials: foil pie plate, bread crumbs, wooden spoon, cookie sheet

Students should observe the crumbs move. The energy of sound waves moving through the air disturbs the crumbs.

5 ▶ Interpret Visuals

Which wave is a back-and-forth wave? the sound wave

6 ▶ Inquiry Skills

Plan and Conduct Simple Investigations Have students use a coiled spring toy to create up-and-down and back-and-forth waves. Have them relate the direction of the wave to the direction of the motion used to create it. **How does the direction of the back-and-forth wave compare to the direction of the motion that produced it?** They are in the same direction. **How does the direction of the up-and-down wave compare to the direction of the motion that produced it?** They are in different directions.

7 ▶ Main Idea and Details

Answer: energy

Reaching All Learners

ESL / ESOL Support

Below On-Level ESL Advanced

Background and Experience

Use students' understanding of the word *carry* to explain the phrase *carry energy.*

Beginning Ask students to act out carrying an object. Discuss the meaning of the term *carry.*

Intermediate Ask students to identify synonyms for *carry,* such as *lift* or *move.*

Advanced Have students draw a picture of a person carrying an object; then have them draw a picture of how they imagine a wave carries energy. Discuss the drawings in small groups. Guide students to the understanding that waves move energy the way a person moves an object by carrying it.

For strategies and lesson support, see *ESL Support* pp. 216–219.

8 ► Develop Science Vocabulary

crest and **trough** Have students compare *crest* and *trough* with more familiar things. Display a picture or draw a diagram of a hill and of a feeding trough. **How is the crest of a wave like the crest of a hill?** Both are rounded and peaked at the top. **How is the trough of a wave like a feeding trough**? Both are rounded at the bottom.

wavelength Write *wave/length* on the board to show the two roots of the term. Review the meanings of *wave* and *length*. Discuss that wavelength describes the length of a wave by measuring the distance between adjacent crests or troughs.

9 ► Key Science Concepts

What is the crest of a wave? The trough? The crest is the highest point on the wave. The trough is the lowest point.

How does force affect wave energy? The larger the force that makes a vibration, the more energy the wave will have.

10 ► Critical Thinking

What do the crest, trough, and wavelength of a wave all have in common? They are distances that can be measured.

11 ► Inquiry Skills

Use Numbers Provide students with accurate drawings of up-and-down (transverse) waves, perhaps generated on a computer. Have them identify and mark two adjacent crests and then measure the wavelength. Have them confirm the measurement by finding the distance between two adjacent troughs.

12 ► Main Idea and Details

Answer: the distance from its crest to its trough

Measuring Waves

8 Waves have parts that can be measured. The **crest** is the highest point
9 ►of a wave. The **trough** is the lowest point of a wave. The greater the distance between these two points, the larger the wave is and the more energy it carries.

Forces affect the amount of energy that waves carry. A rock thrown into a pond will make bigger waves than a pebble will. Suppose you beat hard on a drum. The sound is louder than if you beat softly.

Scientists also measure another
10 ►characteristic of waves. **Wavelength** is the distance from one point of one wave to the same point of the next wave.

12 **MAIN IDEA AND DETAILS** What measurement tells how much energy a wave carries?

Wavelength can be measured as the distance from one crest to the next crest or from one trough to the next trough.

Measuring a wave is easy if you think of it as hills and valleys. ▼

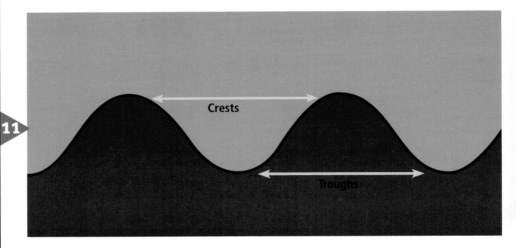

Crests

11 ►

Troughs

516

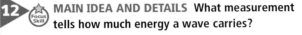

1. MAIN IDEA AND DETAILS Copy and complete this concept map.

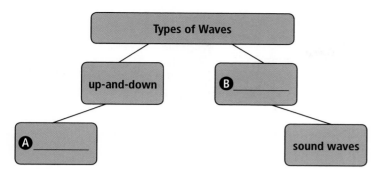

Types of Waves

up-and-down

B _____

 A _____

sound waves

2. SUMMARIZE Write two sentences that tell what this lesson is mainly about.

3. DRAW CONCLUSIONS Why can ocean waves wash away rocks on the beach?

4. VOCABULARY Make a quiz question for each vocabulary term in this lesson. Provide the answers.

Test Prep

5. How can the length of a wave be measured?
   A. from trough to crest
   B. from crest to wavelength
   C. from crest to trough
   D. from crest to crest

Links

Writing

Narrative
Suppose you are a wave. Write a **description** of yourself. Tell what type of wave you are, how you move, and how your energy is measured. Describe how the amount of energy you carry can change.

💻 **For more links and activities, go to www.hspscience.com**

Math

Measure Wavelength
Look at the two pictures of waves. Measure their wavelengths. How much longer is Wave A than Wave B?

A.

B.

517

Lesson Quick Study

The Lesson Quick Study in **Reading Support and Homework** provides the opportunity for students to practice inquiry skills, review lesson vocabulary, apply reading skills, and use critical thinking and problem solving. Students can use the second page of the Lesson Quick Study to complete the graphic organizer from the Reading Review. The graphic organizer is also available on overhead and electronic transparencies.

Reading Support and Homework

p. RS 116

p. RS 117

---

3 Assess and Extend

Graphic Organizer

Transparency GO 50
Electronic Transparency
GO 3011

1. **Ⓐ** radio or light waves [B] back-and-forth

2. Possible answer: Waves result when things vibrate. They can be up-and-down waves or back-and-forth waves.

3. Waves carry energy that can move the rocks.

4. Possible answers: **What is a wave?** a disturbance in matter or space **How is a wave crest different from a trough?** The crest is a wave's highest point and the trough is the lowest point. **How do you measure wavelength?** You measure the distance from crest to crest or from trough to trough.

5. D, crest to crest

Links

Writing Be sure students identify themselves as back-and-forth or up-and-down waves in their stories. Before students write, suggest that they first act out their motion as a wave. They can start their stories by writing about how they traveled around the room.

 Students can consult the *Writing Models* in **Teaching Resources** as they complete the link. Rubrics are also provided.

Math The wavelength of B is twice as long as the wavelength of A.

Technology

■ Investigate how models can be used by scientists and inventors.

1 Introduce

Preview the Reading

Have students look closely at the pictures and preview the reading. Ask students to identify what they think the machine shown is used for and how it operates.

2 Teach

Chapter Concepts

Students' knowledge about forces and motion will help students to better understand how the *SoloTrek* and *Dragonfly* work.

How does a pilot use force to change the motion of the *SoloTrek*? The pilot uses forces to tilt the ducts in the direction the pilot wants to travel.

How could firefighters use a device like *Dragonfly* to help fight fires? Possible answer: the *Dragonfly* could carry firefighters into inaccessible areas.

Inquiry Skills

Order The scientists who developed *SoloTrek* and *Dragonfly* worked in stages. First, they developed the prototype. Then, they improved upon the prototype by making a similar vehicle that could carry more. Work with students to order the steps scientists took in developing the personal aircraft. Tell students to think about steps that were not mentioned in the article but would be needed between the design of the prototype and the test flight.

SCIENCE Spin™ from WEEKLY READER®
Technology

Taking to the Air

Michael Moshier always believed he could fly. Now a lot of other people believe that he can, too.

Not long ago, Moshier flew about 60 cm (2 ft) into the air. That might not sound like much, but he flew only with the help of a special flying backpack that he invented, called the *SoloTrek*.

518

Science Background

Personal Aircraft NASA and many private companies are developing different types of personal aircraft to make transportation easier in the future. You may want to share the following information about personal aircraft with your class:

■ The first flying car was developed in 1946 and was called Airphibian. It was a three-wheeled vehicle that could fly. However, it was not a commercial success.

■ The only other flying car that was approved by the U.S. government was called Aerocar. This car could fly at 120 miles (194 kilometers) per hour, but it did not meet all of the regulations for cars.

■ Scientists continue to work on a personal aircraft that will help make traveling faster, and more fun, for everyone.

Straight Up

The *SoloTrek* was what scientists call a prototype, or a test version of something. It weighs about 147 kg (325 pounds) and is a personal flying machine. The machine is lifted into the air by two propellers, called ducts. The ducts force air in the direction they are pointed. For example, if the pilot tilts the ducts to face forward, the aircraft flies forward. If the ducts are tilted to face upward, the aircraft flies up.

Bigger and Better

Since the *SoloTrek* prototype, Trek Aerospace has built several more test vehicles that can lift people or cargo have been built. One new machine is called the *Dragonfly*. The *Dragonfly* is 4 m (13.1 ft) long and can carry a cargo of 205 kg (450 pounds), about the same weight as five third graders. The machine can fly at a maximum speed of about 378 km (235 miles) per hour.

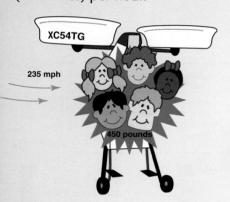

XC54TG

235 mph

450 pounds

Flying Solo

Dragonfly is being tested in both a piloted and unpiloted version. An unpiloted version could someday be used by the military or firefighters to carry supplies to dangerous areas.

The company that makes *Solo Trek*, has high hopes for its machines. The first purchases might be made by the military or firefighters. The company also hopes that families might some day buy these personal flying machines to get around town. Who knows, when you're old enough you might drive your kids to soccer practice in your own personal aircraft.

THINK ABOUT IT

1. During its test flight, how was the *SoloTrek* put into motion?

2. How would you use your own personal aircraft?

Find out more! Log on to **www.hspscience.com**

519

3 Wrap Up and Assess

Think About It

1. The *SoloTrek* was put into motion by two propellers that lifted the personal aircraft off the ground.

2. Answers may vary; accept all reasonable answers.

Writing Link

Persuasive Writing Personal aircraft are an interesting and exciting means of transportation for the future. Write a e-mail to a friend, giving your opinion about personal aircraft and how they will be used in the future.

Inspire Inquiry

Inquiry starts with wonder and with asking questions. Sometimes the questions are just about things people want to know. Sometimes they are problems that people want to solve.

- Have students suggest questions that scientists might have been asking when they began to design and build *SoloTrek* and *Dragonfly*.
- Ask students what questions they have about personal aircraft. Write the questions on the board.
- Ask students to suggest ways they might begin to answer the questions they have asked. List the steps. Encourage interested students to explore more and to develop ways to answer their questions through research and experimentation.

Objectives

- Discuss how the airplane has changed people's lifestyles in the last 100 years.
- Describe the Young Eagles program.

1 Introduce

Preview/Set a Purpose

Ask students, **Is it easy to fly?** Students might answer that it would be really hard to fly.

2 Teach

The Work of Scientists

Help students conclude that the work of the Wright brothers made flying possible and that improvements over the past 100 years has made flying easier.

What did Michael Zollars do? He flew a plane.

How old was he? 10 years old

How many years have passed since the airplane was invented? about 100 years

3 Wrap Up and Assess

Think About It

Have students infer how inventors use science to make their inventions.

Who invented the first powered airplane that actually flew? Wilbur and Orville Wright

What did they have to do before their airplane could fly? Possible answer: They had to learn what other scientists had done as they tried to make an airplane fly. Then they had to do experiments to test their ideas.

SCIENCE Spin from WEEKLY READER

People

KIDS TAKE FLIGHT

Ten-year-old Michael Zollars recently went on the ride of his life. He and a pilot flew in a small airplane. "It was fun!" Michael said. "I got to take the controls for a while."

Michael was taking part in the Young Eagles program. The goal of the program was to give one million children free rides in private airplanes. The program ended on December 17, 2003, the 100th anniversary of the first powered flight made by the Wright brothers. Wilbur and Orville Wright built their first powered airplane, the Flyer, in 1903 and tested it at Kitty Hawk, North Carolina.

1903	1927	1939	1958	1961	1969
Wright brothers make first powered flight.	Charles Lindbergh makes first nonstop solo flight across Atlantic Ocean.	Jet plane makes first successful flight.	Jet passenger service across Atlantic Ocean begins.	Russians launch first person into space.	U.S. astronauts land on moon.

 Find out more! Log on to **www.hspscience.com**

Reaching All Learners
Challenge

Below · On-Level · Advanced · ESL

More Inquiry

Present students with the following problem:

Can you make a wing for an airplane?

- Preparation: Obtain coarse sandpaper and small blocks of plastic foam. Cut blocks to 3 inches x 1.5 inches x 4 inches. Place a wooden dowel in the plastic foam from one 3-inch by 1.5-inch side to the other. Obtain an electric fan and pictures of cross sections of airplane wings.
- Have students look at the pictures of wing cross sections and use sandpaper to sand the blocks of plastic foam into the shape of a wing—flat on the bottom and curved over the top.
- Have them hold the wing at an angle (back edge down) in front of the running fan. They should feel the wing being pushed upward as the air blows across it.

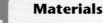

SCIENCE Projects
for Home or School

You Can Do It!

Quick and Easy Project

Net Force

Procedure

Materials
• book

1. Lay a book on a table or on the floor. Push on one side of the book. How does the book move?

2. Push on the side next to the side you just pushed. How does the book move?

3. Push on both of these sides at the same time. In which direction does the book move?

Draw Conclusions

Why did the book move in a new direction in Step 3?
What do you think would happen if you pushed on opposite sides of the book?

Design Your Own Investigation

Friction

Friction is a force that you can't see. It causes objects to slow down when two surfaces rub against each other. Design an investigation to find out more about friction. Find some surfaces that are smooth and some that are rough. Then choose an object, and try moving it across the different surfaces. Do smooth surfaces or rough surfaces cause more friction?

521

You Can Do It!

Quick and Easy Project

Net Force

Objectives

■ Observe that an object moves in the direction of a force applied to it.

■ Observe that an object moves in the direction of the net forces acting on it.

• Tips and Hints

Students can work as partners to coordinate the application of forces in Step 3.

• Draw Conclusions

1. The two forces together created a net force in the direction that the book moved.

2. The two forces would cancel each other out; the book would not move.

• Extend the Activity

Have three students push on the book in various combinations to investigate how the net force of three forces affects the motion of the book.

Design Your Own Investigation

Friction

Objectives

■ Determine whether smooth or rough surfaces have more friction.

Inspire Inquiry

Use this activity as an at-home investigation or suggestion for a science fair project. Have students use the investigation as a starting point for developing their own questions and ideas for research. Ask students to share their plans and ideas with you and the class and to work together to help make the investigation procedure better.

A reproducible copy of this page is provided in *Teaching Resources*.

LESSON 3 ■ 521

Chapter 15

Vocabulary Review (5 pts. each)

1. crest
2. motion
3. weight
4. force
5. wavelength
6. speed
7. wave
8. trough
9. gravity
10. distance

Check Understanding (5 pts. each)

11. B, toward the right
12. F, energy
13. A, The net force is twice the force of each horse alone.
14. F, distance
15. C, It doesn't move.
16. G, gravity

Vocabulary Review

Use the terms below to complete the sentences. The page numbers tell you where to look in the chapter if you need help.

motion p. 499
distance p. 500
speed p. 502
force p. 506
gravity p. 510
weight p. 510
wave p. 514
crest p. 516
trough p. 516
wavelength p. 516

1. The highest point of a wave is the _____.
2. A change in position is _____.
3. The measure of the force of gravity on an object is the object's _____.
4. A push or a pull is a _____.
5. The distance between two crests or two troughs is the _____.
6. The distance an object moves in a certain period of time is its _____.

7. A disturbance that travels through matter or space is a _____.
8. The lowest point of a wave is the _____.
9. The force that pulls two objects toward each other is _____.
10. How far an object moves is _____.

Check Understanding

Write the letter of the best choice.

11. A boy pushes a box across the floor. The box moves to the right. In which direction is the boy probably pushing?
    A. toward the left
    B. toward the right
    C. downward
    D. upward

12. What do waves carry with them from place to place?
    F. energy   H. speed
    G. motion   J. wavelength

Harcourt School Publishers
Online Assessment

Harcourt School Publishers Online Assessment provides even more options. For a preview, go to:
www.hspscience.com

Portfolio Assessment

Have students select their best work from the following suggestions:

- **Investigate,** pp. 497, 505, 513
- **Reading Skill Mini-Lesson,** pp. 498, 506, 514
- **Writing Link,** pp. 503, 511, 513

See *Assessment Guide* pp. xx-xxiv.

13. **COMPARE AND CONTRAST** Two horses pull a wagon in the same direction with the same force. How does the net force compare to the force of each horse?
    - **A.** The net force is twice the force of each horse alone.
    - **B.** The net force is half the force of each horse alone.
    - **C.** The net force is equal to the force of each horse alone.
    - **D.** The net force is zero.

14. **MAIN IDEA AND DETAILS** To figure speed, what else do you need to know besides time?
    - **F.** distance   **H.** motion
    - **G.** force   **J.** wavelength

15. In the picture, the two girls start pushing the trunk with equal force. How does it move?
    - **A.** It moves toward the right.
    - **B.** It moves toward the left.
    - **C.** It doesn't move.
    - **D.** It moves slowly.

16. Which force holds your book on your desk?
    - **F.** electricity
    - **G.** gravity
    - **H.** magnetism
    - **J.** surface tension

Inquiry Skills

17. Interpret the data shown in the pictures. Which wave has the shortest wavelength? How do you know?

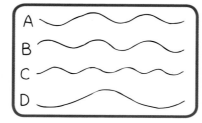

18. Compare two different types of waves.

Critical Thinking

19. Look around the room. Find three objects that can move, and describe their motions. Tell what forces are needed to make these objects move.

20. Weigh some objects in your classroom. Record the weights. Which object does gravity pull on the hardest? How do you know?

Inquiry Skills (5 pts. each)

17. C; The distance between adjacent crests or between adjacent troughs is the shortest of the four waves.

18. There are up-and-down waves and back-and-forth waves, so they vary in their motion. Both waves have crests and troughs, and both carry energy.

Critical Thinking (5 pts. each)

19. Words to describe motion can include zigzag, straight-line, or back-and-forth. Forces are most likely to be pushes and pulls applied by people or gravity.

20. The object pulled the hardest by gravity is the heaviest. Weight is a measure of the pull of gravity between objects, so a greater weight shows a harder pull.

Chapter Test

See **Assessment Guide** pages AG 115–120 for a Chapter Test and *Performance Task*, with rubric. Assessment options appear on page 494H.

Performance Assessment

The Way Things Move

Give students a rubber ball, rope, and a spring toy. Tell them to demonstrate three types of motion, including two types of wave motion, using one object at a time and each object at least once. Ask students to use one of the objects to demonstrate a fourth kind of motion.

Rubric for Performance Assessment

Preparation Obtain rubber balls, ropes, and toy springs.

Scoring Rubric—Performance Indicators

_____ Uses a ball to demonstrate rolling motion, back-and-forth bouncing, or other type of motion.

_____ Uses a rope to demonstrate up-and-down wave motion.

_____ Uses the toy spring to demonstrate back-and-forth wave motion.

_____ Uses the ball, rope, or toy spring to demonstrate one additional type of motion.

Observations and Rubric Scores

| 3 | 2 | 1 | 0 |

CHAPTER 16 LESSON PLANNER

Lesson	Pacing	Vocabulary	Objectives & Reading Focus	Resources & Technology
1 What Is Work? pp. 526–533	2 days	work	■ Explain how a force can cause an object to move. ■ Define *work*. ■ Identify what is needed to measure work. 🟊 **MAIN IDEA AND DETAILS** Look for details about work. Main Idea detail — detail — detail	■ Lab Manual pp. LM187–189 📦 Transparencies DI51, IS51, RS51, GO 51 ◎ Electronic Transparencies ■ Activity Video/DVD 3012 ◉ ESL Support pp. 222–225 ■ Reading Support and Homework pp. RS119–120
2 What Are Some Simple Machines? pp. 534–543	2 days	simple machine lever fulcrum wheel-and-axle pulley	■ Explain the advantages and disadvantages of performing a task with and without the help of a machine. ■ Define *simple machine*. ■ Describe a lever, a wheel-and-axle, and a pulley. 🟊 **MAIN IDEA AND DETAILS** Look for details about simple machines. Main Idea detail — detail — detail	■ Lab Manual pp. LM73–75 📦 Transparencies DI17, IS17, RS17, GO 17 ◎ Electronic Transparencies ■ Activity Video/DVD 3013 ◉ ESL Support pp. 64–67 ■ Reading Support and Homework pp. RS37–38
3 What Are Some Other Simple Machines? pp. 544–551	2 days	inclined plane wedge screw	■ Describe the mechanical advantage of using a ramp. ■ Describe an inclined plane, a wedge, and a screw. ■ Explain the relationship between an inclined plane and a screw. 🟊 **COMPARE AND CONTRAST** Look for ways inclined planes, wedges, and screws are *alike* and *different*. alike — different	■ Lab Manual pp. LM193–195 📦 Transparencies DI53, IS53, RS53, GO 53 ◎ Electronic Transparencies ■ Activity Video/DVD 3014 ◉ ESL Support pp. 230–233 ■ Reading Support and Homework pp. RS123–124
End of Chapter pp. 552–557	2 days		■ Evaluate relationships of science, technology, and society ■ Review chapter concepts	■ Intervention, On-Level, and Above-Level Readers ■ Assessment Guide pp. AG121–126

Science Projects for Home or School
p. 555 *Teaching Resources* p. TR 26

Unit Experiment pp. 493A–B; *Lab Manual* pp. LM 9–11 and *Science Fair Projects Lab Manual* LM 196–201

Lab Manual (cont.)

Lesson 2 — p. LM 190

Date _____

Help from Simple Machines

Materials

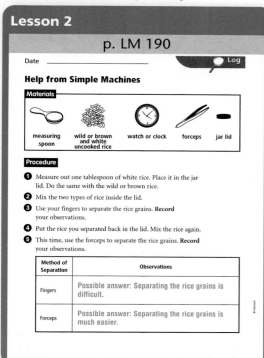

measuring spoon | wild or brown and white uncooked rice | watch or clock | forceps | jar lid

Procedure

1. Measure out one tablespoon of white rice. Place it in the jar lid. Do the same with the wild or brown rice.
2. Mix the two types of rice inside the lid.
3. Use your fingers to separate the rice grains. **Record** your observations.
4. Put the rice you separated back in the lid. Mix the rice again.
5. This time, use the forceps to separate the rice grains. **Record** your observations.

Method of Separation	Observations
Fingers	Possible answer: Separating the rice grains is difficult.
Forceps	Possible answer: Separating the rice grains is much easier.

Use with *Student Edition* p. 535.

Lesson 2 — p. LM 191

1. Which way of separating the rice grains was easier? Why? Separating the rice grains with the forceps should be easier. Since the forceps have a smaller grasp than a person's fingers, it is easier to separate the rice grains.

2. Which would be a safer way of handling food, using your fingers or using forceps?
   Using forceps would be more sanitary, as long as the forceps are clean.

3. **Inquiry Skill—Measure** Would it make a difference if time was important in completing this task? Repeat the Investigate and **measure** how long it takes to separate the rice.
   Answers will vary depending on the skill of the student.

Inquiry Skill Tip
You can use a clock or a watch to **measure** time. Make sure you **record** the time you begin and the time you finish.

Investigate Self-Assessment	Agree	Not Sure	Disagree
I made observations that helped me with this investigation.			
I used the measuring spoon to **measure** out the rice.			
I was able to **measure** the amount of time I took to separate the rice.			

Lesson 2 — Investigate — p. LM 192

Date _____

Investigate Further

You have measured how long it takes to separate the rice. Compare your time with four other classmates by making a bar graph. Were there differences? Why do you think so?

Materials

Here are some materials that you might use. List additional materials that you need.
- graph paper

1. Write the sorting time for each of the four classmates.
   Times will vary.

2. Use the times to make a bar graph.

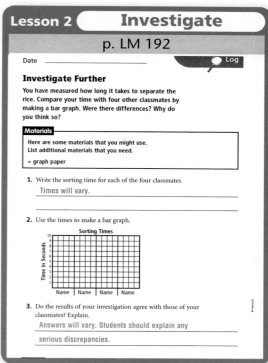

Sorting Times

3. Do the results of your investigation agree with those of your classmates? Explain.
   Answers will vary. Students should explain any serious discrepancies.

Lesson 3 — p. LM 193

Date _____

Inclined to Help

Materials

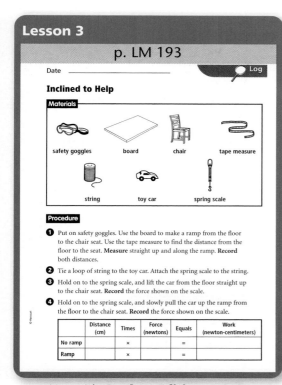

safety goggles | board | chair | tape measure
string | toy car | spring scale

Procedure

1. Put on safety goggles. Use the board to make a ramp from the floor to the chair seat. Use the tape measure to find the distance from the floor to the seat. **Measure** straight up and along the ramp. **Record** both distances.
2. Tie a loop of string to the toy car. Attach the spring scale to the string.
3. Hold on to the spring scale, and lift the car from the floor straight up to the chair seat. **Record** the force shown on the scale.
4. Hold on to the spring scale, and slowly pull the car up the ramp from the floor to the chair seat. **Record** the force shown on the scale.

	Distance (cm)	Times	Force (newtons)	Equals	Work (newton-centimeters)
No ramp		×		=	
Ramp		×		=	

Use with *Student Edition* p. 545.

Lesson 3 — p. LM 194

1. How did the ramp affect the force needed to lift the car?
   The force needed should be less when the ramp is used.

2. How did the ramp affect the distance?
   The distance increased.

3. **Inquiry Skill—Interpret Data** Scientists **interpret data** to draw conclusions. What conclusions can you draw from your data?
   Students may conclude that a ramp makes work easier.

Inquiry Skill Tip
When you **interpret data**, you decide what the data means. Interpreting data involves other processes, such as inferring and making predictions.

Investigate Self-Assessment	Agree	Not Sure	Disagree
I followed the directions for this investigation.			
I used a tape measure and spring scale to make measurements.			
I **interpreted data** to make conclusions about what I observed.			

Lesson 3 — Investigate — p. LM 195

Date _____

Investigate Further

What might affect the force needed to lift the car? Plan and conduct a simple investigation to test some ideas.

Materials

Here are some materials that you might use. List additional materials that you need.
- safety goggles
- board
- chair
- tape measure
- string
- toy car
- spring scale

1. Write a prediction for your investigation.
   Answers will vary depending on the type of investigation. Students should predict the effects of different variables on the amount of force needed to lift the car.

2. Use the following table to record your measurements.

Method of Lifting	Force (newtons)

3. What can you conclude from your results?
   Answers will depend on the variables students test. Possible answer: Increasing the length of a ramp means less force is needed to lift the car.

READING SUPPORT AND HOMEWORK

Pages available online.
www.hspscience.com

Reading Support and Homework also includes Vocabulary Power, and Vocabulary Cards and Activities.

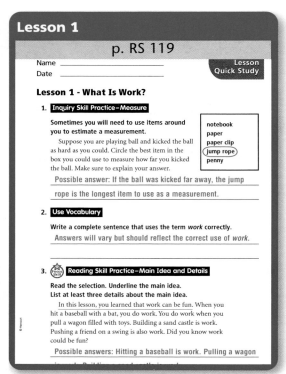

Lesson 1

p. RS 119

Name _____
Date _____

Lesson Quick Study

Lesson 1 - What Is Work?

1. **Inquiry Skill Practice–Measure**

Sometimes you will need to use items around you to estimate a measurement.

Suppose you are playing ball and kicked the ball as hard as you could. Circle the best item in the box you could use to measure how far you kicked the ball. Make sure to explain your answer.

notebook
paper
paper clip
jump rope
penny

Possible answer: If the ball was kicked far away, the jump rope is the longest item to use as a measurement.

2. **Use Vocabulary**

Write a complete sentence that uses the term *work* correctly.
Answers will vary but should reflect the correct use of *work*.

3. **Reading Skill Practice–Main Idea and Details**

Read the selection. Underline the main idea.
List at least three details about the main idea.

In this lesson, you learned that work can be fun. When you hit a baseball with a bat, you do work. You do work when you pull a wagon filled with toys. Building a sand castle is work. Pushing a friend on a swing is also work. Did you know work could be fun?

Possible answers: Hitting a baseball is work. Pulling a wagon

Use with **Student Edition** pp. 526–533.

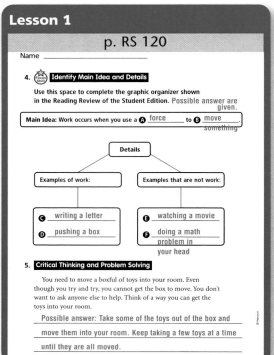

Lesson 1

p. RS 120

Name _____

4. **Identify Main Idea and Details**

Use this space to complete the graphic organizer shown in the Reading Review of the Student Edition. Possible answer are given.

Main Idea: Work occurs when you use a Ⓐ force to Ⓑ move something.

Details

Examples of work:
Ⓒ writing a letter
Ⓓ pushing a box

Examples that are not work:
Ⓔ watching a movie
Ⓕ doing a math problem in your head

5. **Critical Thinking and Problem Solving**

You need to move a boxful of toys into your room. Even though you try and try, you cannot get the box to move. You don't want to ask anyone else to help. Think of a way you can get the toys into your room.

Possible answer: Take some of the toys out of the box and move them into your room. Keep taking a few toys at a time until they are all moved.

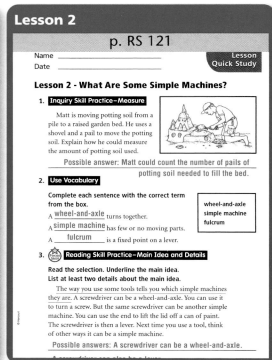

Lesson 2

p. RS 121

Name _____
Date _____

Lesson Quick Study

Lesson 2 - What Are Some Simple Machines?

1. **Inquiry Skill Practice–Measure**

Matt is moving potting soil from a pile to a raised garden bed. He uses a shovel and a pail to move the potting soil. Explain how he could measure the amount of potting soil used.

Possible answer: Matt could count the number of pails of potting soil needed to fill the bed.

2. **Use Vocabulary**

Complete each sentence with the correct term from the box.

wheel-and-axle
simple machine
fulcrum

A wheel-and-axle turns together.
A simple machine has few or no moving parts.
A fulcrum is a fixed point on a lever.

3. **Reading Skill Practice–Main Idea and Details**

Read the selection. Underline the main idea.
List at least two details about the main idea.

The way you use some tools tells you which simple machines they are. A screwdriver can be a wheel-and-axle. You can use it to turn a screw. But the same screwdriver can be another simple machine. You can use the end to lift the lid off a can of paint. The screwdriver is a lever. Next time you use a tool, think of other ways it can be a simple machine.

Possible answers: A screwdriver can be a wheel-and-axle.
A screwdriver can also be a lever.

Use with **Student Edition** pp. 534–543.

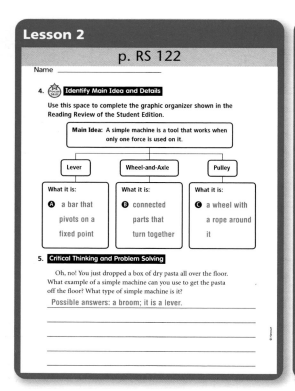

Lesson 2

p. RS 122

Name _____

4. **Identify Main Idea and Details**

Use this space to complete the graphic organizer shown in the Reading Review of the Student Edition.

Main Idea: A simple machine is a tool that works when only one force is used on it.

Lever — What it is: Ⓐ a bar that pivots on a fixed point

Wheel-and-Axle — What it is: Ⓑ connected parts that turn together

Pulley — What it is: Ⓒ a wheel with a rope around it

5. **Critical Thinking and Problem Solving**

Oh, no! You just dropped a box of dry pasta all over the floor. What example of a simple machine can you use to get the pasta off the floor? What type of simple machine is it?

Possible answers: a broom; it is a lever.

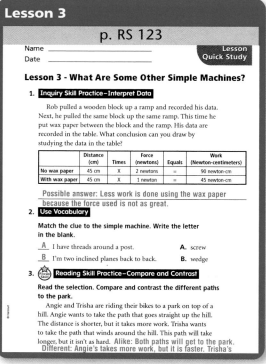

Lesson 3

p. RS 123

Name _____
Date _____

Lesson Quick Study

Lesson 3 - What Are Some Other Simple Machines?

1. **Inquiry Skill Practice–Interpret Data**

Rob pulled a wooden block up a ramp and recorded his data. Next, he pulled the same block up the same ramp. This time he put wax paper between the block and the ramp. His data are recorded in the table. What conclusion can you draw by studying the data in the table?

	Distance (cm)	Times	Force (newtons)	Equals	Work (Newton-centimeters)
No wax paper	45 cm	X	2 newtons	=	90 newton-cm
With wax paper	45 cm	X	1 newton	=	45 newton-cm

Possible answer: Less work is done using the wax paper because the force used is not as great.

2. **Use Vocabulary**

Match the clue to the simple machine. Write the letter in the blank.

A I have threads around a post.   A. screw
B I'm two inclined planes back to back. B. wedge

3. **Reading Skill Practice–Compare and Contrast**

Read the selection. Compare and contrast the different paths to the park.

Angie and Trisha are riding their bikes to a park on top of a hill. Angie wants to take the path that goes straight up the hill. The distance is shorter, but it takes more work. Trisha wants to take the path that winds around the hill. This path will take longer, but it isn't as hard. Alike: Both paths will get to the park. Different: Angie's takes more work, but it is faster. Trisha's

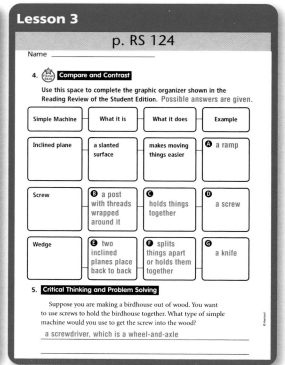

Lesson 3

p. RS 124

Name _____

4. **Compare and Contrast**

Use this space to complete the graphic organizer shown in the Reading Review of the Student Edition. Possible answers are given.

Simple Machine	What it is	What it does	Example
Inclined plane	a slanted surface	makes moving things easier	Ⓐ a ramp
Screw	Ⓑ a post with threads wrapped around it	Ⓒ holds things together	Ⓓ a screw
Wedge	Ⓔ two inclined planes place back to back	Ⓕ splits things apart or holds them together	Ⓖ a knife

5. **Critical Thinking and Problem Solving**

Suppose you are making a birdhouse out of wood. You want to use screws to hold the birdhouse together. What type of simple machine would you use to get the screw into the wood?

a screwdriver, which is a wheel-and-axle

Use with **Student Edition** pp. 544–551.

ASSESSMENT OPTIONS

Formal Assessment
- Chapter Review and Test Preparation SE pp. 555–556
- Chapter Test AG pp. 121–124

Standardized Test Preparation
- Reading Review and Test Preparations SE pp. 533, 543, 551

 Harcourt School Publishers Online Assessment
- Chapter test taking and automatic scoring
- Banks of items from which to build tests

Ongoing Assessment
- Assess Prior Knowledge
- Daily Inquiry Transparencies
- Teacher Edition questions throughout
- Focus Skill questions throughout SE
- Reaching All Learners throughout TE
- Reading Review SE pp. 311, 319, 327
- Observation Checklist AG

Performance Assessment
- Long-Option AG pp. AG 125–126
- Short-Option TE p. 557

Student Self–Assessment
- Investigate Self-Assessment Lab Manual
- Self-Assessment AG

Portfolio Assessment
- Using Portfolio Assessment AG
- Suggested work samples TE p. 556

Chapter Test

p. AG 121

Name _____
Date _____

Chapter Assessment

Work and Machines

Vocabulary 4 points each

Match each term in Column B with its meaning in Column A.

Column A		Column B
G	1. Two inclined planes placed back to back	A. fulcrum
D	2. A wheel with a rope around it	B. inclined plane
A	3. The fixed point on a lever	C. lever
E	4. A nail with threads wrapped around it	D. pulley
H	5. Using force to move an object	E. screw
B	6. A simple machine that makes moving and lifting things easier	F. simple machine
C	7. A bar that turns on a fixed point	G. wedge
F	8. A machine that needs only one force to make it work	H. work

Science Concepts 4 points each

Write the letter of the best choice.

D **9.** What type of simple machine is a screwdriver?
- A. inclined plane
- B. lever
- C. pulley
- D. wheel-and-axle

F **10.** Tasha is making a poster to show pictures of levers. Which object should **not** be on her poster?
- F. nail
- G. rake
- H. broom
- J. crowbar

p. AG 122

Name _____

D **11.** How is the shovel being used in this picture?
- A. as a wheel-and-axle
- B. as a wedge
- C. as an inclined plane
- D. as a lever

F **12.** A screw is made of a post and another kind of simple machine. What is that other kind of simple machine?
- F. inclined plane
- G. pulley
- H. wedge
- J. wheel-and-axle

B **13.** Levon's class is learning about simple machines. His teacher has written the names of four simple machines in a table on the board. As she points to each name, Levon gives an example of that machine. She writes down what he says. Which simple machine is correctly paired with its example?
- A. lever
- B. wedge
- C. pulley
- D. inclined plane

Simple Machine	Example
lever	wheelchair ramp
wedge	knife
pulley	screwdriver
inclined plane	seesaw

H **14.** A jar lid has threads. These threads help hold the lid tightly on the jar. What simple machine is a jar lid?
- F. lever
- G. pulley
- H. screw
- J. wedge

p. AG 123

Name _____

D **15.** Which of these is **not** an example of work?
- A. lifting a book
- B. opening a door
- C. drawing with a marker
- D. adding numbers in your head

F **16.** Mr. Lopez is telling his class about the human body. He describes how some athletes lift weights to make their arms stronger. An athlete holds a weight in her hand and bends her arm at the elbow. The elbow acts as a fulcrum.

In his example, the arm is a simple machine. Which machine is it?
- F. lever
- G. pulley
- H. screw
- J. wheel-and-axle

Inquiry Skills 8 points each

17. Megan needs to keep a door propped open. **Predict** which simple machine Megan will choose to do the job. Explain.

Megan will choose a wedge. She will push the wedge between the door and the floor. The wedge will keep the door open.

18. **Interpret** the pictures to decide which screw is easier to turn. Explain.

Screw A is easier to turn, because it has threads that are closer together.

p. AG 124

Name _____

Critical Thinking 10 points each

19. The pictures show two simple machines. Tell how the machines are alike.

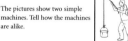

Possible answer: Both are simple machines that can be used to raise an object. When a person pulls down on one end of the pulley rope, the other end—with the bucket—moves upward. In the same way, when a person pushes down on one end of the lever, the other end—with the bucket—moves upward.

20. Luis has made two ramps. Ramp A is steeper than Ramp B. Which ramp will make it easier for Luis to move the block of wood? Tell how you know.

A   B

Possible answer: Ramp B will be easier, because it is less steep. This means that Luis will use less force to pull the block of wood up Ramp B than up Ramp A.

Performance Task

p. AG 125

Name _____
Date _____

Performance Assessment

Student Task

Lever and Fulcrum

Materials

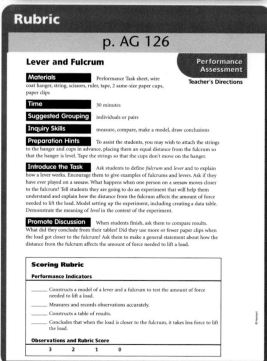

wire coat hanger   string   scissors   ruler

tape   2 same-size paper cups   paper clips

Procedure

1. Use string to hang a wire hanger by its top. The top is a fulcrum.
2. Measure to find the middle of the bottom part of the hanger. Mark the middle with a small piece of tape. This shows the position of the fulcrum on top of the hanger.
3. Label one cup L for load and the other cup F for force. Hang each cup an equal distance from the center of the hanger, as shown. Tape the strings so they don't slide.
4. Put 10 paper clips in Cup L. Add paper clips one by one to Cup F until the hanger is level. Record the number of paper clips you add.
5. Move Cup L 4 cm closer to the fulcrum mark, and retape it. Then repeat Step 4. Again, record the number of paper clips you add to make the hanger level. How does the distance from the fulcrum relate to the force that lifts the load?

Rubric

p. AG 126

Lever and Fulcrum

Performance Assessment

Teacher's Directions

Materials Performance Task sheet, wire coat hanger, string, scissors, ruler, tape, 2 same-size paper cups, paper clips

Time 30 minutes

Suggested Grouping individuals or pairs

Inquiry Skills measure, compare, make a model, draw conclusions

Preparation Hints To assist the students, you may wish to attach the strings to the hanger and cups in advance, placing them at an equal distance from the fulcrum so that the hanger is level. Tape the strings so that the cups don't move on the hanger.

Introduce the Task Ask students to define *fulcrum* and *lever* and to explain how a lever works. Encourage them to give examples of fulcrums and levers. Ask if they have ever played on a seesaw. What happens when one person on a seesaw moves closer to the fulcrum? Tell students they are going to do an experiment that will help them understand and explain how the distance from the fulcrum affects the amount of force needed to lift the load. Model setting up the experiment, including creating a data table. Demonstrate the meaning of *level* in the context of the experiment.

Promote Discussion When students finish, ask them to compare results. What did they conclude from their tables? Did they use more or fewer paper clips when the load got closer to the fulcrum? Ask them to make a general statement about how the distance from the fulcrum affects the amount of force needed to lift a load.

Scoring Rubric

Performance Indicators

____ Constructs a model of a lever and a fulcrum to test the amount of force needed to lift a load.

____ Measures and records observations accurately.

____ Constructs a table of results.

____ Concludes that when the load is closer to the fulcrum, it takes less force to lift the load.

Observations and Rubric Score

3	2	1	0

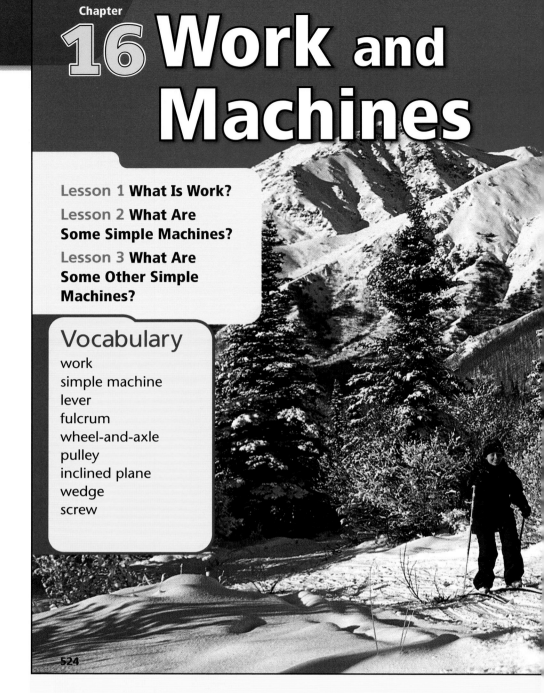

Chapter 16 Work and Machines

Lesson 1 **What Is Work?**

Lesson 2 **What Are Some Simple Machines?**

Lesson 3 **What Are Some Other Simple Machines?**

Vocabulary

work
simple machine
lever
fulcrum
wheel-and-axle
pulley
inclined plane
wedge
screw

524

Assess Prior Knowledge

Use the photograph to get students interested in the chapter topic. Ask students to examine the different objects in the photograph. You may want to point out that the skiers are skiing uphill.

Have students discuss their ideas about these questions: **What kinds of simple machines are being used here? What others can you think of?** Note their answers as a key to prior knowledge and misconceptions. (See also the Science Background.) Students may incorrectly identify the skis as levers and the poles as screws.

Later, as students read about simple machines in Lessons 2 and 3, they will have an opportunity to reevaluate the questions. They should then be able to identify the hill in this picture as an inclined plane, the poles as levers, and name all six kinds of simple machines.

Generate Science Questions

Have students write down questions they have about simple machines. Record students' questions on the board or on chart paper. Encourage students to refer to the list of questions as they complete the chapter.

PROFESSIONAL DEVELOPMENT Science Background To Address Misconceptions

What is a force?

Assess Prior Knowledge *Ask:* How would you define the word force? What is a force?

Students May Think of force as some imaginary power.

Scientists Explain that a force is a push or a pull exerted on one object by another object. If it is strong enough, a force can make a stationary object move or a moving object stop moving or change direction.

What You Can Do Ask students to suggest examples of pushes and pulls, such as kicking a soccer ball and towing a car. Explain that both the soccer ball and the car change speed and direction because a force is acting on them. You may want to solicit examples of each of the possible effects of a force listed above.

What do YOU wonder?

Simple machines can be found everywhere. What kinds of simple machines are being used here? What others can you think of?

525

Vocabulary

Opportunities for developing chapter vocabulary include:

- Develop Science Vocabulary strategies at point-of-use in the teaching plan
- Vocabulary questions in each Reading Review and the Chapter Review and Test
- Vocabulary sections on the Quick Study pages in **Reading Support and Homework**
- Vocabulary cards and activities and Vocabulary Power worksheet in **Reading Support and Homework**

Students can use the **Vocabulary Power** worksheet below to preview and explore more about the chapter vocabulary.

Reading Support and Homework

p. RS 118

Work and Machines

A. **Explore Word Meanings**

Think about the meaning of the underlined words. Then write your answer to each question.

1. A wedge is a machine that splits one thing into two. What is something that can be split apart with a wedge?
   Possible answer: Wood can be split with a wedge.

2. A fulcrum is the point that doesn't move on a lever. What is the fulcrum on a seesaw?
   The fulcrum is the stand that the seesaw rests on.

3. What would a carpenter use a screw for?
   A carpenter might use a screw to attach pieces of wood.

4. A rake and a broom are examples of levers. What is another example of a lever?
   Possible answer: a shovel

5. Name a rolling machine that uses a wheel-and-axle?
   Possible answer: a child's wagon

6. An inclined plane can help make moving and lifting things easier. Give an example of an inclined plane.
   Possible answer: a mountain trail

Reading Focus Skills

The content of each lesson is organized to focus on a key reading skill. The skill is reinforced by questions that appear at the end of each section and the graphic organizer at the end of the lesson. Additional practice is also provided in **Reading Support and Homework.**

The Reading Focus Skills for this chapter are:	
Lesson 1	Main Idea and Details
Lesson 2	Main Idea and Details
Lesson 3	Compare and Contrast
All Lessons	Draw Conclusions; Summarize

Strategies for other reading skills also appear in the Reading Mini-Lessons throughout the chapter.

ESL/ESOL Support

Spanish-speaking students may already be familiar with English words such as these cognates:

inclined plane/plano inclinado
machine/máquina
simple machine/máquina simple

Objectives

- Explain how a force can cause an object to move.
- Define *work.*
- Identify what is needed to measure work.

Transparency DI 51

Electronic Transparency DI 3012

Daily Inquiry

Yarn Lengths

tape measure

Other Materials: yarn, scissors, paper, pencil

Review Skill: Measure, Predict

What to Do

- Cut three lengths of yarn. Predict how many centimeters each piece is. Write your predictions on a chart.
- Measure each length of yarn three times. Record your measurements on a chart.

1 Introduce

Build on Prior Knowledge

Use the Fast Fact for a discussion starter about the lesson topic.

Why would you say the girl is doing work?

How would you define *work?*

Can work be fun?

When *Minutes* Count . . .

If time is short, consider these options.

Conduct the Investigate as a **whole-class demonstration**. Be sure students understand that you are applying a force to the checker, even though you are not touching it.

Use the Activity Video/DVD to model the Investigate. After previewing, students can conduct the Investigate in small groups.

Lesson **1**

What Is Work?

Fast Fact

Hard Work! This girl weighs less than the dog. However, she does work and uses simple machines to pull him through the park. In the Investigate, you will also use work to move an object.

526

Science Background

Work The term *work* has a scientific meaning that is different from its meaning in everyday conversation. In science, work is using a force to move an object. If no force is applied, no work has been done. If force is applied to an object that doesn't move, no work has been done on the object. Many activities that are usually thought of as work, such as solving a mental math problem, are not work in the scientific sense. Many activities that are usually thought of as fun, such as throwing a ball and swinging a bat, are work in the scientific sense. Measuring how much work has been done requires two pieces of information: how much force was applied and how far the object moved in the direction of the applied force.

Webliography
Keyword work
www.hspscience.com

Work with Me

Materials (Be Safe) safety goggles • graph paper • checker • drinking straw

Procedure

1. **Caution:** Put on the safety goggles. Work with a partner. On a piece of paper, make a start line. Place the checker on the paper behind the start.

2. Put one end of the straw in your mouth, and touch the other end to one edge of the checker. Blow hard through the straw.

3. Place the checker back at the same point on the paper. Have your partner press down on the checker while you repeat Step 2. **Record** your observations.

Step 2

Step 3

Draw Conclusions

1. Was the force of blowing on the checker the same or different each time? Explain.

2. Was the result the same or different each time? Explain.

3. **Inquiry Skill** Scientists often measure things during an experiment. How could you use the piece of paper to measure how much the checker moved?

Investigate Further

Predict how using a stack of two checkers might affect your results each time. Try it!

527

Inquiry Skill Mini-Lesson

Measure Display the Transparency. Lead students in a discussion about why making accurate measurements is important during investigations.

Inquiry Skill practice is provided in **Reading Support and Homework**.

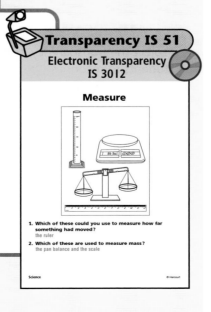

Transparency IS 51

Electronic Transparency IS 3012

Measure

1. Which of these could you use to measure how far something had moved?
the ruler

2. Which of these are used to measure mass?
the pan balance and the scale

Science

---

2 Teach

Video Segment 3012

Time 30 minutes

Grouping pairs

Alternative Materials

▶ lined paper instead of graph paper

Lab Manual pages can be used to record results. Inquiry Skill Tip and Self-Assessment are also provided.

Tips and Guided Inquiry

Students will find it easier to make the checker move if they crouch next to the desk and hold the straw horizontally.

How else could you make the checker move? Push it with the straw or a finger.

What is needed to make the checker move? A force must be applied to the checker.

Expected Results

Step 2: The first student moves the checker across the paper. Step 3: The other student cannot move the checker back.

Draw Conclusions

1. The force may or may not have been the same each time.

2. The checker probably moved the first time but not the second time, since the partner pushed down the second time.

3. Possible answer: Each row could be used as a unit of measure.

Investigate Further

Students can use this page in the *Lab Manual* for **Independent Inquiry**.

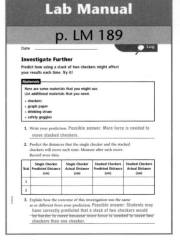

Lab Manual

p. LM 189

Date _____

Investigate Further
Predict how using a stack of two checkers might affect your results each time. Try it!

Materials
Here are some materials that you might use. List additional materials that you need.
• checkers
• graph paper
• drinking straw
• safety goggles

1. Write your prediction. Possible answer: More force is needed to move stacked checkers.

2. Predict the distances that the single checker and the stacked checkers will move each time. Measure after each move. Record your data.

Trial	Single Checker Predicted Distance (cm)	Single Checker Actual Distance (cm)	Stacked Checkers Predicted Distance (cm)	Stacked Checkers Actual Distance (cm)
1				
2				

3. Explain how the outcome of this investigation was the same as or different from your prediction. Possible answer: Students may have correctly predicted that a stack of two checkers would be harder to move because more force is needed to move two checkers than one checker.

LESSON 1 ▪ 527

2 Teach
continued

VOCABULARY For Vocabulary Cards and activities, see *Reading Support and Homework.*

SCIENCE CONCEPTS On the board, begin a list titled Work. Have students suggest examples of work, and add them to the list. Have students review and revise the list as they discuss the lesson.

READING FOCUS SKILL

MAIN IDEA AND DETAILS Tell students that the information in this lesson is organized to help them recognize a main idea and the details that support it. Use the Reading Skill Mini-Lesson below to discuss a strategy that students can use to identify the main idea and supporting details.

1 Critical Thinking

What happens to the jar lid? It doesn't move. **What do you do when solving a math problem? I sit still. What is similar about the two examples?** Neither the student nor the jar lid moves.

2 Interpret Visuals

What are the students pictured doing? They are solving a math problem and trying to remove the lid of a jar.

VOCABULARY
work p. 530

SCIENCE CONCEPTS
▶ what scientists mean by work

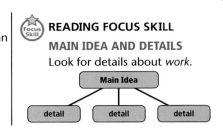
READING FOCUS SKILL
MAIN IDEA AND DETAILS
Look for details about *work*.

Different Types of Work

People use the word *work* all the time. Scientists do, too, but you might be surprised to find out what work means to a scientist.

Suppose your teacher asks you to solve a math problem in your head. You sit still and think hard. Then you get the answer. Your teacher says, "Good work!" However, a scientist would say that you did not do any work.

1 Suppose you want to open a jar. You twist the lid hard, but the lid doesn't move. You feel that you have done a lot of work. Again, however, a scientist would say you had done no work.

Is This Work?

◀ Solving a math problem isn't what scientists call work.

2

If the lid doesn't move, no work is being done. ▶

528

Reading Skill Mini-Lesson

MAIN IDEA AND DETAILS

Project the transparency. Guide students to recognize the main idea and to understand how each of the remaining sentences provides a supporting detail.

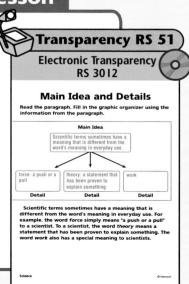

Transparency RS 51

Electronic Transparency
RS 3012

Main Idea and Details

Read the paragraph. Fill in the graphic organizer using the information from the paragraph.

Main Idea

Scientific terms sometimes have a meaning that is different from the word's meaning in everyday use.

force: a push or a pull	theory: a statement that has been proven to explain something	work
Detail	**Detail**	**Detail**

Scientific terms sometimes have a meaning that is different from the word's meaning in everyday use. For example, the word *force* simply means "a push or a pull" to a scientist. To a scientist, the word *theory* means a statement that has been proven to explain something. The word *work* also has a special meaning to scientists.

Science

1. MAIN IDEA AND DETAILS Draw and complete this graphic organizer.

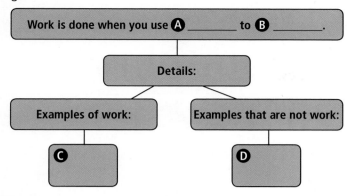

Work is done when you use **A** _____ to **B** _____.

Details:

Examples of work:

Examples that are not work:

C

D

2. SUMMARIZE Use the graphic organizer to write a lesson summary.

3. DRAW CONCLUSIONS Heather wants to carry her laundry basket to the washer. It is too heavy for her to pick up. What can she do to get the laundry to the washer?

4. VOCABULARY Write an example of work being done.

Test Prep

5. Which of these is not an example of work?
   A. sitting and reading
   B. playing fetch with a dog
   C. pulling a chair across a room
   D. pushing a box of books across the floor

Links

Writing

Expository
Think about community workers. List two or three workers who do things that scientists would call work. Write a **description** of how the workers' jobs include work.

Art

Working Art
Make a drawing of someone doing work. Then, on the back of your paper, list the ways you did work while you were making the drawing.

 For more links and activities, go to www.hspscience.com

533

---

3 Assess and Extend

Graphic Organizer
Transparency GO 51
Electronic Transparency IS 3012

1. A force; **B** move something; **C** Answers should include examples in which an object is being moved. **D** Answers should include examples in which an object is *not* being moved.

2. Possible answer: Work happens when a force moves an object.

3. Possible responses: Heather could take some clothes out of the basket so she can carry it and then make a second trip to the washer. She could also get someone to help her so there would be enough force to move the basket.

4. Check students' examples.

5. A, sitting still and waiting

Links

Writing If students need help getting started, suggest occupations such as construction workers, mail carriers, warehouse workers, and people who deliver appliances and furniture. Then have students pick two or three of these workers and tell how they do things that scientists would describe as work.

 Students can consult *Writing Models* in **Teaching Resources** as they complete the link. Rubrics are also provided.

Lesson Quick Study

The Lesson Quick Study in **Reading Support and Homework** provides the opportunity for students to practice inquiry skills, review lesson vocabulary, apply reading skills, and use critical thinking and problem solving. Students can use the second page of the Lesson Quick Study to complete the graphic organizer from the Reading Review. The graphic organizer is also available on overhead and electronic transparencies.

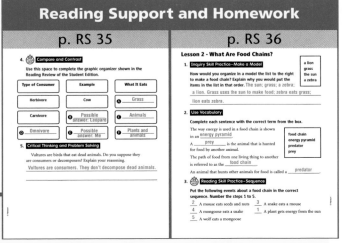

Reading Support and Homework

p. RS 35

4. Compare and Contrast
Use this space to complete the graphic organizer shown in the Reading Review of the Student Edition.

Type of Consumer	Example	What It Eats
Herbivore	Cow	**A** Grass
Carnivore	**B** Possible answer: Leopard	**C** Animals
D Omnivore	**E** Possible answer: Me	Plants and animals

5. Critical Thinking and Problem Solving
Vultures are birds that eat dead animals. Do you suppose they are consumers or decomposers? Explain your reasoning.
Vultures are consumers. They don't decompose dead animals.

p. RS 36

Lesson 2 - What Are Food Chains?

1. Inquiry Skill Practice–Make a Model
How would you organize in a model the list to the right to make a food chain? Explain why you would put the items in the list in that order. The sun; grass; a zebra; a lion. Grass uses the sun to make food; zebra eats grass; lion eats zebra.

a lion
grass
the sun
a zebra

2. Use Vocabulary
Complete each sentence with the correct term from the box.
The way energy is used in a food chain is shown in an energy pyramid
A prey is the animal that is hunted for food by another animal.
The path of food from one living thing to another is referred to as the food chain
An animal that hunts other animals for food is called a predator

food chain
energy pyramid
predator
prey

3. Reading Skill Practice–Sequence
Put the following events about a food chain in the correct sequence. Number the steps 1 to 5.
_2_ A mouse eats seeds and nuts   _3_ A snake eats a mouse
_4_ A mongoose eats a snake   _1_ A plant gets energy from the sun
_5_ A wolf eats a mongoose

Objectives

- Explain the advantages and disadvantages of performing a task with and without the help of a machine.
- Define *simple machine*.
- Describe a lever, a wheel-and-axle, and a pulley.

Transparency DI51

Electronic Transparency DI 3013

Daily Inquiry

Look at This!

 forceps, hand lens

Other Materials: penny, other small objects

Review Skill: Observe

What to Do
- Use the forceps to gently pick up one of the objects. Observe it closely. Use the hand lens to observe it. Record your observations. Repeat for other objects.
- What else might you observe in this way?

1 Introduce

Build on Prior Knowledge

Use the Fast Fact for a discussion starter about the lesson topic.

When *Minutes* Count . . .

If time is short, consider these options.

Conduct the Investigate as a **whole-class demonstration**.

Use the Activity Video/DVD to model . After previewing, conduct the Investigate in small groups.

Lesson **2**

What Are Some Simple Machines?

Fast Fact

Important Levers We use levers to do many things. Did you know that the nutcracker you use to crack a nut is a lever? In the investigate you will learn more about the importance of levers.

534

 Science Background

PROFESSIONAL DEVELOPMENT

Simple Machines A simple machine has few or no moving parts and requires only one force (for example, to use a pulley, you just pull on the rope). Simple machines are often classified into two groups. The ones in this lesson—the lever, wheel-and-axle, and pulley—involve turning around a central point. The ones in the next lesson—the inclined plane, wedge, and screw—involve a sloping surface.

Work has two components: force and distance. Some simple machines decrease the force required but increase the distance. Others increase the force required but decrease the distance. The amount of work done doesn't change, but changing the force and the distance can make a task easier.

Webliography
Key Word simple machines
www.hspscience.com

Help from Simple Machines

Materials
- measuring spoon
- jar lid
- white rice and brown rice, uncooked
- forceps
- two paper plates

Procedure

1. Measure out one tablespoon of white rice. Place it in the jar lid. Do the same with the wild or brown rice.

2. Mix the two types of rice in the lid.

3. Use your fingers to separate the types of rice. **Record** your observations.

4. Put the rice you separated back in the lid. Mix the rice again.

5. This time, use the forceps to separate the types of rice. **Record** your observations.

Step 3

Step 5

Draw Conclusions

1. Which way of separating the rice grains was easier? Why?

2. Which would be a safer way of handling food, using your fingers or using forceps?

3. **Inquiry Skill** Would using fingers or forceps make a difference if time was important in completing this task? Repeat the Investigate and **measure** the time.

Investigate Further

You have measured how long it takes to separate the rice. **Compare** your time with 4 other classmates by making a bar graph. Were there differences? Why do you think so?

535

Inquiry Skill Mini-Lesson

Predict Remind students that this skill involves careful observation of what is currently happening, combined with prior knowledge both of science facts and of occurrences in everyday life. Display the Transparency, and discuss the questions.

Inquiry Skill practice is provided in **Reading Support and Homework**.

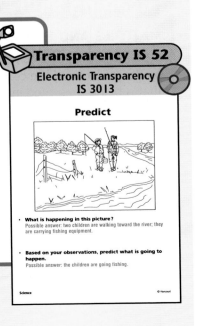

Transparency IS 52

Electronic Transparency IS 3013

Predict

- **What is happening in this picture?**
  Possible answer: two children are walking toward the river; they are carrying fishing equipment.

- **Based on your observations, predict what is going to happen.**
  Possible answer: the children are going fishing.

Science

© Harcourt

---

2 Teach

Video Segment 3013

Time 30 minutes

Grouping individuals

Lab Manual pages can be used to record results. Inquiry Skill Tips and Self-Assessment are also provided.

Tips and Guided Inquiry

Some students may have trouble grasping a rice grain with the forceps. Suggest they hold the forceps close to the tips for better control.

Why was it important to try picking up grains with your fingers before you used the forceps? Students may point out that using their fingers helped them compare whether using the forceps was easier.

Expected Results

Step 3: Students should be able to separate a few grains. Step 5: Students may be able to separate more grains because it is easier to pick up individual grains by using the forceps.

Draw Conclusions

1. Using forceps should be easier. The forceps have a smaller grasp to separate the rice grains.

2. forceps (as long as they are clean)

3. Possible answer: The forceps might take longer to use, but there might be fewer mistakes in the separation.

Investigate Further

Students can use this page in the *Lab Manual* for **Independent Inquiry**.

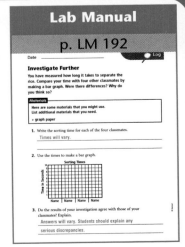

Lab Manual

p. LM 192

Date _____

Investigate Further
You have measured how long it takes to separate the rice. Compare your time with four other classmates by making a bar graph. Were there differences? Why do you think so?

Materials
Here are some materials that you might use. List additional materials that you need.
- graph paper

1. Write the sorting time for each of the four classmates.
   Times will vary.

2. Use the times to make a bar graph.

   Sorting Times

3. Do the results of your investigation agree with those of your classmates? Explain.
   Answers will vary. Students should explain any serious discrepancies.

2 Teach
continued

VOCABULARY For Vocabulary cards and activities, see Reading Support and Homework.

SCIENCE CONCEPTS Have students turn each statement into a question and then use their prior knowledge to suggest responses. List the responses on the board. Have students review and revise them as they discuss the lesson.

 READING FOCUS SKILL

MAIN IDEA AND DETAILS Tell students that the information in this lesson is organized to help them identify a main idea and the details that support it.

Key Science Concepts

What are some examples of machines? leaf blower, car, dishwasher, bicycle

What is an example of a simple machine? Possible answer: a rake

What is the main difference between a leaf blower and a simple machine? A leaf blower has many moving parts. A simple machine, such as a rake, has only one.

VOCABULARY	SCIENCE CONCEPTS	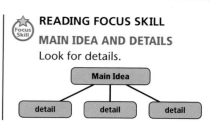 READING FOCUS SKILL
simple machine p. 537	▶ what simple machines are	**MAIN IDEA AND DETAILS** Look for details.
lever p. 538	▶ how levers, wheel-and-axles, and pulleys make work easier	
fulcrum p. 538		
wheel-and-axle p. 540		
pulley p. 542		

Simple Machines

Imagine that the lawn is covered with leaves. Your job is to clear them away. You grab a handful of leaves and put them in a trash bag. Then you pick up another handful of leaves, and another, and another. This is going to take a very long time!

1 The job might go faster if you used a machine. A machine is anything that changes the way work is done. For example, a leaf blower is a machine. This machine would make clearing up the leaves easy and fast.

Other examples of machines include cars, dishwashers, and bicycles. These machines have many parts. All the parts together make the machines work.

This leaf blower has an engine. The engine supplies the force to do the work.

Reading Skill Mini-Lesson

 **TITLES AND HEADINGS**

Titles and headings can help a reader understand the content that is being presented in a passage. Project the transparency, and have volunteers read each section aloud. Then have the class suggest a title for the article and a heading for each section.

Transparency RS 52

Electronic Transparency RS 3013

Using Titles and Headings

Read the paragraphs below and add a title for the page and a heading for each paragraph.

Possible answer: Work

Possible answer: The Meaning of Work

In science, the word *work* has a special meaning. It means using a force to move an object. The word has several other meanings in ordinary conversation. But to a scientist, it only has one.

Possible answer: Force and Distance

Work can be broken into two parts: force and distance. If you move a heavier object, you have to use more force. The more force you use, the more work you do. If you want to move an object farther, you have to apply the force over a greater distance. The greater the distance, the more work you do.

Possible answer: Machines and Work

A machine is anything that changes the way work is done. A machine might allow you to use less force to move an object. That would make the work easier. However, you would have to apply that smaller force over a greater distance. So you would still do the same amount of work. The machine made the work easier, but it didn't change the amount of work you have to do.

Science

Not all machines have a lot of parts. If you don't have a leaf blower, you could use a rake to help you clear up the leaves. A rake is a machine, even though it has no engine. A rake is an example of a **simple machine**.

A simple machine has few or no moving parts. The rake has no moving parts. To use a simple machine, you apply only one force. To use a rake, you pull on it with one hand.

MAIN IDEA AND DETAILS What is a simple machine?

3

4 ◄ With the rake, the boy provides the force that gets the work done.

Math in Science
Interpret Data

5

Gavin raked all the leaves in the yard. Then he scattered them across the yard and used a leaf blower. How much time did using the leaf blower save?

Clearing Leaves	
Leaf Blower	🍂
Rake	🍂 🍂 🍂

Key: Each 🍂 = 1 hour

537

---

2 ## Develop Science Vocabulary

simple machine Explain that *simple machine* is a compound term. Point out that the leaf blower has many parts. Learning to use and repair it would be difficult. By contrast, the rake is one piece. It is easier to use and repair. A *machine* is anything people use to make work easier. A *simple machine* has few parts and can be used to make work easier. A rake is a simple machine.

3 ## Inquiry Skills

Observe and Infer Ask students to observe the picture carefully. **Where do you hold the rake?** the middle of the handle **Which part of the rake does useful work?** the end of the rake; the tines

4 ## Critical Thinking

Where does the energy come from to: operate a dishwasher? electricity **a simple machine, such as a shovel?** the person using it

5 ## Interpret Data

Answer: 10 minutes

6 ## Main Idea and Details

a machine with few or no moving parts

LESSON 2 ▪ 537

Develop Science Vocabulary

lever Students may be familiar with this word as part of the term *leverage*. Point out that leverage is increased ability to make something happen. A lever is a machine that increases a person's ability to do work.

fulcrum Students may not understand that even though the location of a fulcrum is fixed, its location varies with the type of lever. For each example on these pages, have students identify which parts of the lever move and which do not.

Inquiry Skills

Compare **Compare the levers shown on these pages.** Students should notice that the fulcrums are in different places of the various levers. Some students may notice that the force a person exerts on the lever is not always in the same direction as the force the lever exerts on an object.

The Lever

7 A rake is a lever. A **lever** is a bar that pivots, or turns, on a fixed point. A fixed point is a point that doesn't move. The fixed point on a lever is called the **fulcrum** (FUHL•kruhm).

Think about how you hold a rake when you use it. One hand holds the end of the handle. That hand stays still. It is the fulcrum. The other hand pulls the middle of the handle. The end of the rake gathers the leaves.

Your hand moves the middle of the rake's handle a certain distance. The end of the rake moves a greater distance, so it gathers more leaves. That's what makes the work easier.

Do all levers work this way? No, but a broom and a fishing pole are levers that work this way. So is your arm. Your elbow joint is the fulcrum.

A broom is a lever that helps you clean up an area more easily. Where is the fulcrum? ▼

fulcrum

Insta-Lab

Turn, Turn, Turn
Fold a chenille stick in half, and twist the halves together. Hold one end and twirl the stick. Then make two bends in the stick to form a crank (a kind of wheel-and-axle). Turn the crank to twirl the stick. Which way is easier?

8

538

PROFESSIONAL DEVELOPMENT Science Background To Address Misconceptions

How are levers used?

Assess Prior Knowledge *Ask:* What other example can you give me of a lever being used?

Students May Think they have a grasp on the application of the lever but still have difficulty communicating those applications.

Scientists Explain that there are many levers that are not as simple as those listed here but that all levers are bars that pivot on a fixed point.

What You Can Do Have each student use a ruler to model the levers shown on these pages. For each one, explain where the fulcrum is, where the force is applied, and where the work is done. Allow students time to examine their models and come up with real-life examples.

Source: Stepans, J. *Targeting Students' Science Misconceptions.* Riverview, FL: Idea Factory, Inc. 1994

Inclined to Help

Materials (Be Safe) safety goggles • board • chair • tape measure
• string • toy car • spring scale

Procedure

1 **CAUTION:** Put on safety goggles. Use the board to make a ramp from the floor to the chair seat. Measure to find the distance from the floor to the seat. Measure straight up and along the ramp. Record both distances.

	Distance (cm)	Times	Force (newtons)	Equals	Work (newton-cm)
No Ramp		x		=	
Ramp		x		=	

2 Tie a loop of string to the toy car. Attach the spring scale to the string.

3 Hold on to the spring scale, and lift the car from the floor straight up to the chair seat. Record the force shown on the scale.

4 Hold on to the spring scale, and slowly pull the car up the ramp from the floor to the chair seat. Record the force shown on the scale.

Step 4

Draw Conclusions

1. How did the ramp affect the force needed to lift the car?

2. How did the ramp affect the distance?

3. **Inquiry Skill** Scientists interpret data to draw conclusions. What conclusions can you draw from your data?

Investigate Further

What might affect the force needed to lift the car? **Plan and conduct a simple investigation** to test some variables.

545

Inquiry Skill Mini-Lesson

Interpret Data Remind students that *data* means "information." Data can be acquired by measuring something, by performing an experiment and recording the results, or simply by observation. Display the Transparency, and discuss the questions.

Inquiry Skill practice is provided in *Reading Support and Homework*.

Transparency IS 53

Electronic Transparency IS 3014

Interpret Data

1. **Which carton has more mass?**
Students should observe that the carton marked "27 kg" has more mass.

2. **Which carton requires more force in order to make it move?**
Students should realize that the carton with more mass will require more force to move.

3. **Which girl has to do more work in order to put the carton in the van?**
Students should realize that they do not have enough information to answer this question. The two components of work are force and distance. The girl with the carton of feathers used less force to move her carton, but without knowing how far she moved it, it is impossible to determine how much work she did.

Science   © Harcourt

---

2 Teach

Video Segment 3014

Time 30 minutes

Grouping individuals

Alternative Materials

▶ corrugated cardboard instead of a board

Lab Manual pages can be used to record results. Inquiry Skill Tip and Self-Assessment are also provided.

Tips and Guided Inquiry

Students may have difficulty reading the spring scale. Suggest they stand at the side of the chair opposite the ramp and pull the scale toward them. The scale should be pulled parallel to the ramp as shown in the photo for Step 4.

What does the reading on the spring scale mean? how much force is being used to move the car

Would it be helpful to repeat the procedure? Why? Yes; repeating the procedure will either confirm the first results or reveal an error.

Expected Results

Step 4: The reading on the scale should be lower than it was in Step 3.

Draw Conclusions

1. It reduced the force needed.

2. It increased.

3. A ramp changed the work by increasing the distance and decreasing the force. It didn't change the amount of work done.

Investigate Further

Students can use this page in the *Lab Manual* for **Independent Inquiry**.

Lab Manual

p. LM 195

Investigate Further
What might affect the force needed to lift the car?
Plan and conduct a simple investigation to test some ideas.

Materials
Here are some materials that you might use.
List additional materials that you need.
- safety goggles   - string
- board   - toy car
- chair   - spring scale
- tape measure

1. Write a prediction for your investigation.
Answers will vary depending on the type of investigation.
Students should predict the effects of different variables on
the amount of force needed to lift the car.

2. Use the following table to record your measurements.

Method of Lifting	Force (newtons)

3. What can you conclude from your results?
Answers will depend on the variables students test. Possible
answer: Increasing the length of a ramp means less force is
needed to lift the car.

LESSON 3 ▪ 545

2 Teach
continued

VOCABULARY For Vocabulary cards and activities, see *Reading Support and Homework.*

SCIENCE CONCEPTS Have students look at the illustrations in the chapter to see where the science concepts might be addressed.

READING FOCUS SKILL

COMPARE AND CONTRAST Tell students that the information in this lesson is organized to help them compare and contrast science facts and ideas.

1 Critical Thinking

Draw a right triangle on the board to represent a ramp. Which would require less force—lifting a heavy box straight up or dragging it up along the ramp? dragging it up along the ramp

Draw a staircase with the same slope as the ramp. Which would require less force—lifting a heavy box straight up or dragging it up along the stairs? Both would require the same amount of force. Why? You'd still have to lift the box straight up each step, and the total vertical distance is the same each way.

VOCABULARY	SCIENCE CONCEPTS	**READING FOCUS SKILL**
inclined plane p. 546	▶ how inclined planes, wedges, and screws are used	**COMPARE AND CONTRAST** Look for ways inclined planes, wedges, and screws are alike and different.
wedge p. 548		
screw p.550		

alike ——— different

The Inclined Plane

Suppose you wanted to get to the top of this hill. You could take the direct route and ride up the hill. That would be hard to do, and you might be very tired after you did it.

Instead, you could ride up the path that spirals around the hill. The path is longer than the route up the hill, but it's easier to ride up a gentle slope.

The path is an inclined plane. An **inclined plane** is a simple machine that makes moving and lifting things easier.

> Going up the straight path doesn't take as long, but it is more work. Taking the winding path is less work, but it takes longer..

546

Reading Skill Mini-Lesson

 USING CONTEXT CLUES

Remind students that many words have more than one meaning. Then ask them to recall the different meanings of *work* discussed in Lesson 1. Tell students that to determine which meaning of a word is intended, the reader can use context clues within the sentence. Project the transparency, and have students determine the meaning of the underlined word in each sentence.

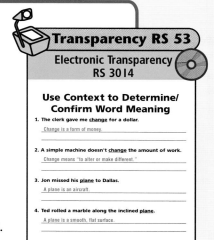

Transparency RS 53

Electronic Transparency RS 3014

Use Context to Determine/ Confirm Word Meaning

1. The clerk gave me <u>change</u> for a dollar.
   Change is a form of money.

2. A simple machine doesn't <u>change</u> the amount of work.
   Change means "to alter or make different."

3. Jon missed his <u>plane</u> to Dallas.
   A plane is an aircraft.

4. Ted rolled a marble along the inclined <u>plane</u>.
   A plane is a smooth, flat surface.

Science   © Harcourt

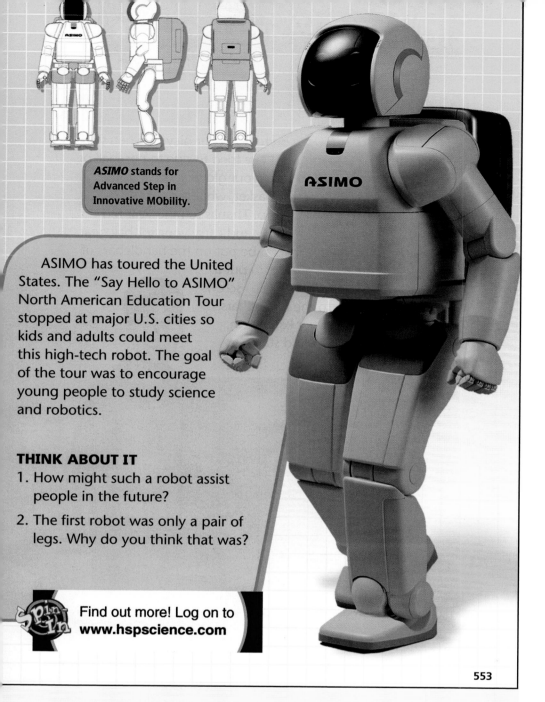

ASIMO stands for Advanced Step in Innovative MObility.

ASIMO has toured the United States. The "Say Hello to ASIMO" North American Education Tour stopped at major U.S. cities so kids and adults could meet this high-tech robot. The goal of the tour was to encourage young people to study science and robotics.

THINK ABOUT IT

1. How might such a robot assist people in the future?
2. The first robot was only a pair of legs. Why do you think that was?

Find out more! Log on to **www.hspscience.com**

553

3 Wrap Up and Assess

Think About It

1. The robot may be able to help disabled people with household tasks like cleaning and maybe cooking. It could carry or help move heavy things. It might answer the door and serve as protection for a family.

2. Because a whole robot is a very complicated machine. By building just the legs, researchers could test a machine to see if it could balance and walk before they added other, more difficult, tasks.

Writing Link

Expository Writing Have students write a newspaper release that describes the development of ASIMO as well as lists some of the jobs for which he will be used in the future. Have students illustrate the article using either computer-drawn art or their own drawings.

Inspire Inquiry

Inquiry starts with wonder and with asking questions. Sometimes the questions are just about things people want to know. Sometimes they are problems that people want to solve.

- Have students suggest questions that scientists might have been asking as they began to design and build this robot.
- Ask students what questions they have about robots. List their questions on the board.
- Ask students to suggest ways that they might begin to answer the questions they have asked. List the steps. Encourage interested students to explore more and to develop ways to answer their questions through research and experimentation.

Objectives

- Describe how Austin Meggitt contributed to science.
- Discuss the science knowledge and processes that Austin used to solve a problem.

1 Introduce

Preview/Set a Purpose

Ask students, **Who can be a scientist?** Students may answer that scientists have a college education. Then have them look at the picture. Ask them if Austin is a scientist.

2 Teach

The Work of Scientists

Have students conclude that an inventor is a kind of scientist.

What problem did Austin Meggitt face? He needed to carry a lot of gear on his bicycle and wanted to do so safely.

What difficulties do you think Austin might have had? Some of his designs may have failed. He may not have had the materials or tools that he needed.

What did Austin need to know to build his baseball gear carrier? He had to understand how simple machines worked. He needed to know what he wanted to do and how to do it most simply.

3 Wrap Up and Assess

Think About It

Have students infer that they can be scientists.

How did Austin act like a scientist? He identified a problem and used what he knew to think of ways to solve the problem. He probably experimented with different designs until he finally found a solution.

How can you be a scientist? I can be a scientist by thinking of questions and using what I already know to find the answers.

People

Bikes and Baseball Bats

You know how hard it can be to ride your bicycle when you have a lot to carry. Maybe you have tried to ride to baseball or softball practice and had to carry your glove and bat at the same time. If you don't have a basket, what can you do?

Now there is something to help. Thanks to nine-year old Austin Meggitt you can ride safely and carry your softball gear. Austin invented a carrier that can be put on the handlebars of any bike. The carrier has a place to put a baseball bat, glove, and ball. It uses screws and clamps to attach to the handlebars. This invention lets the rider keep both hands on the handlebars and stay safe while riding.

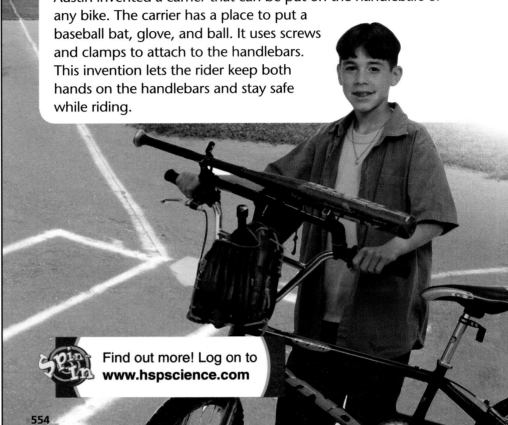

 Find out more! Log on to www.hspscience.com

554

SCIENCE Projects
for Home or School

You Can Do It!

Quick and Easy Project

Making an Elevator

Procedure

1 Tape the pulley wheel to the underside of a desk or table.

2 Pass the string over it.

3 Tape a paper cup to each end of the string.

4 Place pennies in one cup and then in the other. Watch your elevator move.

Materials

- pulley
- 2 paper cups
- string
- pennies
- tape

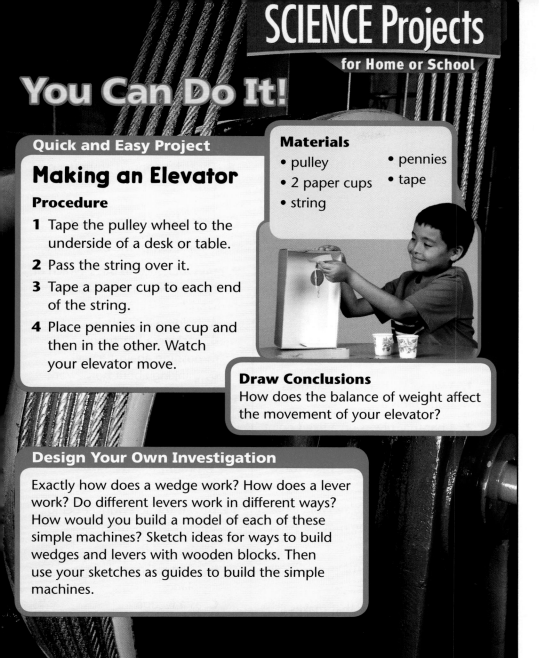

Draw Conclusions

How does the balance of weight affect the movement of your elevator?

Design Your Own Investigation

Exactly how does a wedge work? How does a lever work? Do different levers work in different ways? How would you build a model of each of these simple machines? Sketch ideas for ways to build wedges and levers with wooden blocks. Then use your sketches as guides to build the simple machines.

555

You Can Do It!

Quick and Easy Project
Making an Elevator

Objectives

- Use a model to understand how a pulley works.

• **Tips and Hints**

You can use any ledge or overhang to suspend the pulley.

• **Draw Conclusions**

When the weights are balanced, the cups do not move. When one cup is heavier, it moves down and pulls the other cup up.

• **Extend the Activity**

Have interested students experiment with the pulleys to see if they can find a way to make an "elevator" car go up and down without changing the weight of the car.

Design Your Own Investigation
How Do Simple Machines Work?

Objectives

- Design and conduct a simple investigation to determine how wedges and levers work.

Inspire Inquiry

Use this activity as an at-home investigation or suggestion for a science fair project. Have students use the investigation for a starting point for developing their own questions and ideas for researching simple machines. Ask students to share their plans and ideas with you and the class and work together to make the investigation procedure better.

A reproducible copy of this page is provided in *Teaching Resources*.

Vocabulary Review (5 pts. each)

1. pulley
2. lever
3. wedge
4. simple machine
5. work
6. inclined plane
7. fulcrum
8. screw

Check Understanding (5 pts. each)

9. B, packing a lunch box
10. I, ramp
11. A, as a lever
12. H, lever
13. A, pulley
14. G, screw
15. D, wedge
16. G, seesaw

Vocabulary Review

Use the terms below to complete the sentences. The page numbers tell you where to look in the chapter if you need help.

work p. 528

simple machine p. 537

lever p. 538

fulcrum p. 538

pulley p. 542

inclined plane p. 546

wedge p. 548

screw p. 550

1. A wheel with a rope that goes around it is a _____.
2. A bar that pivots on a fixed point is a _____.
3. Two inclined planes back-to-back form a _____.
4. Anything that makes work easier and has few or no moving parts is a _____.
5. Using a force to move an object is known as _____.
6. A slanted surface that makes it easier to move objects is an _____.

7. When you use a shovel to pry up an object, the ground acts as a _____.
8. Threads wrapped around a post form a _____.

Check Understanding

Write the letter of the best choice.

9. **MAIN IDEA AND DETAILS** Which of the following is an example of work?
   A. holding a baseball
   B. packing a lunch box
   C. pushing against a wall
   D. thinking about homework

10. **COMPARE AND CONTRAST** Compare the simple machines. Which of the following is not a lever?
    F. broom   H. rake
    G. crowbar   J. ramp

11. How is the screwdriver being used in this picture?

    A. as a lever
    B. as an inclined plane
    C. as a wedge
    D. as a wheel-and-axle

Harcourt School Publishers
Online Assessment

Harcourt School Publishers Online Assessment provides even more options. For a preview, go to:
www.hspscience.com

Portfolio Assessment

Have students select their best work from the following suggestions:
- **Links,** pp. 533, 543, 551
- **Investigate,** p. 527, 535, 545
- **Insta-Lab,** p.532, 539, 550
- **Science Projects,** p. 555

See **Assessment Guide** pp. AGxx-AGxxiv.

12. What type of simple machine is a nutcracker?

   F. axle   **H.** lever
   G. inclined plane **J.** screw

13. What simple machine can you use to lift a can of paint to the second floor as you stand on the ground?

   A. pulley   **C.** wedge
   B. ramp   **D.** wheel-and-axle

14. What simple machine is made up of an inclined plane that winds around a post?

   F. fulcrum   **H.** wedge
   G. screw   **J.** wheel-and-axle

15. Leo is using a chisel to shape a piece of wood. What simple machine is he using?

   A. lever   **C.** ramp
   B. pulley   **D.** wedge

16. Which of these objects at a playground is an example of a lever?

   F. ladder   **H.** slide
   G. seesaw   **J.** swing

Inquiry Skills

17. Your teacher asks you to use classroom items to put together a simple machine. You see a ruler and a rubber eraser. What two simple machines could you make using these items? Draw what they would look like. **Compare**.

18. You kicked a soccer ball as far as you could. Explain how you could use a jump rope to **measure** how far the ball was kicked.

Critical Thinking

19. Angie and her family have reached the airport late. They must hurry to catch their flight. Is Angie doing work as she pulls her suitcase up a ramp? Explain.

20. In this picture, Kyle is pushing a large bundle of newspapers up a ramp. What could he do to lessen the amount of force he needs to apply?

Inquiry Skills (5 pts. each)

17. Check students' drawings. Possible answers: a seesaw with the rubber eraser as the fulcrum; a ramp in which the rubber eraser is the load being moved up the ramp

18. Possible response: You could place one end of the jump rope at the point where you kicked the ball and stretch it to also mark the place where the ball landed.

Critical Thinking (5 pts. each)

19. Yes; work is done if something moves when force is applied to it.

20. Possible response: He could make two smaller bundles of papers; he could get another person to help him move the newspapers up the ramp; he could use a ramp that is less steep (a longer ramp).

Chapter Test

See *Assessment Guide* pages AG25–30 for a Chapter Test and Performance Task, with rubric. Assessment options appear on page 152H.

Performance Assessment

Distance and Force

Have students investigate how the length of a ramp affects the force needed to move a rock. In the Investigate, students will use two ramps (made from books) that have the same height but different lengths. Students will make a table to record their data. Remind students to clearly state their conclusions.

Rubric for Performance Assessment

Preparation Provide two boards of different lengths, books, a rock, and a spring scale. Also provide string with which the students can tie the rock to the spring scale.

Scoring Rubric—Performance Indicators

_____ Builds two inclined planes, each having the same height but a different length.

_____ Uses a steady force to pull on the spring scale, moving the rock up the board at a steady speed.

_____ Records the height and length of each ramp and the amount of force needed to move the rock up each ramp.

_____ Concludes that the force needed to move an object up a ramp decreases as the length of the ramp increases.

Observations and Rubric Scores

    3   2   1   0

Teaching Notes

References
and
Resources

References and Resources

STUDENT EDITION REFERENCES

TEACHER RESOURCES

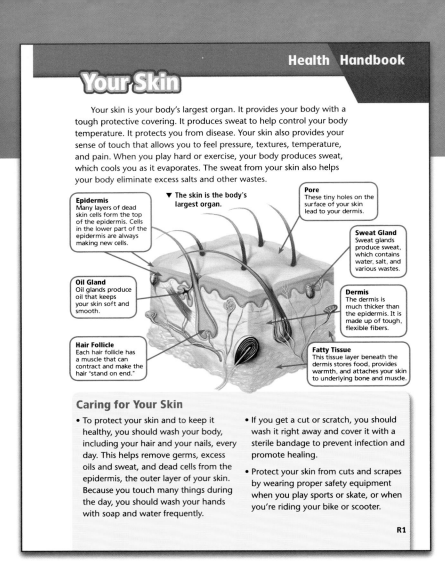

Your Skin

Your skin is your body's largest organ. It provides your body with a tough protective covering. It produces sweat to help control your body temperature. It protects you from disease. Your skin also provides your sense of touch that allows you to feel pressure, textures, temperature, and pain. When you play hard or exercise, your body produces sweat, which cools you as it evaporates. The sweat from your skin also helps your body eliminate excess salts and other wastes.

Epidermis
Many layers of dead skin cells form the top of the epidermis. Cells in the lower part of the epidermis are always making new cells.

▼ The skin is the body's largest organ.

Pore
These tiny holes on the surface of your skin lead to your dermis.

Sweat Gland
Sweat glands produce sweat, which contains water, salt, and various wastes.

Oil Gland
Oil glands produce oil that keeps your skin soft and smooth.

Dermis
The dermis is much thicker than the epidermis. It is made up of tough, flexible fibers.

Hair Follicle
Each hair follicle has a muscle that can contract and make the hair "stand on end."

Fatty Tissue
This tissue layer beneath the dermis stores food, provides warmth, and attaches your skin to underlying bone and muscle.

Caring for Your Skin

- To protect your skin and to keep it healthy, you should wash your body, including your hair and your nails, every day. This helps remove germs, excess oils and sweat, and dead cells from the epidermis, the outer layer of your skin. Because you touch many things during the day, you should wash your hands with soap and water frequently.

- If you get a cut or scratch, you should wash it right away and cover it with a sterile bandage to prevent infection and promote healing.

- Protect your skin from cuts and scrapes by wearing proper safety equipment when you play sports or skate, or when you're riding your bike or scooter.

R1

HEALTH BACKGROUND

Becoming tan is the skin's way of protecting itself from ultraviolet (UV) rays. Malanin, the pigment that gives skin its color, absorbs UV light. When the skin is exposed to UV rays, granules of melanin gather over the nuclei of skin cells and produce a shield that protects important genetic information in the nucleus from damage by UV light. Students may have the misconception that tanning in a tanning bed or under a sun lamp may be safer for skin than being out in the sun. The American Academy of Dermatology states that these alternative ways of tanning are just as damaging to skin as natural sunlight is.

ACTIVITIES

Design Sun Hats Have students draw designs for effective sun hats. The designs can be practical or imaginative. Encourage students to use commonly available materials to make models of their hats.

Investigate Sunscreens Suggest that students choose one brand of sunscreen and make charts to compare the relationships between the prices and the SPF numbers. Direct students to find the best value for each SPF and present their findings to the class.

Your Digestive System

Your digestive system is a series of interconnected organs that breaks down the food you eat and disposes of the leftover wastes your body does not need.

Mouth to Stomach

Digestion begins when you chew your food. Chewing your food breaks it up and mixes it with saliva. When you swallow, the softened food travels down your esophagus to your stomach where it is mixed with digestive juices. These are strong acids that continue the process of breaking your food down into the nutrients your body needs to stay healthy. Your stomach churns your food and turns it into a thick liquid.

Small Intestine and Liver

Your food leaves your stomach and goes into your small intestine. This organ is a long tube just below your stomach. Your liver is an organ that sends bile into your small intestine to continue the process of digesting fats in the food. The walls of the small intestine are lined with millions of small, finger-shaped bumps called villi. Tiny blood vessels in these bumps absorb nutrients from the food as it moves through the small intestine.

Large Intestine

When the food has traveled all the way through your small intestine, it passes into your large intestine. This last organ of your digestive system absorbs water from the food. The remaining wastes are held there until you go to the bathroom.

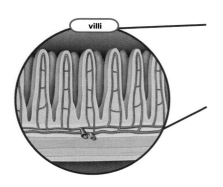

villi

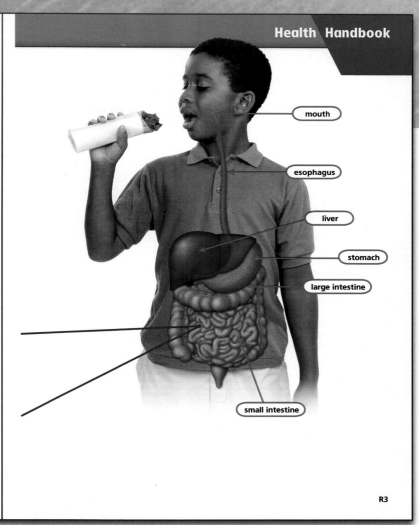

mouth

esophagus

liver

stomach

large intestine

small intestine

R2

R3

HEALTH BACKGROUND

Next to the esophagus lies the passage to the lungs called the trachea. If food "goes down the wrong way," a person can choke. Usually, a flap called the epiglottis moves across the trachea when you swallow, and food passes safely down to the stomach.

ACTIVITIES

Food Travels Have students cut a narrow balloon so that it is open on both ends. Have them put a wad of paper in one end and then squeeze the outside of the balloon to push the paper through and out the other end. Explain that this is similar to how your esophagus pushes food to your stomach.

Length of Intestines Point out that the longest part of the path through the digestive system is the small intestine (about 22 feet) and the large intestine (about 5 feet). Have students measure, cut, and label different colors of yarn to represent the correct lengths of a small and large intestines.

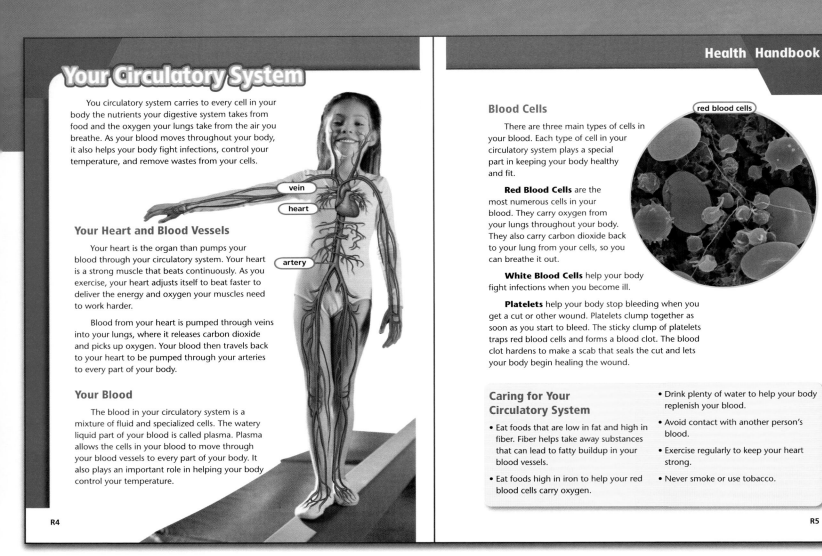

Your Circulatory System

You circulatory system carries to every cell in your body the nutrients your digestive system takes from food and the oxygen your lungs take from the air you breathe. As your blood moves throughout your body, it also helps your body fight infections, control your temperature, and remove wastes from your cells.

vein

heart

artery

Your Heart and Blood Vessels

Your heart is the organ than pumps your blood through your circulatory system. Your heart is a strong muscle that beats continuously. As you exercise, your heart adjusts itself to beat faster to deliver the energy and oxygen your muscles need to work harder.

Blood from your heart is pumped through veins into your lungs, where it releases carbon dioxide and picks up oxygen. Your blood then travels back to your heart to be pumped through your arteries to every part of your body.

Your Blood

The blood in your circulatory system is a mixture of fluid and specialized cells. The watery liquid part of your blood is called plasma. Plasma allows the cells in your blood to move through your blood vessels to every part of your body. It also plays an important role in helping your body control your temperature.

Blood Cells

red blood cells

There are three main types of cells in your blood. Each type of cell in your circulatory system plays a special part in keeping your body healthy and fit.

Red Blood Cells are the most numerous cells in your blood. They carry oxygen from your lungs throughout your body. They also carry carbon dioxide back to your lung from your cells, so you can breathe it out.

White Blood Cells help your body fight infections when you become ill.

Platelets help your body stop bleeding when you get a cut or other wound. Platelets clump together as soon as you start to bleed. The sticky clump of platelets traps red blood cells and forms a blood clot. The blood clot hardens to make a scab that seals the cut and lets your body begin healing the wound.

Caring for Your Circulatory System

- Eat foods that are low in fat and high in fiber. Fiber helps take away substances that can lead to fatty buildup in your blood vessels.
- Eat foods high in iron to help your red blood cells carry oxygen.
- Drink plenty of water to help your body replenish your blood.
- Avoid contact with another person's blood.
- Exercise regularly to keep your heart strong.
- Never smoke or use tobacco.

HEALTH BACKGROUND

Tell students that there is a short loop of blood vessels from the heart to the lungs and back. In these vessels, the arteries carry blood that has little oxygen and lots of carbon dioxide. The veins of this system carry oxygenated blood back to the heart to send out to the rest of the body. For this reason, students should not associate arteries with oxygen, but rather think of them as blood vessels leaving the heart.

ACTIVITIES

Listen to the Beat Have small groups of students make a stethoscope-like instrument by slipping a 1-foot length of rubber tube over the small opening of a funnel. Demonstrate placing the wide end of the funnel over the heart while holding the other end of the tubing to your ear. Have group members listen to their own heartbeat. Explain that the "lubb dup" sound of a heartbeat is produced by the closing of valves in the heart.

Blood Flow in your Arm Have students find the blue lines under the skin in their wrist. Explain that these are veins. Have students press gently and stroke along the lines toward their elbow and then back toward their hand. Explain that stroking toward the elbow will result in the veins disappearing, but gradually reappearing. Stroking toward the hand will result in the lines disappearing and not reappearing until pressure is released. Tell students that the blue in the veins is the blood with little oxygen.

Your Skeletal System

Your skeletal system includes all of the bones in your body. These strong, hard parts of your body protect your internal organs, help you move, and allow you to sit and to stand up straight.

Your skeletal system works with your muscular system to hold your body up and to give it shape.

Your skeletal system includes more than two hundred bones. These bones come in many different shapes and sizes.

Your Skull

The wide flat bones of your skull fit tightly together to protect your brain. The bones in the front of your skull give your face its shape and allow the muscles in your face to express your thoughts and feelings.

Your Spine

Your spine, or backbone, is made up of nearly two dozen small, round bones. These bones fit together and connect your head to your pelvis. Each of these bones, or vertebrae, has a small round hole in the center like a doughnut. Your spinal cord is a bundle of nerves that carries information to and from your brain and the rest of your body. Your spinal cord runs from your brain down your back to your hips through the holes in your vertebrae. There is a soft, flexible disk of cartilage between each of your vertebrae. This allows you to bend and twist your spine. Your spine, pelvis, and leg bones work together to allow you to stand, sit, or move.

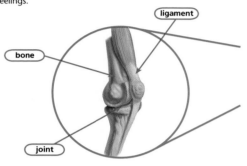

ligament

bone

joint

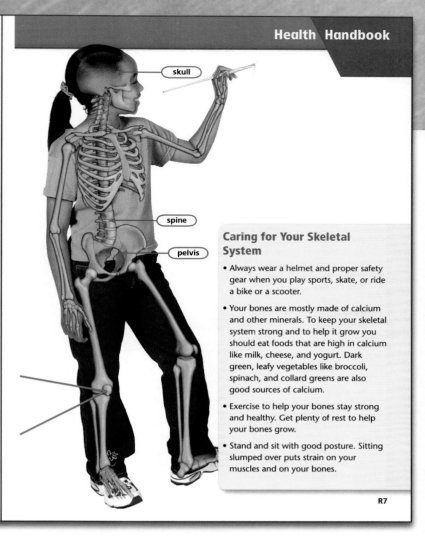

skull

spine

pelvis

Caring for Your Skeletal System

- Always wear a helmet and proper safety gear when you play sports, skate, or ride a bike or a scooter.

- Your bones are mostly made of calcium and other minerals. To keep your skeletal system strong and to help it grow you should eat foods that are high in calcium like milk, cheese, and yogurt. Dark green, leafy vegetables like broccoli, spinach, and collard greens are also good sources of calcium.

- Exercise to help your bones stay strong and healthy. Get plenty of rest to help your bones grow.

- Stand and sit with good posture. Sitting slumped over puts strain on your muscles and on your bones.

HEALTH BACKGROUND

Bones are continuously breaking down and reforming, a process called remodeling. Bones grow in width and length while people are growing. They sometimes grow in width in later life. Bones increase in density until about the age of 30. After that, bones break down faster than they form.

ACTIVITIES

Measure Your Rib Cage Have students use a string to measure around their rib cage. Have them determine how big it is when they breathe in and how big it is when they breathe out. Explain that the ribs move up and out, causing the rib cage to become larger, when the air breathed in expands the lungs. They move down and in, causing the rib cage to become smaller, when you breathe out.

Model Your Spine Have students make a model of their spine using candy rings. Have them run a string down through it and explain that this is how their spinal cord runs through their spine. Explain that there are 24 vertebrae in the spine. Each vertebra is cushioned from the next one by a pad of cartilage, called a disc.

Your Muscular System

A muscle is a body part that produces movement by contracting and relaxing. All of the muscles in your body make up the muscular system.

Voluntary and Involuntary Muscles

Voluntary Muscles are the muscles you use to move your arms and legs, your face, head, and fingers. You can make these muscles contract or stop them to control the way your body moves.

Involuntary Muscles are responsible for movements you usually don't see or control. These muscles make up your heart, your stomach and digestive system, your diaphragm, and the muscles that control your eyelids. Your heart beats and your diaphragm powers your breathing without your thinking about them. You cannot stop the action of these muscles.

How Muscles Help You Move

All muscles pull when they contract. Moving your body in more than one direction takes more than one muscle. To reach out with your arm or to pull it back, you use a pair of muscles. As one muscle contracts to extend your arm, the other relaxes and stretches. As you pull your arm back the muscles reverse their functions.

Your muscles let you do many kinds of things. The large muscles in your legs allow you to walk and run. Tiny muscles in your face allow you to smile.

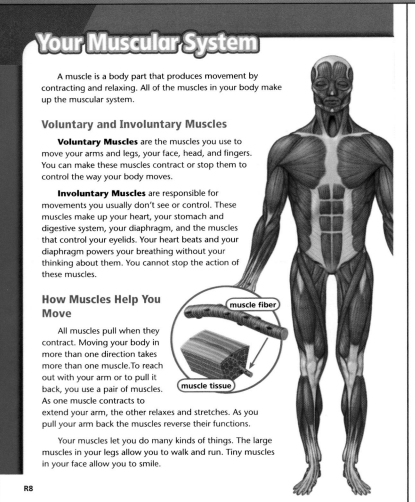

muscle fiber

muscle tissue

R8

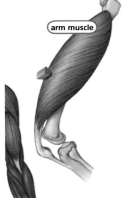

arm muscle

Your Muscles and Your Bones

The muscles that allow you to move your body work with your skeletal system. Muscles in your legs that allow you to kick a ball or ride a bicycle pull on the bones and joints of your legs and lower body. Your muscles are connected to your skeletal system by strong, cordlike tissues called tendons.

Your Achilles tendon just above your heel connects your calf muscles to your heel bone. When you contract those muscles, the tendon pulls on the heel bone and allows you to stand on your toes, jump, or push hard on your bicycle's pedals.

Caring for Your Muscular System

- Always stretch and warm your muscles up before exercising or playing sports. Do this by jogging or walking for at least ten minutes. This brings fresh blood and oxygen into your muscles and helps prevent injury or pain.

- Eat a balanced diet of foods to be sure your muscles have the nutrients they need to grow and remain strong.

- Drink plenty of water when you exercise or play sports. This helps your blood remove wastes from your muscles and helps you build endurance.

- Always cool down after you exercise. Walk or jog slowly for five or ten minutes to let your heartbeat slow and your breathing return to normal. This helps you avoid pain and stiffness after your muscles work hard.

- Stop exercising if your feel pain in your muscles.

- Get plenty of rest before and after you work your muscles hard. They need time to repair themselves and recover from working hard.

R9

HEALTH BACKGROUND

Muscles work in pairs. Each skeletal muscle has another skeletal muscle that works gently against it. When one muscle contracts, the other muscle relaxes. The contracting muscle causes movement. The relaxed muscle stays somewhat tight to help control the movement. To return the body part to its original position, the relaxed muscle contracts and the other muscle relaxes.

ACTIVITIES

Push and Pull Have students pull up on a desk with one hand. Have them feel which muscle is working with the other hand. Next have them push on the desk and let them feel which muscle is working now. Explain that pulling will primarily use the biceps muscle and pushing will primarily use the triceps muscle. Students should be able to feel these muscles tightening and getting shorter and fatter. Reinforce that both muscles are actually involved in both movements, as well as other muscles in the hand, forearm, and shoulder.

Tie Your Shoe Have students tie a shoe without using their thumb. Explain that without the use of their thumb, students will be unable to grasp and manipulate the strings effectively to tie their shoes.

Your Senses

Your Eyes and Vision

Your eyes allow you to see light reflected by the things around you. This diagram shows how an eye works. Light enters through the clear outer surface called the cornea. It passes through the pupil. The lens bends the incoming light to focus it on the retina. The retina sends nerve signals along the optic nerve. Your brain uses the signals to form an image. This is what you "see."

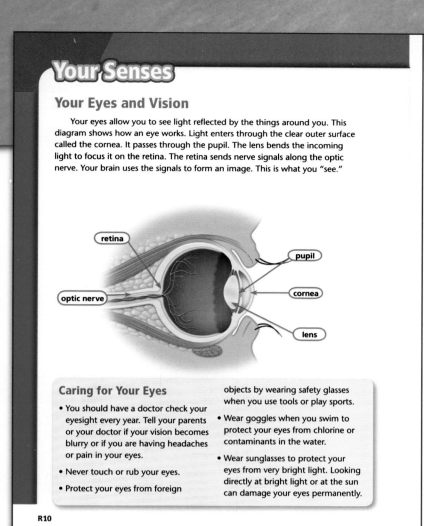

retina

pupil

optic nerve

cornea

lens

Caring for Your Eyes

- You should have a doctor check your eyesight every year. Tell your parents or your doctor if your vision becomes blurry or if you are having headaches or pain in your eyes.
- Never touch or rub your eyes.
- Protect your eyes from foreign objects by wearing safety glasses when you use tools or play sports.
- Wear goggles when you swim to protect your eyes from chlorine or contaminants in the water.
- Wear sunglasses to protect your eyes from very bright light. Looking directly at bright light or at the sun can damage your eyes permanently.

Your Ears and Hearing

Sounds travel through the air in waves. When some of those waves enter your ear you hear a sound. This diagram shows the inside of your ear.

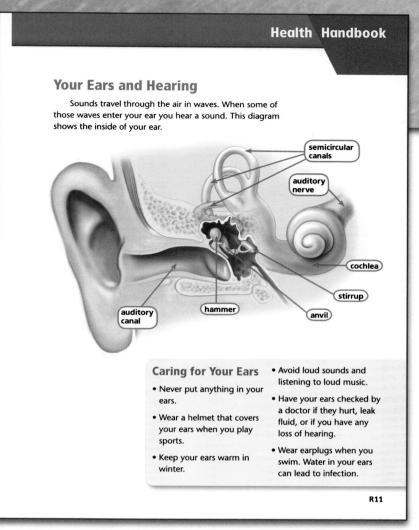

semicircular canals

auditory nerve

cochlea

stirrup

auditory canal

hammer

anvil

Caring for Your Ears

- Never put anything in your ears.
- Wear a helmet that covers your ears when you play sports.
- Keep your ears warm in winter.
- Avoid loud sounds and listening to loud music.
- Have your ears checked by a doctor if they hurt, leak fluid, or if you have any loss of hearing.
- Wear earplugs when you swim. Water in your ears can lead to infection.

HEALTH BACKGROUND

The adult eyeball is about 1 inch wide. The outermost covering is called the sclera. You see the sclera as the "whites of the eyes." Beneath the sclera is a thin layer called the choroid, which has many blood vessels that nourish the eye. The retina is the layer below the choroid. The retina contains many light-sensitive cells that detect light and change it into nerve signals. Most of the eye is filled with a jellylike substance called the vitreous humor. Light that enters the eye through the cornea and lens travels through the vitreous humor to the retina.

ACTIVITIES

Optical Illusions Have students research and copy some examples of optical illusions. Have students present their illusions to the class. If possible, have students explain their illusions and describe why the eye responds to the illusion in the way it does.

"Save Your Hearing" Slogans Have pairs of students work together to think up slogans that encourage others to protect their hearing. Post slogans on the bulletin board or other locations for all to see.

Noisy Situations Have students form teams and make lists of situations that could cause damage to their ears. Have each team circle the situations they think are most dangerous to healthy hearing.

Your Immune System

Pathogens and Illness

You may know someone who had a cold or the flu this year. These illnesses are caused by germs called pathogens. Illnesses spread when pathogens move from one person to another.

Types of Pathogens

There are four kinds of pathogens—viruses, bacteria, fungi, and protozoans. Viruses are the smallest kind of pathogen. They are so small that they can be seen only with very powerful electron microscopes. Viruses cause many types of illness, including colds, the flu, and chicken pox. Viruses are not living things. They must use living cells to reproduce.

Bacteria are tiny single-cell organisms that live in water, in the soil, and on almost all surfaces. Most bacteria can be seen only with a microscope. Not all bacteria cause illness. Your body needs some types of bacteria to work well.

The most common type of fungus infection is athlete's foot. This is a burning, itchy infection of the skin between your toes. Ringworm is another skin infection caused by a fungus. It causes itchy round patches to develop on the skin.

Protozoa are the fourth type of pathogen. They are single-cell organisms that are slightly larger than bacteria. They can cause disease when they grow in food or drinking water.

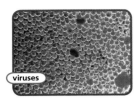
viruses

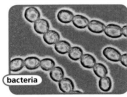
bacteria

fungi

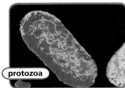
protozoa

Fighting Illness

Pathogens that can make you ill are everywhere. When you become ill, a doctor may be able to treat you. You also can practice healthful habits to protect yourself and others from the spread of pathogens and the illnesses they can cause.

The best way to avoid spreading pathogens is to wash your hands with warm water and soap. This floats germs off of your skin. You should wash your hands often. Always wash them before and after eating, after handling animals, and after using the bathroom. Avoid touching your mouth, eyes, and nose. Never share hats, combs, cups, or drinking straws. If you get a cut or scrape, pathogens can enter your body. It is important to wash cuts and scrapes carefully with soap and water. Then cover the injury with a sterile bandage.

When you are ill, you should avoid spreading pathogens to others. Cover your nose and mouth when you sneeze or cough.

Don't share anything that has touched your mouth or nose. Stay home from school until an adult or your doctor tells you that you are well enough to go back.

Even though pathogens are all around, most people become ill only once in a while because the body has systems that protect it from pathogens. These defenses keep pathogens from entering your body.

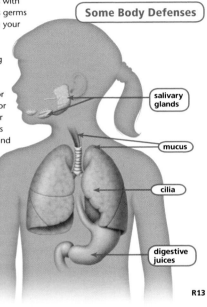
Some Body Defenses
salivary glands
mucus
cilia
digestive juices

HEALTH BACKGROUND

In the 1800s, ringworm was commonly spread by contact with barbers, schoolchildren, and theater seats. This well-known skin infection is not caused by a worm at all, but by one of various kinds of fungi. The disease is easily identified by the rapidly growing circular patches of rough, reddened skin that heals from the center outward. Hence the name ringworm. Today, ringworm can be transmitted by infected people, pets, towels, hairbrushes, or other contaminated objects. Some infections disappear with no treatment at all. In other cases, a topical antifungal medication is applied to the infected area, or other ringworm medication is taken by mouth.

ACTIVITIES

Food Processing Have students research the roles of bacteria or fungi in making foods such as cheese, vinegar, sauerkraut, pickles, yogurt, soy sauce, and olives. Ask students to diagram the process of fermentation in making one of these foods.

Uncommon Diseases in the U.S. Have students research an infectious disease that is not common in the United States today, but is common in other countries or was common in the past. Examples include bubonic plague, malaria, African sleeping sickness (trypanosomiasis), and cholera. Ask students to find out what the symptoms of the disease are, how it spreads, what kind of pathogen causes it, and how it has affected life in the areas where it is, or was, common.

Staying Healthy

Eat a Balanced Diet

Eating the foods that your body needs to grow and fight illness is the most important thing you can do to stay healthy. A balanced diet of healthful foods gives your body energy. Your body's systems need nutrients to function properly and work together.

Choosing unhealthful foods can cause you to gain excess weight and to lack energy. Inactivity and poor food choices can lead you to becoming ill more frequently. Unhealthful foods can also cause you to develop noncommunicable diseases. Unlike communicable diseases caused by germs, these illnesses occur because your body systems are not working right.

Exercise Regularly

Exercise keeps your body healthy. Regular exercise helps your heart, lungs, and muscles stay strong. It helps your body digest food. It also helps your body fight disease. Exercising to keep your body strong also helps prevent injury when you play sports.

Exercise allows your body to rest more effectively. Getting enough sleep prepares your body for the next day. It allows your muscles and bones to grow and recover from exercise. Resting also helps keep your mind alert so you can learn and play well.

HEALTH BACKGROUND

Students do not always apply what they learn in class to their own lives. As you teach these pages, encourage students to apply the information about a healthful diet when they make food choices in the school cafeteria or elsewhere each day. Encourage students to apply the information on exercise when they decide what to do on weekends and after school.

ACTIVITIES

Have a Good Meal Have students plan a healthful lunch or dinner. Ask students to make a drawing that shows all the foods that make up the meal.

Exercise Journal Have students keep track of the exercise they do for one week. Have them make a table with two columns. In the left-hand column, they should list the activities they do each day. In the right-hand column, they should write how much time they spend doing each activity.

All Different Kinds Have small groups of students look in magazines for pictures of people engaged in different physical activities. Remind students that physical activities involve moving the body and can include raking leaves, walking a dog, and flying a kite. Have students cut out one or two pictures. Ask them to write a caption for the each picture, describing the benefits of the activity.

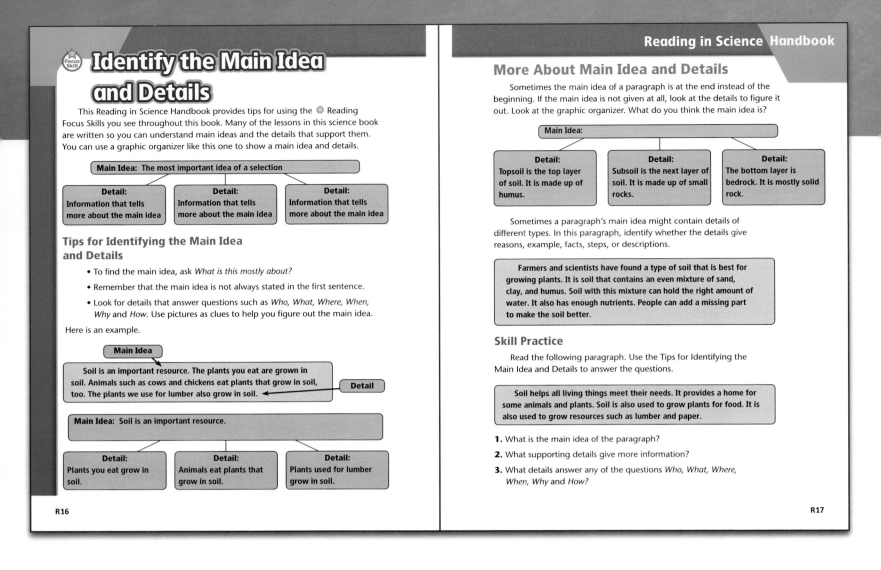

Identify the Main Idea and Details

This Reading in Science Handbook provides tips for using the ◉ Reading Focus Skills you see throughout this book. Many of the lessons in this science book are written so you can understand main ideas and the details that support them. You can use a graphic organizer like this one to show a main idea and details.

Main Idea: The most important idea of a selection

| **Detail:** Information that tells more about the main idea | **Detail:** Information that tells more about the main idea | **Detail:** Information that tells more about the main idea |

Tips for Identifying the Main Idea and Details

- To find the main idea, ask *What is this mostly about?*
- Remember that the main idea is not always stated in the first sentence.
- Look for details that answer questions such as *Who, What, Where, When, Why* and *How.* Use pictures as clues to help you figure out the main idea.

Here is an example.

Main Idea

Soil is an important resource. The plants you eat are grown in soil. Animals such as cows and chickens eat plants that grow in soil, too. The plants we use for lumber also grow in soil. **Detail**

Main Idea: Soil is an important resource.

| **Detail:** Plants you eat grow in soil. | **Detail:** Animals eat plants that grow in soil. | **Detail:** Plants used for lumber grow in soil. |

R16

More About Main Idea and Details

Sometimes the main idea of a paragraph is at the end instead of the beginning. If the main idea is not given at all, look at the details to figure it out. Look at the graphic organizer. What do you think the main idea is?

Main Idea:

| **Detail:** Topsoil is the top layer of soil. It is made up of humus. | **Detail:** Subsoil is the next layer of soil. It is made up of small rocks. | **Detail:** The bottom layer is bedrock. It is mostly solid rock. |

Sometimes a paragraph's main idea might contain details of different types. In this paragraph, identify whether the details give reasons, example, facts, steps, or descriptions.

Farmers and scientists have found a type of soil that is best for growing plants. It is soil that contains an even mixture of sand, clay, and humus. Soil with this mixture can hold the right amount of water. It also has enough nutrients. People can add a missing part to make the soil better.

Skill Practice

Read the following paragraph. Use the Tips for Identifying the Main Idea and Details to answer the questions.

Soil helps all living things meet their needs. It provides a home for some animals and plants. Soil is also used to grow plants for food. It is also used to grow resources such as lumber and paper.

1. What is the main idea of the paragraph?
2. What supporting details give more information?
3. What details answer any of the questions *Who, What, Where, When, Why* and *How?*

R17

TEACH/MODEL

Have students explain why it is helpful to identify the main idea and details of a selection. *to know what a passage is mostly about* Point out the graphic organizer, and discuss the Tips for Identifying the Main Idea and Details. Have students read the paragraph in the example.

Read aloud the following model to help students see how to record in the graphic organizer information from the paragraph.

This paragraph is mostly about soil is an important resource. I put this in the Main Idea box of the graphic organizer. One detail is that plants you eat grow in soil. Another detail is animals eat plants that grow in soil. A third detail is that plants used for lumber grow in soil. I write these in the boxes marked Details.

PRACTICE/APPLY

Have students work in small groups to look at the information given on the graphic organizer. Discuss with students what is most likely the main idea given the set of details provided. *There are different levels in a food chain.*

Read aloud the paragraph. Help students identify and analyze the details to determine into which category each detail would fall. *Examples are given.*

Skill Practice

Have students use the Tips for Identifying the Main Idea and Details to answer the questions.

1. Soil helps all living things meet their needs.
2. It provides a home for some animals and plants and it is used to grow plants for food.
3. It is also used to grow resources such as lumber and paper.

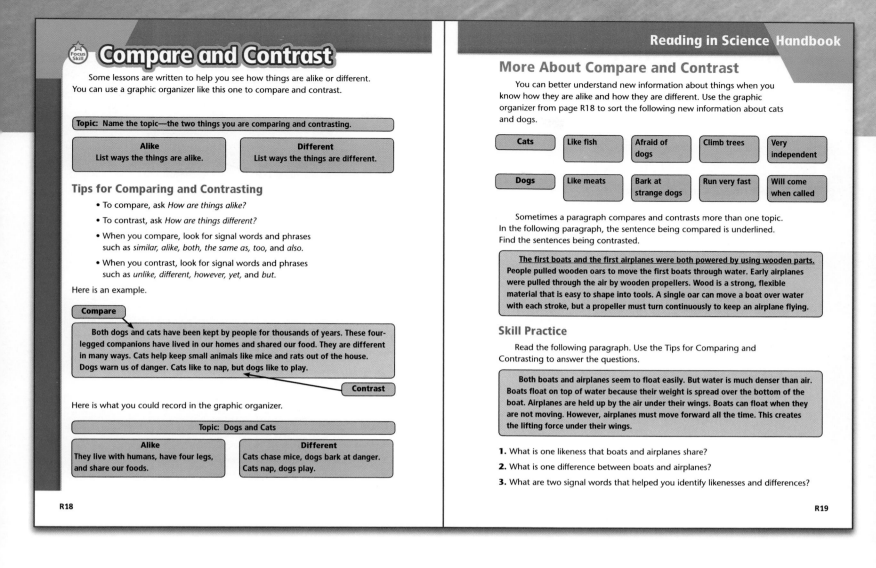

Compare and Contrast

Some lessons are written to help you see how things are alike or different. You can use a graphic organizer like this one to compare and contrast.

Topic: Name the topic—the two things you are comparing and contrasting.	
Alike List ways the things are alike.	**Different** List ways the things are different.

Tips for Comparing and Contrasting

- To compare, ask *How are things alike?*
- To contrast, ask *How are things different?*
- When you compare, look for signal words and phrases such as *similar, alike, both, the same as, too,* and *also.*
- When you contrast, look for signal words and phrases such as *unlike, different, however, yet,* and *but.*

Here is an example.

Compare

Both dogs and cats have been kept by people for thousands of years. These four-legged companions have lived in our homes and shared our food. They are different in many ways. Cats help keep small animals like mice and rats out of the house. Dogs warn us of danger. Cats like to nap, but dogs like to play.

Contrast

Here is what you could record in the graphic organizer.

Topic: Dogs and Cats	
Alike They live with humans, have four legs, and share our foods.	**Different** Cats chase mice, dogs bark at danger. Cats nap, dogs play.

More About Compare and Contrast

You can better understand new information about things when you know how they are alike and how they are different. Use the graphic organizer from page R18 to sort the following new information about cats and dogs.

Cats	Like fish	Afraid of dogs	Climb trees	Very independent
Dogs	Like meats	Bark at strange dogs	Run very fast	Will come when called

Sometimes a paragraph compares and contrasts more than one topic. In the following paragraph, the sentence being compared is underlined. Find the sentences being contrasted.

The first boats and the first airplanes were both powered by using wooden parts. People pulled wooden oars to move the first boats through water. Early airplanes were pulled through the air by wooden propellers. Wood is a strong, flexible material that is easy to shape into tools. A single oar can move a boat over water with each stroke, but a propeller must turn continuously to keep an airplane flying.

Skill Practice

Read the following paragraph. Use the Tips for Comparing and Contrasting to answer the questions.

Both boats and airplanes seem to float easily. But water is much denser than air. Boats float on top of water because their weight is spread over the bottom of the boat. Airplanes are held up by the air under their wings. Boats can float when they are not moving. However, airplanes must move forward all the time. This creates the lifting force under their wings.

1. What is one likeness that boats and airplanes share?
2. What is one difference between boats and airplanes?
3. What are two signal words that helped you identify likenesses and differences?

TEACH/MODEL

Have students explain why it is helpful to compare and contrast text. *to understand how things are alike and how they are different* Point out the graphic organizer, and discuss the Tips for Comparing and Contrasting. Have students read the paragraph in the example.

Read aloud the following model to help students see how to record in the graphic organizer information from the paragraph.

I know that my topic is dogs and cats. Dogs and cats are alike in that they live with humans, have four legs, and share our foods. I will write this in the Alike column. Cats chase mice and dogs bark at danger. Cats nap and dogs play. I will write that information in the Different column.

PRACTICE/APPLY

Have students work in small groups to sort the information given in the table.

Remind students that some paragraphs tell about ways a number of things are alike and different. Read aloud the paragraph. Help students write the underlined information from the paragraph in a graphic organizer like the one used in the model. Have students identify the second thing being compared and organize that information in a second graphic organizer.

Skill Practice

Have students use the Tips for Comparing and Contrasting to answer the questions.

1. Both boats and airplanes float easily.

2. *Possible answer:* Boats can float when they are not moving; airplanes must move forward all the time.

3. *Both* and *however* are signal words in this paragraph.

References and Resources **R18–R19**

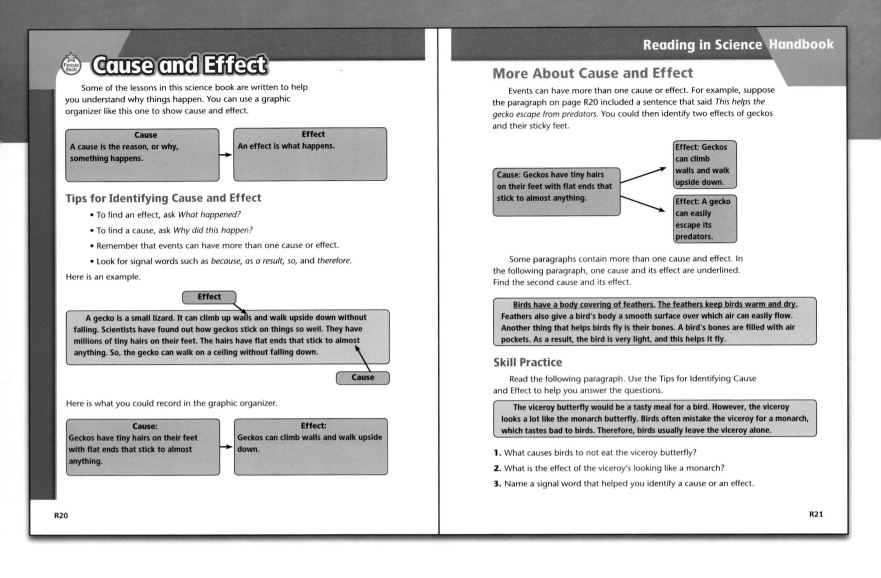

Cause and Effect

Some of the lessons in this science book are written to help you understand why things happen. You can use a graphic organizer like this one to show cause and effect.

Cause	Effect
A cause is the reason, or why, something happens.	An effect is what happens.

Tips for Identifying Cause and Effect

- To find an effect, ask *What happened?*
- To find a cause, ask *Why did this happen?*
- Remember that events can have more than one cause or effect.
- Look for signal words such as *because, as a result, so,* and *therefore.*

Here is an example.

Effect

A gecko is a small lizard. It can climb up walls and walk upside down without falling. Scientists have found out how geckos stick on things so well. They have millions of tiny hairs on their feet. The hairs have flat ends that stick to almost anything. So, the gecko can walk on a ceiling without falling down.

Cause

Here is what you could record in the graphic organizer.

Cause:	Effect:
Geckos have tiny hairs on their feet with flat ends that stick to almost anything.	Geckos can climb walls and walk upside down.

R20

More About Cause and Effect

Events can have more than one cause or effect. For example, suppose the paragraph on page R20 included a sentence that said *This helps the gecko escape from predators.* You could then identify two effects of geckos and their sticky feet.

Cause: Geckos have tiny hairs on their feet with flat ends that stick to almost anything.

Effect: Geckos can climb walls and walk upside down.

Effect: A gecko can easily escape its predators.

Some paragraphs contain more than one cause and effect. In the following paragraph, one cause and its effect are underlined. Find the second cause and its effect.

Birds have a body covering of feathers. The feathers keep birds warm and dry. Feathers also give a bird's body a smooth surface over which air can easily flow. Another thing that helps birds fly is their bones. A bird's bones are filled with air pockets. As a result, the bird is very light, and this helps it fly.

Skill Practice

Read the following paragraph. Use the Tips for Identifying Cause and Effect to help you answer the questions.

The viceroy butterfly would be a tasty meal for a bird. However, the viceroy looks a lot like the monarch butterfly. Birds often mistake the viceroy for a monarch, which tastes bad to birds. Therefore, birds usually leave the viceroy alone.

1. What causes birds to not eat the viceroy butterfly?

2. What is the effect of the viceroy's looking like a monarch?

3. Name a signal word that helped you identify a cause or an effect.

R21

TEACH/MODEL

Have students explain why it is helpful to understand cause-and-effect relationships. *to understand how and why things happen* Point out the graphic organizer and discuss the Tips for Identifying Cause and Effect. Have students read the paragraph in the example.

Read aloud the following model to help students see how to record in the graphic organizer information from the paragraph.

I know that Geckos have tiny hairs on their feet with flat ends that stick to almost anything. I think this is the cause, so I will write it in the Cause box. I see that as a result, Geckos can climb walls and walk upside down. I will write that in the Effect box.

PRACTICE/APPLY

Have students compare the graphic organizer on page R20 with the one on page R21. Lead students to see that the Effect box now has two things listed instead of one.

Remind students that some paragraphs have more than one cause and effect. Read aloud the paragraph. Have students find the second cause and effect in the paragraph. *Cause: Birds' bones are filled with air pockets. Effect: Birds can fly.*

Skill Practice

Have students use the Tips for Identifying Cause and Effect to answer the questions.

1. It looks like a monarch butterfly which tastes bad.

2. Birds leave it alone.

3. *Therefore* is a signal word in this paragraph.

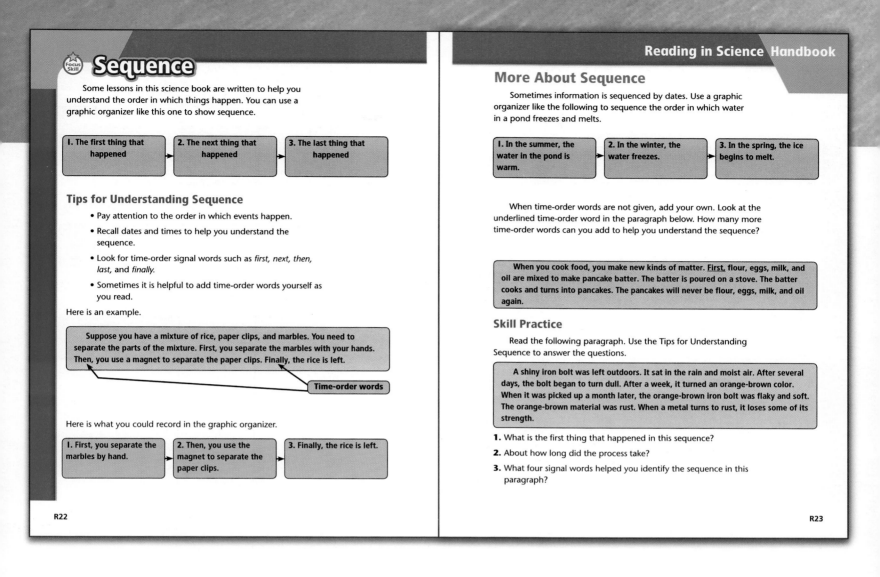

Sequence

Some lessons in this science book are written to help you understand the order in which things happen. You can use a graphic organizer like this one to show sequence.

1. The first thing that happened	→	2. The next thing that happened	→	3. The last thing that happened

Tips for Understanding Sequence

- Pay attention to the order in which events happen.
- Recall dates and times to help you understand the sequence.
- Look for time-order signal words such as *first, next, then, last,* and *finally.*
- Sometimes it is helpful to add time-order words yourself as you read.

Here is an example.

> Suppose you have a mixture of rice, paper clips, and marbles. You need to separate the parts of the mixture. First, you separate the marbles with your hands. Then, you use a magnet to separate the paper clips. Finally, the rice is left.

Time-order words

Here is what you could record in the graphic organizer.

1. First, you separate the marbles by hand.	→	2. Then, you use the magnet to separate the paper clips.	→	3. Finally, the rice is left.

R22

More About Sequence

Sometimes information is sequenced by dates. Use a graphic organizer like the following to sequence the order in which water in a pond freezes and melts.

1. In the summer, the water in the pond is warm.	→	2. In the winter, the water freezes.	→	3. In the spring, the ice begins to melt.

When time-order words are not given, add your own. Look at the underlined time-order word in the paragraph below. How many more time-order words can you add to help you understand the sequence?

> When you cook food, you make new kinds of matter. <u>First,</u> flour, eggs, milk, and oil are mixed to make pancake batter. The batter is poured on a stove. The batter cooks and turns into pancakes. The pancakes will never be flour, eggs, milk, and oil again.

Skill Practice

Read the following paragraph. Use the Tips for Understanding Sequence to answer the questions.

> A shiny iron bolt was left outdoors. It sat in the rain and moist air. After several days, the bolt began to turn dull. After a week, it turned an orange-brown color. When it was picked up a month later, the orange-brown iron bolt was flaky and soft. The orange-brown material was rust. When a metal turns to rust, it loses some of its strength.

1. What is the first thing that happened in this sequence?
2. About how long did the process take?
3. What four signal words helped you identify the sequence in this paragraph?

R23

TEACH/MODEL

Have students explain why it is helpful to pay attention to the sequence of events. *Knowing the order in which things happen can help you understand what you read.* Point out the graphic organizer and discuss the Tips for Understanding Sequence. Have students read the paragraph in the example.

Read aloud the following model to help students see how to record in the graphic organizer information from the paragraph.

I know that my topic is about separating parts of a mixture. I read that the first thing you do is separate the marbles with your hands. I write that on the graphic organizer. I see from the signal word *then* that the second thing you do is use a magnet to separate the paperclips. The last signal word, *finally*, tells me that the third thing you do is see what is left. I write this in my graphic organizer.

PRACTICE/APPLY

Have students look at the events written in sequence on the graphic organizer.

Remind students that some paragraphs don't include time-order words. This can make it harder to understand an event's sequence. Read the paragraph aloud. Students should find places to add time-order words: *first, then,* and *finally.*

Skill Practice

Have students use the Tips for Understanding Sequence to answer the questions.

1. A shiny iron bolt was left outdoors.
2. one month
3. *After several days, after a week,* and *a month later* are signal words in this paragraph.

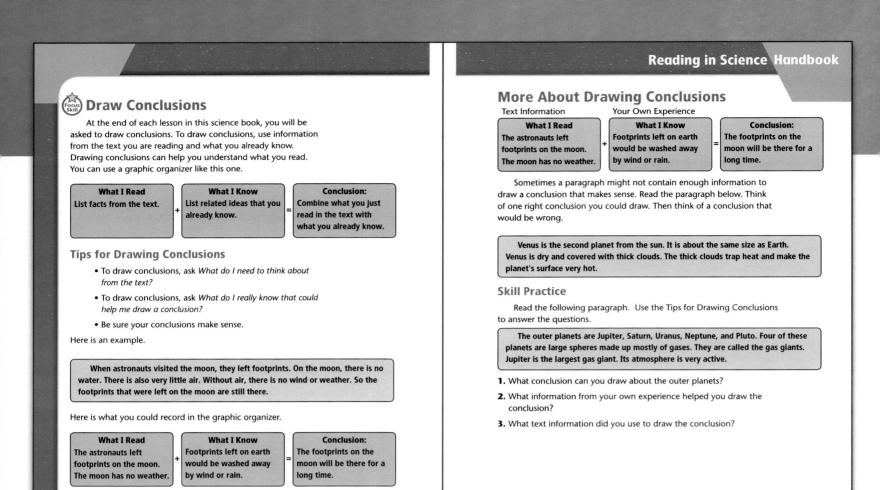

Draw Conclusions

At the end of each lesson in this science book, you will be asked to draw conclusions. To draw conclusions, use information from the text you are reading and what you already know. Drawing conclusions can help you understand what you read. You can use a graphic organizer like this one.

What I Read		What I Know		Conclusion:
List facts from the text.	+	List related ideas that you already know.	=	Combine what you just read in the text with what you already know.

Tips for Drawing Conclusions

- To draw conclusions, ask *What do I need to think about from the text?*
- To draw conclusions, ask *What do I really know that could help me draw a conclusion?*
- Be sure your conclusions make sense.

Here is an example.

> When astronauts visited the moon, they left footprints. On the moon, there is no water. There is also very little air. Without air, there is no wind or weather. So the footprints that were left on the moon are still there.

Here is what you could record in the graphic organizer.

What I Read		What I Know		Conclusion:
The astronauts left footprints on the moon. The moon has no weather.	+	Footprints left on earth would be washed away by wind or rain.	=	The footprints on the moon will be there for a long time.

R24

More About Drawing Conclusions

Text Information — Your Own Experience

What I Read		What I Know		Conclusion:
The astronauts left footprints on the moon. The moon has no weather.	+	Footprints left on earth would be washed away by wind or rain.	=	The footprints on the moon will be there for a long time.

Sometimes a paragraph might not contain enough information to draw a conclusion that makes sense. Read the paragraph below. Think of one right conclusion you could draw. Then think of a conclusion that would be wrong.

> Venus is the second planet from the sun. It is about the same size as Earth. Venus is dry and covered with thick clouds. The thick clouds trap heat and make the planet's surface very hot.

Skill Practice

Read the following paragraph. Use the Tips for Drawing Conclusions to answer the questions.

> The outer planets are Jupiter, Saturn, Uranus, Neptune, and Pluto. Four of these planets are large spheres made up mostly of gases. They are called the gas giants. Jupiter is the largest gas giant. Its atmosphere is very active.

1. What conclusion can you draw about the outer planets?
2. What information from your own experience helped you draw the conclusion?
3. What text information did you use to draw the conclusion?

R25

TEACH/MODEL

Have students explain why it is helpful to draw conclusions about text. *When not all of the information is given, readers must use text information and their own knowledge to understand what is written.* Point out the graphic organizer and discuss the Tips for Drawing Conclusions. Have students read the paragraph in the example.

Read aloud the following model to help students see how to record in the graphic organizer information from the paragraph.

I read that astronauts left footprints on the moon. I wrote this in the What I Read box of the graphic organizer. For the What I Know box, I wrote that footprints left on earth would be washed away by wind or rain. For the Conclusion box, I figured out that the footprints on the moon may be there for a long time.

PRACTICE/APPLY

Remind students that some paragraphs might not contain enough information to draw a valid conclusion. Read aloud the paragraph. Help students arrive at one valid conclusion. *It is too hot on Venus for plants or animals to live.*

Skill Practice

Have students use the Tips for Drawing Conclusions to answer the questions.

1. The larger the gas giant, the more active its atmosphere.

2. I know that gases are active compared with solids.

3. Jupiter, the largest gas giant, has the most active atmosphere.

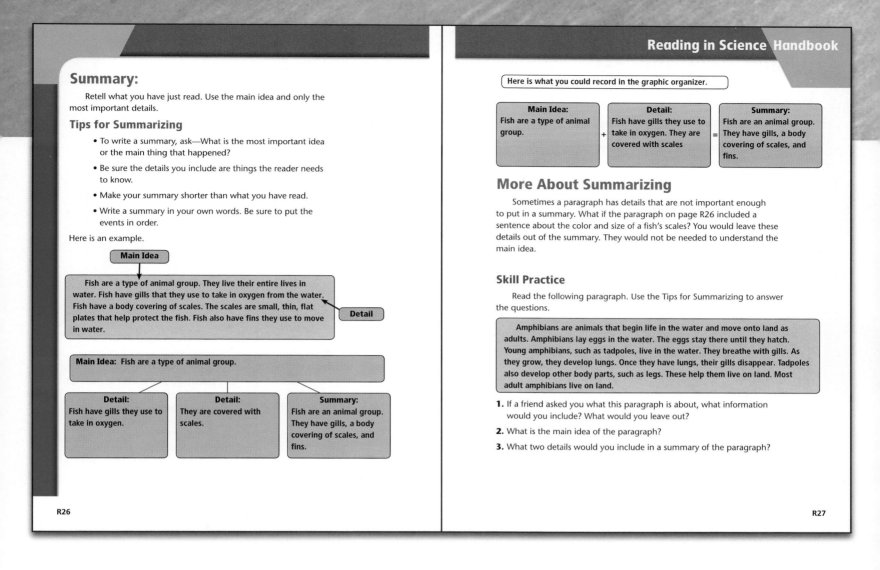

Summary:

Retell what you have just read. Use the main idea and only the most important details.

Tips for Summarizing

- To write a summary, ask—What is the most important idea or the main thing that happened?
- Be sure the details you include are things the reader needs to know.
- Make your summary shorter than what you have read.
- Write a summary in your own words. Be sure to put the events in order.

Here is an example.

Main Idea

Fish are a type of animal group. They live their entire lives in water. Fish have gills that they use to take in oxygen from the water. Fish have a body covering of scales. The scales are small, thin, flat plates that help protect the fish. Fish also have fins they use to move in water.

Detail

Main Idea: Fish are a type of animal group.

Detail: Fish have gills they use to take in oxygen.

Detail: They are covered with scales.

Summary: Fish are an animal group. They have gills, a body covering of scales, and fins.

Here is what you could record in the graphic organizer.

| Main Idea: Fish are a type of animal group. | Detail: Fish have gills they use to take in oxygen. They are covered with scales | Summary: Fish are an animal group. They have gills, a body covering of scales, and fins. |

More About Summarizing

Sometimes a paragraph has details that are not important enough to put in a summary. What if the paragraph on page R26 included a sentence about the color and size of a fish's scales? You would leave these details out of the summary. They would not be needed to understand the main idea.

Skill Practice

Read the following paragraph. Use the Tips for Summarizing to answer the questions.

Amphibians are animals that begin life in the water and move onto land as adults. Amphibians lay eggs in the water. The eggs stay there until they hatch. Young amphibians, such as tadpoles, live in the water. They breathe with gills. As they grow, they develop lungs. Once they have lungs, their gills disappear. Tadpoles also develop other body parts, such as legs. These help them live on land. Most adult amphibians live on land.

1. If a friend asked you what this paragraph is about, what information would you include? What would you leave out?

2. What is the main idea of the paragraph?

3. What two details would you include in a summary of the paragraph?

R26

R27

TEACH/MODEL

Have students explain why it is important to summarize a passage. *to understand how to tell about the most important parts* Point out the graphic organizer, and discuss the Tips for Summarizing. Have students read the paragraph in the example.

Read aloud the following model to help students see how to record in the graphic organizer information from the paragraph.

I know that the main idea of the paragraph is that fish are a type of animal group. I write that in the Main Idea box. The paragraph includes the details that fish have gills they use to take in oxygen and they are covered with scales. I write those details in the Details box. I write a summary statement by using my own words: Fish are an animal group. They have gills, a body covering of scales, and fins.

PRACTICE/APPLY

Remind students that a summary includes only the most important details of a passage.

Often the main idea of a paragraph is in the first sentence of the paragraph. However, it can be elsewhere in the paragraph. Read the paragraph aloud. Have students identify the main idea of the paragraph.

Skill Practice

Have students use the Tips for Summarizing to answer the questions.

1. Amphibians begin life in the water. Most adult amphibians live on land. Answers will vary.

2. Amphibians are animals that begin life in the water and move onto land as adults.

3. Amphibians lay eggs in the water. They develop lungs and legs as they grow, which help them live on land.

Using Tables, Charts, and Graphs

As you do investigations in science, you collect, organize, display, and interpret data. Tables, charts, and graphs are good ways to organize and display data so that others can understand and interpret your data.

The tables, charts, and graphs in this Handbook will help you read and understand data. You can also use the information to choose the best ways to display data so that you can use it to draw conclusions and make predictions.

Reading a Table

A third-grade class is studying the length of different sea animals. They want to find out how the lengths vary. The table shows some of the data the students have collected.

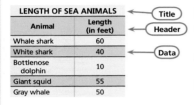

LENGTH OF SEA ANIMALS	
Animal	**Length (in feet)**
Whale shark	60
White shark	40
Bottlenose dolphin	10
Giant squid	55
Gray whale	50

Title ← Header ← Data

How to Read a Table

1. Read the title to find out what the table is about.

2. Read the headings to find out what information is given.

3. Study the data. Look for patterns.

4. Draw conclusions. If you display the data in a graph, you might be able to see patterns easily.

By studying the table, you can see the length of different sea animals. However, suppose the students want to look for patterns in the data. They might choose to display the data in a different way, such as in a bar graph.

R28

Reading a Bar Graph

The data in this bar graph is the same as in the table. A bar graph can be used to compare the data about different events or groups.

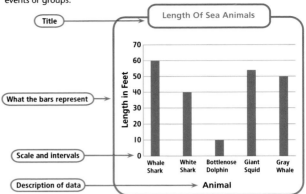

Title
What the bars represent
Scale and intervals
Description of data

How to Read a Bar Graph

1. Look at the graph to determine what kind of graph it is.

2. Read the graph. Use the labels to guide you.

3. Analyze the data. Study the bars to compare the measurements. Look for patterns.

4. Draw conclusions. Ask yourself questions like those on the right.

Skills Practice

1. How long is a gray whale?

2. How much longer is a whale shark than a white shark?

3. Which two sea animals vary in length by 40 feet?

4. Predict Which of these sea animals might you find in an aquarium at an animal park?

5. Was the bar graph a good choice for displaying this data? Explain your answer.

R29

TEACH/MODEL

Tables are used to help organize data. Displaying data in a table helps students develop representational-thinking skills. Ask students what data is represented in the second column of this table. *the length of the sea animals*

Explain that bar graphs can be used to organize and display data. The same data can be displayed using either a horizontal bar graph or a vertical bar graph. Point out that the data on this page is represented in a vertical bar graph. Bar graphs are used to compare data.

PRACTICE/APPLY

Review How to Read a Table and How to Read a Bar Graph with students.

Skill Practice

1. A gray whale is 50 feet long.

2. A whale shark is 20 feet longer than a white shark.

3. A bottlenose dolphin and a gray whale vary in length by 40 feet.

4. You might find a bottlenose dolphin in an aquarium at an animal park.

5. Yes; bar graphs are good to use when comparing data.

Using Metric Measurements

Reading a Line Graph

The data in this bar graph is the same as in the table. A bar graph can be used to compare the data about different events or groups.

TEMPERATURES IN ANCHORAGE, ALASKA	
Month	Normal Temperature in Degrees Fahrenheit
August	55
September	50
October	35
November	20
December	15

Here is the same data displayed in a line graph. A line graph is used to show changes over time.

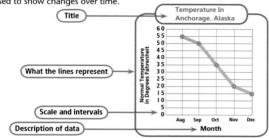

- Title
- What the lines represent
- Scale and intervals
- Description of data

How to Read a Line Graph

1. Look at the graph to determine what kind of graph it is.
2. Read the graph. Use the labels to guide you.
3. Analyze the data. Study the points along the lines. Look for patterns.
4. **Draw conclusions.** Ask yourself questions like those on the right.

Skills Practice

1. In what month is the normal temperature 35 degrees?
2. **Predict** How will the temperature change from December to August?
3. Was the line graph a good choice for displaying this data? Explain why.

R30

Reading a Circle Graph

A family went bird watching on an island. They counted 50 birds on the island. They wanted to know which birds they saw most often. They classified the birds by making a table. Here is the data they collected.

BIRD SIGHTINGS	
Bird	Number Observed
Pelicans	4
Bald Head Eagles	1
Ospreys	10
Egrets	15
Sandpipers	20

The circle graph shows the same data as the table. A circle graph can be used to show data as a whole made up of different parts.

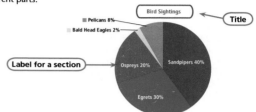

- Title
- Label for a section

How to Read a Circle Graph

1. Look at the title of the graph to learn what kind of information is shown.
2. Read the graph. Look at the label of each section to find out what information is shown.
3. Analyze the data. Compare the sizes of the sections to determine how they are related.
4. **Draw conclusions.** Ask yourself questions like those on the right.

Skills Practice

1. Which type of bird did they see most often?
2. **Predict** If they return to the island in a month, should they expect to see a bald head eagle?
3. Was the circle graph a good choice for displaying this data? Explain why.

R31

TEACH/MODEL

Line graphs are similar to bar graphs in that they have a title, scale, and labels. However, line graphs use a line to show how data change over time. Line graphs show continuous data—connected points that show change. Emphasis in the line graph is determining the amount of change from point to point.

PRACTICE/APPLY

Review How to Read a Line Graph with students.

Skill Practice

1. In October the normal temperature is 35 degrees.
2. The temperature will continue to stay low in the winter but will gradually warm as the summer approaches.
3. Yes; a line graph is good to use

TEACH/MODEL

A circle graph shows data as a whole made up of different parts. Guide students to understand how to read in a circle by suggesting that they find the largest colored area and then read around the circle in a clockwise direction.

PRACTICE/APPLY

Review How to Read a Circle Graph with students.

Skill Practice

1. Sandpipers were seen most often.
2. They should not expect to see a bald eagle.
3. Yes; a circle graph made it easy to see which part of the total number of birds they saw were different types.

Using Metric Measurements

A measurement is a number that represents a comparison of something being measured to a unit of measurement. Scientists use many different tools to measure objects and substances as they work. Scientists almost always use the metric system for their measurements.

Measuring Length in Metric Units

When you measure length, you find the distance between two points. The distance may be in a straight line, along a curved path, or around a circle. The table shows the metric units of length and how they are related.

Equivalent Measures
1 centimeter (cm) = 10 millimeters (mm)
1 decimeter (dm) = 10 centimeters (cm)
1 meter (m) = 1,000 millimeters
1 meter = 10 decimeters
1 kilometer (km) = 1,000 meters

You can use these comparisons to help you understand the size of each metric unit of length.

A millimeter (mm) is about the thickness of a dime.

A centimeter (cm) is about the width of your index finger.

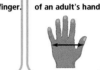

A decimeter (dm) is about the width of an adult's hand.

A meter (m) is about the width of a door.

Sometimes you may need to change units of length. The following diagram shows how to multiply and divide to change to larger and smaller units.

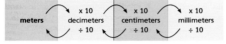

| meters | x 10 / ÷ 10 | decimeters | x 10 / ÷ 10 | centimeters | x 10 / ÷ 10 | millimeters |

To change larger units to smaller units, you need more of the smaller units. So, multiply by 10, 100, or 1,000.

Example: 500 dm = ___ cm

R32

Measuring Capacity in Metric Units

When you measure capacity, you find the amount a container can hold when it is filled. The table shows the metric units of capacity and how they are related.

A milliliter (mL) is the amount of liquid that can fill part of a medicine dropper.

A liter (L) is the amount of liquid that can fill a plastic bottle.

You can use multiplication to change liters to milliliters.

You can use division to change milliliters to liters.

2 L = ___ mL	4,000 mL = ___ L
Think: There are 1,000 mL in 1 L.	Think: There are 1,000 mL in 1 L.
2L = 2 x 1,000 = 2,000 mL	4,000 ÷ 1,000 = 4
So, 2L = 2,000 mL.	So, 4,000 mL = 4 L.

Skills Practice

Complete. Tell whether you multiply or divide by 1,000.

1. 4 L = ___ mL

2. 5,000 mL = ___ L

3. 3,000 mL = ___ L

4. 6 L = ___ mL

R33

TEACH/MODEL

The metric units for length are expressed by attaching the metric prefixes to the meter—the basic unit of length.

The basic metric measurement unit for capacity is the liter. Other metric units for capacity are named by attaching the metric prefixes to the base unit of liter.

PRACTICE/APPLY

Review with students that to convert metric measures from a larger unit to a smaller unit, multiply the larger unit by the smaller unit to find a larger number of small units. Conversely, to convert from a smaller metric unit to a larger unit, divide the smaller unit by the larger unit to find a small number of large units.

Skills Practice

1. 4,000; multiply by 1,000
2. 5; divide by 1,000
3. 3; divide by 1,000
4. 6,000; multiply by 1,000

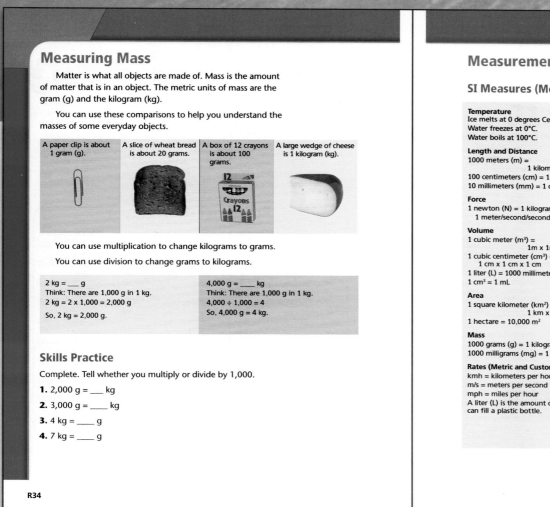

Measuring Mass

Matter is what all objects are made of. Mass is the amount of matter that is in an object. The metric units of mass are the gram (g) and the kilogram (kg).

You can use these comparisons to help you understand the masses of some everyday objects.

A paper clip is about 1 gram (g).	A slice of wheat bread is about 20 grams.	A box of 12 crayons is about 100 grams.	A large wedge of cheese is 1 kilogram (kg).

You can use multiplication to change kilograms to grams.

You can use division to change grams to kilograms.

2 kg = ___ g	4,000 g = ____ kg
Think: There are 1,000 g in 1 kg.	Think: There are 1,000 g in 1 kg.
2 kg = 2 x 1,000 = 2,000 g	4,000 ÷ 1,000 = 4
So, 2 kg = 2,000 g.	So, 4,000 g = 4 kg.

Skills Practice

Complete. Tell whether you multiply or divide by 1,000.

1. 2,000 g = ___ kg

2. 3,000 g = ____ kg

3. 4 kg = ____ g

4. 7 kg = ____ g

Measurement Systems

SI Measures (Metric)

Temperature
Ice melts at 0 degrees Celsius (°C).
Water freezes at 0°C.
Water boils at 100°C.

Length and Distance
1000 meters (m) =
                    1 kilometer (km)
100 centimeters (cm) = 1 m
10 millimeters (mm) = 1 cm

Force
1 newton (N) = 1 kilogram x
    1 meter/second/second (kg-m/s^2)

Volume
1 cubic meter (m^3) =
                    1m x 1m x 1m
1 cubic centimeter (cm^3) =
    1 cm x 1 cm x 1 cm
1 liter (L) = 1000 millimeters (mL)
1 cm^3 = 1 mL

Area
1 square kilometer (km^2) =
                    1 km x 1 km
1 hectare = 10,000 m^2

Mass
1000 grams (g) = 1 kilogram (kg)
1000 milligrams (mg) = 1 g

Rates (Metric and Customary)
kmh = kilometers per hour
m/s = meters per second
mph = miles per hour
A liter (L) is the amount of liquid that can fill a plastic bottle.

Customary Measures

Volume of Fluids
2 cups (c) = 1 pint (pt)
2 pt = 1 quart (qt)
4 qt = 1 gallon (gal)

Temperature
Ice melts at 32 degrees Fahrenheit (°F).
Water freezes at 32°F.
Water boils at 212°F.

Length and Distance
12 inches (in.) = 1 foot (ft)
3 ft = 1 yard (yd)
5,280 ft = 1 mile (mi)

Weight
16 ounces (oz) = 1 pound (lb)
2,000 pounds = 1 ton (T)

TEACH/MODEL

Explain to students that although they are often used interchangeably, weight and mass are different measures. Mass is a measure of an object's resistance to movement, while weight measures the force of gravity on an object. The weight of an object decreases as it is moved away from Earth, but the mass of the object remains constant regardless of its position.

The standard metric unit for mass is the gram. The metric system is related to the base-ten system in which the gram is divided or multiplied by powers of 10 as a means of selecting the appropriate unit.

PRACTICE/APPLY

Review the comparisons with students to help them understand the masses of everyday objects. Based on the comparisons, ask students what the mass of a nickel, a cat, and a child would be. 5 grams; 5 kilograms; 15 kilograms

Skill Practice

1. 2; divide by 1,000

2. 3; divide by 1,000

3. 4,000; multiply by 1,000

4. 7,000; multiply by 1,000

Safety in Science

Doing investigations in science can be fun, but you need to be sure you do them safely. Here are some rules to follow.

1. **Think ahead.** Study the steps of the investigation so you know what to expect. If you have any questions, ask your teacher. Be sure you understand any caution statements or safety reminders.

2. **Be neat.** Keep your work area clean. If you have long hair, pull it back so it doesn't get in the way. Roll or push up long sleeves to keep them away from your experiment.

3. **Oops!** If you spill or break something, or if you get cut, tell your teacher right away.

4. **Watch your eyes.** Wear safety goggles anytime you are directed to do so. If you get anything in your eyes, tell your teacher right away.

5. **Yuck!** Never eat or drink anything during a science activity.

6. **Don't get shocked.** Be especially careful if an electric appliance is used. Be sure that electrical cords are in a safe place where you can't trip over them. Never pull a plug out of an outlet by pulling on the cord.

7. **Keep it clean.** Always clean up when you have finished. Put everything away and wipe your work area. Wash your hands.

Visit the Multimedia Science Glossary to see illustrations of these words and to hear them pronounced.
www.hspscience.com

Glossary

As you read your science book, you will notice that new or unfamiliar words have been respelled to help you pronounce them. Those respellings are *phonetic respellings*. In this Glossary, you will see the same kind of respellings.

In the phonetic respellings, syllables are separated by a bullet (•). Small, uppercase letters show stressed syllables.

The boldfaced letters in the examples in the Pronunciation Key below identify the letters and combinations of letters that the respellings represent.

The page number in (parentheses) at the end of a definition tells you where to find the term defined in your Grade 3, vocabulary book.

Pronunciation Key

Sound	As in	Phonetic Respelling	Sound	As in	Phonetic Respelling
a	bat	(BAT)	oh	over	(OH•ver)
ah	lock	(lahk)	oo	pool	(pool)
air	rare	(rair)	ow	out	(owt)
ar	argue	(AR•gyoo)	oy	foil	(foyl)
aw	law	(law)	s	cell	(sel)
ay	face	(fays)		sit	(sit)
ch	chapel	(CHAP•uhl)	sh	sheep	(sheep)
e	test	(test)	th	that	(that)
	metric	(MEH•trik)		thin	(thin)
ee	eat	(eet)	u	pull	(pul)
	feet	(feet)	uh	medal	(MED•uhl)
	ski	(skee)		talent	(TAL•uhnt)
er	paper	(PAY•per)		pencil	(PEN•suhl)
	fern	(fern)		onion	(UHN•yuhn)
eye	idea	(eye•DEE•uh)		playful	(PLAY•fuhl)
i	bit	(bit)		dull	(duhl)
ing	going	(GOH•ing)	y	yes	(yes)
k	card	(kard)		ripe	(ryp)
	kite	(kyt)	z	bags	(bagz)
ngk	bank	(bangk)	zh	treasure	(TREZH•er)

Multimedia Science Glossary: www.hspscience.com

A

absorbed [ab•SAWRBD] Taken in by an object. **(474)**

adaptation [ad•uhp•TAY•shuhn] Any trait that helps a plant or animal survive. **(142)**

amphibian [am•FIB•ee•uhn] A type of vertebrate that has moist skin; and legs as an adult. **(101)**

anemometer [an•uh•MAHM•uht•er] A weather instrument that measures wind speed. **(325)**

atmosphere [AT•muhs•feer] The air around Earth. **(322)**

axis [AK•sis] A line—that you cannot see—from the top of Earth through the center of Earth to the bottom. **(338)**

B

bird [BERD] A type of vertebrate that has feathers. **(99)**

C

camouflage [KAM•uh•flahzh] Colors, patterns, and shapes that disguise an animal and help it hide. **(146)**

canyon [KAN•yuhn] A valley with steep sides. **(234)**

carnivore [KAR•nuh•vawr] An animal that eats other animals. **(167)**

cell [SEL] A tiny building block that makes up every part of an organism. **(34)**

chlorophyll [KLAWR•uh•FIL] The green substance inside leaves that helps a plant use light energy. **(75)**

circuit [SER•kuht] A path that electricity follows. **(437)**

clay [KLAY] Soil with very, very tiny grains of rock. **(275)**

combustion [kuhm•BUS•chuhn] Another word for burning. **(419)**

community [kuh•MYOO•nuh•tee] All the populations of organisms that live in an ecosystem at the same time. **(129)**

condensation [kahn•duhn•SAY•shuhn] The process by which water vapor changes into liquid water. **(316, 388)**

conduction [kuhn•DUHK•shuhn] The movment of heat between objects that are touching each other. **(463)**

conductor [kuhn•DUHK•ter] An object that heat can move through easily. **(463)**

conservation [kahn•ser•VAY•shuhn] The saving of resources by using them wisely. **(288)**

constellation [kahn•stuh•LAY•shuhn] A group of stars that appear to form the shape of an animal, a person, or an object. **(360)**

consumer [kuhn•SOOM•er] A living thing that gets its energy by eating other living things as food. **(165)**

crest [KREST] The highest point of a wave. **(516)**

current electricity [KER•uhnt ee•lek•TRIS•uh•tee] Electricity that moves through a wire. **(437)**

D

deciduous [dee•SIJ•oo•uhs] Relating to plants that lose all their leaves at the same time every year. **(67)**

decomposer [dee•kuhm•POHZ•er] A living thing that breaks down dead organisms for food. **(165)**

density [DEN•suh•tee] The mass of matter compared to its volume. **(379)**

desert [DEZ•ert] An ecosystem that is very dry. **(134)**

distance [DIS•tuhns] How far one location is from another. **(500)**

E

earthquake [ERTH•kwayk] The shaking of Earth's surface caused by movement in Earth's crust. **(248)**

ecosystem [EE•koh•sis•tuhm] The living and nonliving things that interact in an environment. **(128)**

energy [EN•er•jee] The ability to make something move or change. **(410)**

energy pyramid [EN•er•jee PIR•uh•mid] A diagram that shows how energy gets used in a food chain. **(174)**

environment [en•VY•ruhn•muhnt] The things, both living and nonliving, that surround a living thing. **(127)**

erosion [uh•ROH•zhuhn] The movement of weathered rock and soil. **(242)**

evaporation [ee•vap•uh•RAY•shuhn] The process by which liquid water changes into water vapor. **(317, 388)**

evergreen [EV•er•green] A plant that stays green and makes food all year long. **(67)**

experiment [ek•SPAIR•uh•muhnt] A test done to see if a hypothesis is correct or not. **(21)**

F

fish [FISH] A type of vertebrate that breathes through gills and spends its life in water. **(102)**

flood [FLUHD] A large amount of water that covers normally dry land. **(252)**

food chain [FOOD CHAYN] The path of food from one living thing to another. **(172)**

food web [FOOD WEB] Food chains that overlap. **(180)**

force [FAWRS] A push or a pull. **(506)**

forceps [FAWR•seps] A tool used to pick up and hold on to objects. **(5)**

forest [FAWR•uhst] An ecosystem in which many trees grow. **(138)**

formulate [FAWR•myoo•layt] To come up with a plan for something. **(16)**

fossil [FAHS•uhl] A trace or the remains of a living thing that died a long time ago. **(216)**

fossil fuel [FAHS•uhl FYOO•uhl] A resource that comes from the remains of plants and animals that lived long ago. **(425)**

fresh water [FRESH WAWT•er] Water that has very little salt in it. **(307)**

fulcrum [FUL•kruhm] The fixed point on a lever. **(538)**

G

gas [GAS] A kind of matter that has no definite shape or volume. **(387)**

generator [JEN•er•ayt•er] A device that uses a magnet to make a current of electricity. **(450)**

glacier [GLAY•sher] A huge sheet or block of ice. **(244, 308)**

grassland [GRAS•land] An area of land that is generally hot in the summer and cold in the winter. The main plants found in this ecosystem are grasses. **(135)**

Multimedia Science Glossary: www.hspscience.com

gravity [GRAV•ih•tee] A force that pulls two objects toward each other. **(510)**

groundwater [GROWND•waw•ter] An underground supply of water. **(308)**

habitat [HAB•h•tat] The place where a population lives in an ecosystem. **(129)**

heat [HEET] The movement of thermal energy from hotter to cooler objects. **(462)**

herbivore [HER•buh•vawr] An animal that eats only plants. **(166)**

hibernate [HY•ber•nayt] To go into a sleeplike state for the winter. **(144)**

humus [HYOO•muhs] The part of soil made up of broken-down parts of dead plants and animals. **(272)**

hypothesis [hy•PAHTH•uh•sis] A possible answer to a question that can be tested to see if it is correct. **(21)**

igneous rock [IG•nee•uhs RAHK] Rock that was once melted and then cooled and hardened. **(206)**

inclined plane [in•KLYND PLAYN] A simple machine that makes moving or lifting things easier. **(546)**

infer [in•FER] To draw a conclusion about something. **(13)**

inherit [in•HAIR•it] To have a trait passed on from parents. **(44)**

inquiry [IN•kwer•ee] A question that is asked about something, or a close study of something. **(4)**

instinct [IN•stingkt] A behavior that an animal knows without being taught. **(142)**

insulator [IN•suh•layt•er] An object that doesn't conduct heat well. **(464)**

invertebrate [in•VER•tuh•brit] An animal without a backbone. **(106)**

investigation [in•ves•tuh•GAY•shuhn] A study that a scientist does. **(20)**

kinetic energy [kih•NET•ik EN•er•jee] The energy of motion. **(412)**

landform [LAND•fawrm] A natural shape on Earth's surface. **(232)**

larva [LAHR•vuh] The stage of complete metamorphosis, or change, after an organism hatches from its egg. **(43)**

leaf [LEEF] The part of a plant that grows out of the stem, and is where a plant makes food. **(58)**

lever [LEV•er] A simple machine made up of a bar that pivots, or turns, on a fixed point. **(538)**

life cycle [LYF SY•kuhl] The changes that happen to an organism during its life. **(40)**

liquid [LIK•wid] A kind of liquid matter that has a volume that stays the same but a shape that can change. **(386)**

loam [LOHM] Soil that is a mixture of humus, sand, silt, and clay. **(276)**

loudness [LOWD•nuhs] The amount of energy a sound has. **(482)**

lunar cycle [LOON•er CY•kuhl] The pattern of phases of the moon. **(347)**

lunar eclipse [LOON•er ih•KLIPS] An event in which Earth blocks sunlight from reaching the moon. **(348)**

magnetic [mag•NET•ik] Attracting objects that have iron in them. **(442)**

mammal [MAM•uhl] A type of vertebrate that has hair or fur and gives birth to live young. **(98)**

mass [MAS] The amount of matter in an object. **(378)**

matter [MAT•er] Anything that takes up space. **(374)**

metamorphic rock [met•uh•MAWR•fik RAHK] Rock that has been changed by heat or pressure. **(207)**

metamorphosis [met•uh•MAWR•fuh•sis] A series of changes in appearance that some organisms go through. **(42)**

migrate [MY•grayt] To travel from one place to another and back again. **(145)**

mimicry [MIM•ik•ree] The imitating of the look of another animal. **(146)**

mineral [MIN•er•uhl] A solid object found in nature that has never been alive. **(198)**

mixture [MIKS•cher] A substance that has two or more different kinds of matter. **(394)**

moon phases [MOON FAYZ•uhz] The different shapes that the moon seems to have in the sky when it is observed from Earth. **(346)**

motion [MOH•shuhn] A change of position. **(499)**

mountain [MOWNT•uhn] A place on Earth's surface that is much higher than the land around it. **(233)**

nonrenewable resource [nahn•rih•NOO•uh•buhl REE•sawrs] A resource that, when it is used up, will not exist again during a human lifetime. **(268, 426)**

nutrients [NOO•tree•uhntsz] The parts of the soil that helps plants grow and stay healthy. **(58)**

omnivore [AHM•nih•vawr] A consumer that eats both plants and animals. **(168)**

opaque [oh•PAYK] Relating to objects that don't let light pass through. **(475)**

orbit [AWR•bit] The path a planet takes as it revolves around the sun. **(354)**

organism [AWR•guh•niz•uhm] Any living thing. **(32)**

oxygen [AHK•sih•juhn] A gas that people need to live and that plants give off into the air. **(89, 322)**

photosynthesis [foht•oh•SIN•thuh•sis] The process that plants use to make sugar. **(74)**

physical property [FIZ•ih•kuhl PRAHP•er•tee] Any thing that you can observe about an object by using one or more of your senses. **(376)**

Multimedia Science Glossary: www.hspscience.com

pitch [PICH] The highness or lowness of a sound. **(483)**

plain [PLAYN] A wide, flat area on Earth's surface. **(235)**

planet [PLAN•it] A large body of rock or gas in space. **(354)**

plateau [pla•TOH] A flat area higher than the land around it. **(236)**

pollution [puh•LOO•shuhn] Any harmful material in the environment. **(282)**

population [pahp•yuh•LAY•shuhn] A group of organisms of the same kind that live in the same place. **(128)**

potential energy [poh•TEN•shuhl EN•er•jee] Energy of position. **(412)**

precipitation [pree•sip•uh•TAY•shuhn] Rain, snow, sleet, or hail. **(318)**

predator [PRED•uh•ter] An animal that hunts another animal for food. **(176)**

prey [PRAY] An animal that is hunted by a predator. **(176)**

producer [pruh•DOOS•er] A living thing that makes its own food. **(165)**

pulley [PUL•ee] A simple machine made up of a wheel with a rope around it. **(542)**

pupa [PYOO•puh] The stage of complete change, or metamorphosis, where an organism is wrapped in a cocoon. **(43)**

recycle [ree•SY•kuhl] To reuse a resource by breaking it down and making a new product. **(292)**

reduce [ree•DOOS] To use less of a resource. **(290)**

reflection [rih•FLEK•shuhn] The bouncing of light off an object. **(468)**

refraction [rih•FRAK•shuhn] The bending of light as it moves from one material to another. **(469)**

renewable resource [rih•NOO•uh•buhl REE•sawrs] A resource that can be replaced quickly. **(266, 426)**

reptile [REP•tyl] A type of vertebrate that has dry skin covered with scales. **(100)**

resource [REE•sawrs] A material that is found in nature and that is used by living things. **(151, 264, 425)**

reusable resource [ree•YOOZ•uh•buhl REE•sawrs] A resource that can be used again and again. **(267)**

reuse [ree•YOOZ] To use a resource again and again. **(291)**

revolution [rev•uh•LOO•shuhn] The movement of Earth one time around the sun. **(339)**

rock [RAHK] A naturally formed solid made of one or more minerals. **(202)**

root [ROOT] The part of a plant that grows underground and takes water and nutrients from the soil. **(58)**

rotation [roh•TAY•shuhn] The spinning of Earth on its axis. **(338)**

sand [SAND] Soil with grains of rock that you can see with your eyes alone. **(275)**

scientific method [sy•uhn•TIF•ik METH•uhd] An organized plan that scientists use to conduct a study. **(20)**

screw [SKROO] A simple machine you turn to lift an object or hold two or more objects together. **(550)**

sedimentary rock [sed•uh•MEN•ter•ee RAHK] Rock made when materials settle into layers and get squeezed until they harden into rock. **(207)**

seed [SEED] The first stage of life for many plants. **(65)**

shadow [SHAD•oh] A dark area that forms when an object blocks the path of light. **(470)**

silt [SILT] Soil with grains of rock that are too small to see with your eyes alone. **(275)**

simple machine [SIM•puhl muh•SHEEN] A tool with few or no moving parts that helps people do work. **(537)**

solar eclipse [SOH•ler ih•KLIPS] An event that occurs when the moon blocks the sunlight from reaching Earth and the moon's shadow falls on Earth. **(350)**

solar system [SOH•ler SIS•tuhm] The sun, the planets and their moons, and the small objects that orbit the sun. **(354)**

solid [SAHL•id] A kind of matter with a volume and a shape that both stay the same. **(385)**

solution [suh•LOO•shuhn] A mixture in which the different kinds of matter mix evenly. **(395)**

speed [SPEED] The distance that an object moves in a certain period of time. **(502)**

star [STAR] A hot ball of glowing gases that gives off energy. **(355)**

static electricity [STAT•ik ee•lek•TRIS•uh•tee] An electric charge that builds up in an object. **(436)**

stem [STEM] The part of a plant that grows above ground and helps hold the plant up. **(58)**

valley [VAL•ee] A low area between higher lands such as mountains. **(234)**

variable [VAIR•ee•uh•buhl] One thing that changes in a science inquiry or experiment. **(15)**

vertebrate [VER•tuh•brit] An animal with a backbone. **(97)**

vibration [vy•BRAY•shuhn] A series of back-and-forth movements. **(482)**

volcano [vahl•KAY•noh] An opening in Earth's surface from which lava flows. **(250)**

volume [VAHL•yoom] The amount of space that matter takes up. **(379)**

water cycle [WAW•ter SY•kuhl] The movement of water from Earth's land, through rivers toward the ocean, to the air, and back to the land. **(318)**

wave [WAYV] A disturbance that travels through matter or space. **(514)**

wavelength [WAYV•length] The distance from one point of one wave to the same point on the next wave. **(516)**

weather [WETH•er] What is happening in the atmosphere at a certain place and time. **(324)**

weathering [WETH•er•ing] The breaking down of rocks into smaller pieces. **(240)**

wedge [WEJ] A simple machine that is made up of two inclined planes placed back-to-back. **(548)**

weight [WAYT] The measure of the force of gravity on an object. **(510)**

wheel-and-axle [weel•and•AK•suhl] A simple machine made up of an axle and a wheel that are connected and turn together. **(540)**

work [WERK] The use of a force to move an object. **(530)**

Teaching Notes

Teaching Notes

Bibliography

Science Trade Books

This bibliography has been compiled from the trade books listed within each chapter. The National Science Teachers Association (NSTA) has chosen many of the books cited here as outstanding science trade books for students. Members of the NSTA book review panel and The Children's Book Council have reviewed these books following rigorous selection criteria. They have determined that substantial science content is provided; the information is presented in a clear, accurate, and up-to-date manner; the theories and facts are clearly distinguished; and other similar standards have been met. In addition, the reviewers have correlated the content of the books to the National Science Content Standards. Many other selections are also award-winning titles, or their authors have received awards.

As with all materials you share with your class, we suggest you review the books first to ensure their appropriateness. While titles are current at time of publication, they may go out of print without notice.

Albert Einstein, by Lola M. Schaefer and Wyatt S. Schaefer (Pebble Books, 2004), illustrates and describes the life of physicist Albert Einstein.

And the Good Brown Earth, by Kathy Henderson (Candlewick, 2003), shows how a boy and his grandmother grow a garden, with the help of the good brown earth.

Antarctic Ice, by Jim Mastro and Norbert Wu (Henry Holt, 2003), describes food webs and life, both above and below the ice during the short Antarctic summer. *NSTA Trade Book*

Autumn Leaves, by Ken Robbins (Scholastic, 1998), takes the reader on a walking tour to see the 13 best-known autumn leaves and their trees. *NSTA Trade Book*

Castles, Caves, and Honeycombs, by Lauren Stringer (Harcourt, 2001), describes some unique places where animals build their homes, such as in a heap of twigs, in a cave, or in a hollow space inside a tree.

Clay, by Mary Firestone (Capstone, 2005), discusses where clay comes from and some of its features and uses.

Cloud Dance, by Thomas Locker (Harcourt, 2000), attains a superb level of poetic text and spectacular drawings; technical information about clouds adds useful detail. *NSTA Trade Book*

Crawdad Creek, by Scott Russell Sanders (National Geographic, 1999), encourages readers to go out, find moving water, and open their eyes, ears, and hearts to investigate the natural world. *NSTA Trade Book*

Dandelions, by Kathleen V. Kudlinski (Lerner, 1999), is an excellent resource for learning about the life cycle of the dandelion plant; includes interesting facts about the plant's history and its uses. *NSTA Trade Book*

Earth Friends at Play: Reduce, Reuse, Recycle, by Francine Galko (Heinemann, 2004), discusses the importance of reducing waste, recycling, and reusing products in the context of playing at home and outdoors.

Energy, by Christine Webster (Capstone, 2005), introduces the concept of energy and provides instructions for an activity to demonstrate some of its characteristics.

Flick a Switch: How Electricity Gets to Your Home, by Barbara Seuling (Holiday House, 2003), describes how electricity was discovered, how early devices were invented to make use of it, and how it is generated in power plants and then distributed for many different uses. *Award-Winning Author*

Forces, by Robert Snedden (Heinemann, 1999), discusses various aspects of force, including gravity, magnetism, Newton's laws, inertia, friction, action and reaction, velocity, acceleration, balanced forces, combined forces, and elastic energy. *Award-Winning Author*

Forces: Science All Around Me, by Karen Bryant-Mole (Heinemann, 1997), explains the basic principles of forces and movement through direct observation and through looking at everyday experiences.

The Great Kapok Tree, by Lynne Cherry (Harcourt, 2000), describes the many different animals that live in a great kapok tree in the Brazilian rain forest and discusses their importance to the preservation of ecology. *NSTA Trade Book*

Green Plants: From Roots to Leaves, by Louise and Richard Spilsbury (Heinemann, 2004), describes how plants grow and change.

Gulls...Gulls...Gulls, by Gail Gibbons (Holiday House, 1997), uses detailed text and clear illustrations to describe nearly every aspect of gulls, from their appearance to migration and more. *NSTA Trade Book*

Hot and Cold, by Karen Bryant-Mole (Heinemann, 2002), introduces the scientific properties of heat and cold, examining such topics as temperature, thermometers, freezing, and melting.

How Does a Trumpet Work?: Projects About Sound, by Trevor Day (Copper Beech Books, 2002), describes how and why things make sound.

How Mountains Are Made, by Kathleen Weidner Zoehfeld (HarperCollins, 1995), describes different types of mountains and how they are made. *NSTA Trade Book*

Into the Woods: John James Audubon Lives His Dream, by Robert Burleigh (Atheneum, 2003), encourages the reader to view the natural world through Audubon's eyes and to gain a greater appreciation for the man as a naturalist and an artist. *NSTA Trade Book*

The Light Bulb, by Marc Tyler Nobleman (Capstone, 1998), explores the history of the light bulb and describes how a light bulb works.

Machines We Use, by Sally Hewitt (Children's Press, 1998), examines various simple machines and how they are used to make work easier; also provides activities using wheels, levers, pulleys, screws, and more.

Make It Change, by David Evans and Claudette Williams (Dorling Kindersley, 1992), uses simple observations and experiments to explore how various materials are changed by such processes as heating, wetting, and stirring.

Me and My Place in Space, by Joan Sweeney (Crown, 1998), describes how the earth, sun, and planets are part of our solar system, which is just one small part of the universe.

My World: Seasons, by Tammy J. Schlepp (Copper Beech Books, 2000), describes the changes that occur during the four seasons as well as characteristics of each.

Nature's Paintbrush: The Patterns and Colors Around You, by Susan Stockdale (Simon & Schuster, 1999), encourages children to observe, think about, and enjoy colors and patterns in the natural world. *NSTA Trade Book*

One Tiny Turtle, by Nicola Davies (Candlewick, 2001), describes the life cycle of the loggerhead turtle. *Teacher's Choice*

Our Big Home: An Earth Poem, by Linda Glaser (Millbrook, 2000), details children and animals through delightful multicultural drawings from around the world. *NSTA Trade Book*

People Change the Land, by David Bauer (Yellow Umbrella, 2004), explores ways in which people change the land, from building houses and bridges to planting gardens.

Polar Bear, Polar Bear, What Do You Hear?, by Bill Martin Jr. (Henry Holt, 1991), introduces the distinctive sounds made by various zoo animals, while giving children the chance to learn these sounds through imitation. *Children's Choice*

Pumpkin Circle: The Story of a Garden, by George Levenson (Tricycle, 1999), captures each phase of the pumpkin's life cycle with time-lapse photography: seeds sprouting, flowers blooming, bees buzzing, pumpkins growing, and finally a pumpkin returning to the earth. *NSTA Trade Book*

River of Life, by Debbie S. Miller (Clarion, 2000), explains the life cycle that unfolds along a river ecosystem, as winter melts into spring and spring becomes the warm days of summer. *NSTA Trade Book*

Science with Light and Mirrors, by Kate Woodward (Usborne, 1991), features an array of safe scientific activities that help children learn about the properties of light.

Science with Magnets, by Helen Edom (Usborne, 1992), reveals the properties and basic scientific principles relating to magnetism, while offering safe, fun, and simple experiments designed to teach through personal experience and observation.

Slugs, by Anthony D. Fredericks (Lerner, 2000), is a resource that describes the physical characteristics, habitat, and behavior of slugs. *NSTA Trade Book*

Spinning Spiders, by Melvin Berger (HarperCollins, 2003), shows several species of spiders and how their different kinds of webs help them capture, secure, or store their prey and how spiders that don't spin webs catch their prey. *NSTA Trade Book*

Spring Thaw, by Steven Schnur (Viking, 2000), explores the changes in farmland as the signs of spring appear. *NSTA Trade Book*

Sun, by Steve Tomecek (National Geographic, 2001), describes the physics and characteristics of the sun.

A Symphony of Whales, by Steve Schuch (Harcourt, 1999), is a true story about the efforts of a group of people working to save whales trapped in an ice-enclosed bay. *NSTA Trade Book*

Temperature, by Rebecca Olien (Capstone, 2005), introduces the concept of temperature and provides instructions for an activity to demonstrate some of its characteristics.

Water Cycle, by Monica Hughes (Heinemann, 2004), describes the different forms of water and introduces the concepts of evaporation and condensation. *Award-Winning Author*

Water Dance, by Thomas Locker (Harcourt, 1997), involves readers in a question-and-answer format, observing the natural movement of water. *NSTA Trade Book*

Water, Water Everywhere, by Mark J. Rauzon and Cynthia Overbeck Bix (Sierra Club, 1994), describes the forms water takes, how it has shaped Earth, and its importance to life.

Weather Around You, by Angela Royston (Raintree Steck-Vaughn, 1998), presents basic information about the weather, the different forms it takes, and its effect on our lives. *Award-Winning Author*

What Computers Do, by Holly J. Endres (Yellow Umbrella, 2004), introduces the various ways in which people use computers.

What Do You Do When Something Wants to Eat You?, by Steven Jenkins (Houghton Mifflin, 1997), introduces young readers to the specialized adaptations animals use to avoid the constant threat of becoming another animal's meal. *NSTA Trade Book*

What Makes a Magnet?, by Franklyn M. Branley (HarperCollins, 1996), describes how magnets work and includes instructions for making a magnet and a compass. *Award-Winning Author*

Wheels and Cranks, by Angela Royston (Heinemann, 2001), introduces the basic principles, design, and technology of wheels and cranks and shows how these simple machines help power more complex machines. *Award-Winning Author*

Why Does a Battery Make It Go?, by Jackie Holderness (Copper Beech Books, 2002), provides simple text and fun experiments to teach children about the properties of electricity.

The Yangtze River, by Nathan Olson (Capstone, 2004), discusses the path of the Yangtze River, its history, uses, people, and importance today.

Teaching Notes for the Leveled Readers

Chapter 1 Types of Living Things

Below-Level/Intervention

Reading Level 1.5-2.0

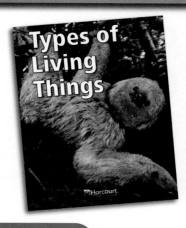
Types of Living Things

The Intervention Reader presents identical chapter content and vocabulary at a below grade reading level. The reader uses a visual glossary, simplified language, and comprehension aids especially designed for struggling readers. The *Intervention Reader Teacher Guide* provides scaffolded strategies for using the reader and student worksheets for vocabulary, fluency, and comprehension.

On-Level/Enrichment

Living Things Grow and Change

This reader promotes success on state science tests by reinforcing tested content objectives, chapter vocabulary, and reading skills. **Reading Level 2.5-3.5**

Summary The differences between living and nonliving things are described. Cells, life cycles, and the differences between plants and animals are covered.

Preview/Set a Purpose Help students preview the book. Point out and discuss the title, headings, and illustrations.

Key Vocabulary
cell   organism
life cycle
metamorphosis

Reading Focus Skills
Compare and Contrast
Sequence

Read for Fluency Have students work in pairs. Ask them to choose and read aloud favorite parts of the book to one another.

Respond—Answers to Think and Write Questions
1. Roots: hold plant in place, take up water; stem: holds plant up straight, moves water and nutrients around; leaves: make food.
2. Possible answers: organisms are living things; organisms use energy to grow, can reproduce, and respond to changes; organisms have parts made of cells. Organisms go through a life cycle. Nonliving things do none of these things.
3. They grow and change physically; they also learn how to survive; they become capable of reproduction.
4. Students should be directed to concentrate on skills that help them survive. Possible answers may include cooking food, crossing streets, going to school in preparation for a job, how to dress for different types of weather, etc.

Advanced/Challenge

Patterns: Do You See What I See?

This interesting nonfiction reader enriches and extends chapter concepts. **Reading Level 4.0-5.5**

Summary The word *pattern* is commonly used in ways that can be confusing. It can mean both a thing that is repeated and the design that results from that repetition. This reader limits the definition of a pattern to something that is repeated, and then presents examples of patterns in nature that you can see, patterns in nature that you can hear and patterns in the development of animals.

Preview/Set a Purpose Have students read the subtitles and look at the illustrations. Ask them if they have ever seen any of the patterns in the pictures on the first four pages.

Key Vocabulary
hexagon   chrysalis
spiral   metamorphosis

Read for Fluency Ask each student to choose his or her favorite pattern in the reader and read aloud to the class the section describing that pattern.

Respond—Answers to Think and Write Questions
1. Accept all naturally occurring objects that are spiral-shaped. Those in the text are the shell of the chambered nautilus, a ram's horn, a hurricane, and the Milky Way Galaxy.
2. Frog
3. The formula says to count the number of chirps a cricket makes in 15 seconds and then to add 37 to that number to get the temperature in degrees Fahrenheit. Here, the cricket chirped 25 times in 15 seconds. $25 + 37 = 62°$ F.
4. Accept all reasonable paragraphs that describe a bird's song and how it repeated.

Chapter 2 Types of Plants

 Below-Level/Intervention

Reading Level 1.5-2.0

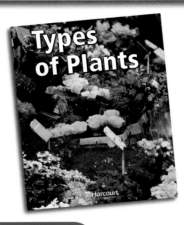

The Intervention Reader presents identical chapter content and vocabulary at a below grade reading level. The reader uses a visual glossary, simplified language, and comprehension aids especially designed for struggling readers. The Intervention Reader Teacher Guide provides scaffolded strategies for using the reader and student worksheets for vocabulary, fluency, and comprehension.

 **On-Level/Enrichment**

This reader promotes success on state science tests by reinforcing tested content objectives, chapter vocabulary, and reading skills. **Reading Level 2.5-3.5**

Summary Describes plant physical structure and systems. Emphasizes how energy is provided to plants by the sun.

Preview/Set a Purpose Have students read the names of the plants, systems, and structures shown in the illustrations. Ask them to tell what they know about plants and what they expect to learn.

Key Vocabulary
leaf
root
stem
photosynthesis

Reading Focus Skills
Compare and Contrast
Main Idea and Details
Cause and Effect

Read for Fluency Have each student choose a section of the book that he or she understands and likes and then reread it aloud to you.

Respond —Answers to Think and Write Questions
1. Soil: to get nutrients; water, self-explanatory; air: uses carbon dioxide to photosynthesize, emits oxygen; sunlight: uses energy to photosynthesize.
2. Bald Cypress roots are deep and spread out wide; this lets it hold firm to the ground and dig deep for nutrients. Cactus roots are shallow to collect as much rainwater as it can.
3. sugar and oxygen
4. Students answers should reflect an understanding that photosynthesis requires light, water, and carbon dioxide. Light gives energy to turn water and carbon dioxide into sugar. Oxygen is exhaled as a byproduct.

 **Advanced/Challenge**

This interesting nonfiction reader enriches and extends chapter concepts. **Reading Level 4.0-5.5**

Summary Description of many highly unusual plants, including the world's largest tree and the world's oldest living plant, and the variety of plants that each produce the world's largest fruit, flower, tuber, seed, and leaf.

Preview/Set a Purpose Have students read the subtitles and look at the illustrations. Ask them to predict what the reader is about and then set a purpose for reading.

Key Vocabulary
fruit   tuber
rafflesia   plant clone

Read for Fluency Have students work in pairs. Ask each student to choose his or her favorite plant in the reader and read aloud the section describing that plant.

Respond Have students respond to the Think and Write questions in the back of the reader. A Hands-on Activity and School-Home Connection are also provided.
Answers to Think and Write Questions

1. First, start the seed indoors before the growing season begins. Then transplant them into rich soil. Then, remove all of the pumpkins from the vines except the ones growing the fastest. Finally, give the plant plenty of water and nutrients.
2. about 2100 kilometers (1300 mi)
3. any part of a flowering plant that contains seeds
4. Paragraph should persuade people to help save the remaining giant sequoias. Accept all reasonable responses.

Chapter 3 Types of Animals

Below-Level/Intervention

Reading Level 1.5-2.0

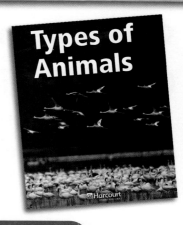

The Intervention Reader presents identical chapter content and vocabulary at a below grade reading level. The reader uses a visual glossary, simplified language, and comprehension aids especially designed for struggling readers. The Intervention Reader Teacher Guide provides scaffolded strategies for using the reader and student worksheets for vocabulary, fluency, and comprehension.

On-Level/Enrichment

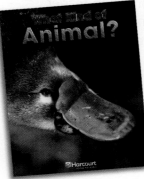

This reader promotes success on state science tests by reinforcing tested content objectives, chapter vocabulary, and reading skills. **Reading Level 2.5-3.5**

Summary The differences between plants and animals are explained. The distinguishing characteristics of vertebrates are discussed in depth.

Preview/Set a Purpose To set a purpose for learning, help students preview the book. Point out and discuss the title, headings, and illustrations.

Key Vocabulary
amphibian
reptile
vertebrate
mammal

 Reading Focus Skills
Main Idea and Details
Compare and Contrast
Sequence
Cause and Effect

Read for Fluency Have students choose and reread aloud the descriptions of their favorite animal.

Respond —Answers to Think and Write Questions
1. A zebra is a mammal, because it has fur covering it. Students may also know that zebras give birth to live animals and make milk for them.
2. Birds have feathers, wings, and hollow bones.
3. Amphibians and reptiles both lay eggs. Amphibians lay them in water, while reptiles lay them on land. Some reptiles can go in water, but they must come up to breathe. Amphibians were born with gills, and lived underwater until they grew lungs.
4. Students' answers should reflect a general understanding of vertebrates, as well as a specific understanding of the vertebrate they choose to write about.

Advanced/Challenge

This interesting nonfiction reader enriches and extends chapter concepts. **Reading Level 4.0-5.5**

Summary Loggerhead nesting behavior is described and the path of a female loggerhead sea turtle is traced from egg to adult.

Preview/Set a Purpose Have students preview the book and predict what they think they will learn.

Key Vocabulary
hatch   threatened
current

Read for Fluency Have each student choose a section of the book that he or she likes and reread it aloud to you.

Respond Have students respond to the Think and Write questions in the back of the reader. A Hands-on Activity and School-Home Connection are also provided.
Answers to Think and Write Questions
1. Sample answer: About one in 1,000 to one in 10,000 hatchlings survive to become adults.
2. Sample Answer: A three year-old loggerhead turtle may be found in the North Atlantic gyre.
3. Sample Answer: Loggerhead sea turtles are graceful, beautiful animals that deserve the chance to survive on Earth. But without our help, they might disappear. We must work together to save the loggerheads!

Chapter 4 Where Living Things Are Found

 Below-Level/Intervention

Reading Level 1.5-2.0

The Intervention Reader presents identical chapter content and vocabulary at a below grade reading level. The reader uses a visual glossary, simplified language, and comprehension aids especially designed for struggling readers. The Intervention Reader Teacher Guide provides scaffolded strategies for using the reader and student worksheets for vocabulary, fluency, and comprehension.

 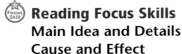 **On-Level/Enrichment**

This reader promotes success on state science tests by reinforcing tested content objectives, chapter vocabulary, and reading skills. **Reading Level 2.5-3.5**

Summary The relationship between plants and animals and their environments is explained. Ecosystems, populations, and communities are described. Adaptation is explained.

Preview/Set a Purpose Have students read the title and look at the illustrations. Ask them to predict what the book is about. Help students set a purpose for reading.

Key Vocabulary
adaptation
ecosystem
environment
habitat

Reading Focus Skills
Main Idea and Details
Cause and Effect

Read for Fluency Have each student choose a section of the reader and read it aloud.

Respond Have students respond to the Think and Write questions in the back of the reader. A Hands-On Activity and a School-Home Connection are also provided.
Answers to Think and Write Questions

1. It is mimicry. The butterfly is trying to look like another, larger insect to scare off predators.
2. Different living things have different needs. Habitats meet those needs. So, habitats are different.
3. The populations will not grow, or will decrease.
4. Students answers will vary according to the animal or plant they choose. Check for accuracy.

 Advanced/Challenge

This interesting nonfiction reader enriches and extends chapter concepts. **Reading Level 4.0-5.5**

Summary Animals are adapted for the environments in which they live. Polar bears are comfortable in extreme cold because they are adapted to it. Likewise, camels live well in the intense heat of the desert.

Preview/Set a Purpose Have students read the title and look at the illustrations. Ask them to compare the camel and the bear. Then have them read the book and see how accurate their comparisons were.

Key Vocabulary
insulate   environment
adaptation

Read for Fluency Have students reread aloud the descriptions of the polar bear and the camel.

Respond Have students respond to the Think and Write questions in the back of the reader. A Hands-on Activity and School-Home Connection are also provided.
Answers to Think and Write Questions

1. They store energy in their fat.
2. Thick, wooly fur and the ability to go for long periods without water.
3. Humans change, or adapt, to their environment to suit their physical needs.
4. Advertisement should include how camel can go for long periods without water, can keep working in the hot desert heat, does not require much food, and so on.

Chapter 5 Living Things Depend on One Another

Below-Level/Intervention

Reading Level I.5-2.0

The Intervention Reader presents identical chapter content and vocabulary at a below grade reading level. The reader uses a visual glossary, simplified language, and comprehension aids especially designed for struggling readers. The Intervention Reader Teacher Guide provides scaffolded strategies for using the reader and student worksheets for vocabulary, fluency, and comprehension.

On-Level/Enrichment

Summary The food chain, energy pyramid, and food web are explained. Highlights of discussion are: predators, prey; herbivore, carnivore, omnivore.

Preview/Set a Purpose Have students read the title and look at the illustrations. Help students set a purpose for reading. Ask them to predict what the book is about.
Reading Level 2.5-3.5

Key Vocabulary
food chain
food web
energy pyramid

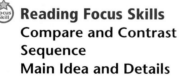 **Reading Focus Skills**
Compare and Contrast
Sequence
Main Idea and Details

Read for Fluency Have students reread aloud pages 8-13, paying special attention to the vocabulary words.

Respond —Answers to Think and Write Questions
1. Possible answer: The neck is an adaptation that helps the animal get leaves from a producer, a tall tree.
2. Possible answer: An animal can first be a predator when it hunts and eats another animal. It can then be prey when an animal hunts it and eats it.
3. Students, answers will vary depending on the food chain they choose. Answers should reflect an accurate understanding of energy being passed from producers to consumers to them. Example: sunlight helps bananas grow. Students eat bananas.
4. Possible answer: Insects are the basis for many food chains and webs. Killing insects would mean less food for animals higher up in the food chain.

Advanced/Challenge

Summary A young girl visits the Smoky Mountains with her family and keeps a journal of the animals and the traces of animals that she sees.

Preview/Set a Purpose Have students read the title and look at the illustrations. Ask them to predict what the book is about. Help students set a purpose for reading.
Reading Level 4.0-5.5

Key Vocabulary
camouflage   binoculars
salamander   opossum

Read for Fluency Have students choose and reread aloud the descriptions of what Sandra's family saw and what they liked the best.

Respond Have students respond to the Think and Write questions in the back of the reader. A Hands-on Activity and School-Home Connection are also provided.
Answers to Think and Write Questions

1. Answers may vary but should include that Sandra looked at all of the evidence that she found. She researched and examined it to come to a conclusion about each instance.
2. Answers may vary but might include that there weren't any mice around, and the fox was very hungry.
3. Answers should include differences between food chains and food webs. They may include that chains have fewer plants and animals within them while webs encompass a much larger variety of life.
4. Letter should discuss conservation of the animals in the Smoky Mountains.

Chapter 6 Minerals and Rocks

Below-Level/Intervention

Reading Level 1.5-2.0

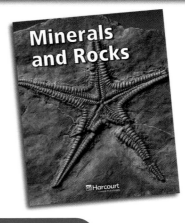

The Intervention Reader presents identical chapter content and vocabulary at a below grade reading level. The reader uses a visual glossary, simplified language, and comprehension aids especially designed for struggling readers. The Intervention Reader Teacher Guide provides scaffolded strategies for using the reader and student worksheets for vocabulary, fluency, and comprehension.

On-Level/Enrichment

Summary Rock and mineral are defined, and the formation of the three kinds of rock–igneous, sedimentary, and metamorphic–is explained. Examples of the different kinds of fossils are given, and the ways that fossils tell us about the past are explained.
Reading Level 2.5-3.5

Preview/Set a Purpose Have students preview the book and predict what they think they will learn.

Key Vocabulary
igneous rock
sedimentary rock
metamorphic rock
fossil

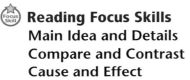
Reading Focus Skills
Main Idea and Details
Compare and Contrast
Cause and Effect

Respond —Answers to Think and Write Questions
1. Possible answers: Fossils tell us about living things that existed in the past. They can tell us about how Earth has changed over time.
2. A sedimentary rock can become a metamorphic rock. Metamorphic rock is made when any kind of rock is placed under high heat and pressure. This includes sedimentary rock.
3. Both the bone and the footprint are fossils. The bone is the remains of an animal. It looks like the actual body part of the animal. The footprint is a mark that an animal left behind. It is called an imprint.
4. Students' answers should reflect an understanding that fossils teach us about how the world has changed over time. They should understand that finding a fossil of a fish in a place means that there was once water in that place.

Advanced/Challenge

Summary The core, mantle, and crust of the earth are described. Students learn what each layer contains. **Reading Level 4.0-5.5**

Preview/Set a Purpose Have students read the first page and look at the illustration. Ask them to describe how a hard-boiled egg might help them learn about the layers of the earth.

Key Vocabulary
mantle   crust
core

Read for Fluency Have each student choose a section of the book and read it aloud to you.

Respond Have students respond to the Think and Write questions in the back of the reader. A Hands-on Activity and School-Home Connection are also provided.
Answers to Questions

1. The yoke represents the core, the white represents the mantle, and the shell represents the crust.
2. No. The outer core is liquid and temperatures inside Earth are too hot. Also, the pressure is too great.
3. Scientists infer what's inside Earth using direct evidence from recordings of seismic waves.
4. Both the inner core and outer core have very high temperatures and high pressure. The inner core consists mostly of solid iron. The outer core consists of liquid nickel and iron.

Chapter 7 Forces That Shape the Land

 Below-Level/Intervention

Reading Level I.5-2.0

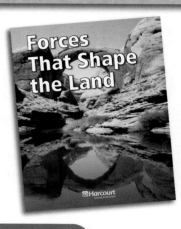

The Intervention Reader presents identical chapter content and vocabulary at a below grade reading level. The reader uses a visual glossary, simplified language, and comprehension aids especially designed for struggling readers. The Intervention Reader Teacher Guide provides scaffolded strategies for using the reader and student worksheets for vocabulary, fluency, and comprehension.

 On-Level/Enrichment

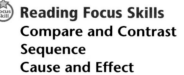

Summary The changes to Earth's surface and structure are explained, including changes due to erosion, natural disasters, and volcanoes.

Preview/Set a Purpose Help students set a purpose for reading the book. Point out and discuss the title, headings, and illustrations. **Reading Level 2.5-3.5**

Key Vocabulary
erosion
earthquake
volcano
weathering

Reading Focus Skills
Compare and Contrast
Sequence
Cause and Effect

Read for Fluency Have students work in pairs. Ask them to choose and read aloud favorite parts of the book to one another, paying special attention to vocabulary words.

Respond —Answers to Think and Write Questions
1. Plates of rock on Earth's surface move, making an earthquake. Possible effects could include knocking down trees, causing landslides, fires, and making mountains.
2. First, weathering breaks up pieces of rock. Then, the pieces are carried away during erosion.
3. Earthquakes take place when Earth's crust shifts. If the plates collide, a mountain can be formed.
4. Students should correctly identify the effects of a volcanic explosion on land. These include lava turning into rock, trees and Earth's surface being burned. Students should explain why the volcano exploded.

 Advanced/Challenge

Summary The reader describes two journeys made by the submersible Alvin to the ocean floor, then gives a general description of landforms found under the ocean, including seamounts, mid-ocean ridges, and the Challenger Deep of the Mariana Trench. **Reading Level 4.0-5.5**

Preview/Set a Purpose Have students read the headings and look at the illustrations. Ask them to predict what the reader is about. Help students set a purpose for reading.

Key Vocabulary
submersible   seamount   trench

Respond —Answers to Think and Write Questions
1. Accept all reasonable answers including: like landforms on land, landforms in the ocean vary in size and shape; landforms in the ocean include volcanoes formed just like volcanoes on land; like landforms on land, landforms in the ocean are always changing.
2. Accept all reasonable answers including: there are not many submersibles because it is expensive to build them; they can only hold a few people.
3. Landforms in the sea change continually because of the flows of lava in the ridges and seamounts; because of the deposition of sediments from ocean water; because of the continual flow of ocean water down through cracks to places where it is heated up and pushed to the surface again; because of the flow of some pieces of the ocean crust below others toward the interior of the earth where it heats up and is pushed up to the surface again as lava.
4. Accept all responses in which the student gives reasons explaining why Alvin was or was not a good way to study the ocean floor.

Chapter 8 Conserving Resources

Below-Level/Intervention

Reading Level I.5-2.0

The Intervention Reader presents identical chapter content and vocabulary at a below grade reading level. The reader uses a visual glossary, simplified language, and comprehension aids especially designed for struggling readers. The Intervention Reader Teacher Guide provides scaffolded strategies for using the reader and student worksheets for vocabulary, fluency, and comprehension.

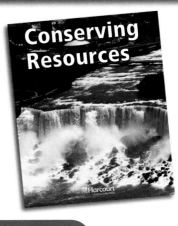

On-Level/Enrichment

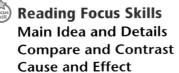

Summary Pollution and its effects are described. Different types of pollution and preventative measures are covered.

Preview/Set a Purpose Have students read the title and look at the illustrations. Ask students to tell what these indicate.
Reading Level 2.5-3.5

Key Vocabulary
conservation
pollution
recycling
resource

Reading Focus Skills
Main Idea and Details
Compare and Contrast
Cause and Effect

Read for Fluency Have each student choose a section of the book that he or she likes and reread it aloud to you.

Respond Have students respond to the Think and Write questions in the back of the reader. A Hands-On Activity and a School-Home Connection are also provided.
Answers to Think and Write Questions

1. Possible answers may include the effects of water, air or land pollution. Water: animals that live there may die; animals and people that drink it may get ill; air: makes it hard for people to breathe, or plants to grow; land: can ruin habitat of animals, can kill plants, and pollute water.
2. This causes land, air and water pollution; it can ruin habitats.
3. Possible answers: coal for electricity, oil and gas for heating and transportation.
4 Students' answers should express an understanding of the effects of littering: it is pollution; animals can eat the litter and get sick; littering pollutes water, etc.

Advanced/Challenge

Summary The great dust storms of the 1930s taught us that we must conserve the soil or we will lose it. This reader describes those storms and some of the measures farmers have taken to keep soil from being blown away by the wind and washed away by water.

Preview/Set a Purpose Have students look at the illustrations and read the captions. Ask them if they have ever seen a dust storm. **Reading Level 4.0-5.5**

Key Vocabulary
no-till farming   runoff crop rotation
wetland   contour stripping

Respond —Answers to Questions
1. The Great Plains farmers tilled, turned, and groomed the soil, making it so fine that it was carried off by the winds. They also left it bare in the spring when the winds came and blew it away.
2. Farmers used methods such as no-till farming, crop rotation, building terraces, contour strips, and strip-cropping.
3. Answers may vary. Possible answer: It was hard for farmers to change their methods because they had been using them for a long time. They were afraid they would lose a whole year's crop if the new methods did not work.
4. Answer may include leaving old plants in the soil, planting new seeds through the old plants, forming terraces on a hillside, making contour strips, and alternating rows of different plants. Students might answer that they are happy or sad. For example, they might be happy because no-till farming requires less work after harvesting; they might be sad because they were comfortable with their old ways of doing things.

Chapter 9 The Water Cycle

Below-Level/Intervention

Reading Level 1.5-2.0

The Intervention Reader presents identical chapter content and vocabulary at a below grade reading level. The reader uses a visual glossary, simplified language, and comprehension aids especially designed for struggling readers. The Intervention Reader Teacher Guide provides scaffolded strategies for using the reader and student worksheets for vocabulary, fluency, and comprehension.

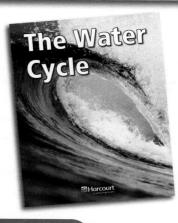

On-Level/Enrichment

This reader promotes success on state science tests by reinforcing tested content objectives, chapter vocabulary, and reading skills. **Reading Level 2.5-3.5**

Summary The states and the processes of water are described, including its relationship to the water cycle and weather.

Preview/Set a Purpose Set a purpose for reading by helping students preview the book. Discuss the title, headings, and illustrations.

Key Vocabulary
condensation
evaporation
precipitation

 Reading Focus Skills
Main Idea and Details
Sequence
Compare and Contrast

Read for Fluency Have each student choose a section of the book that he or she likes and reread it aloud to you.

Respond —-Answers to Think and Write Questions
1. Water from Earth evaporates. Then it condenses to form clouds or fog. When enough condenses, it falls back to Earth as rain. Then it evaporates all over again.
2. Heat makes water evaporate. Removing heat, or cooling, makes vapor condense.
3. Clouds form when water condenses higher above Earth. Fog forms when water condenses close to Earth.
4. Students should be encouraged to be creative. Answer should indicate an understanding of each step of the water cycle and what causes it to occur.

Advanced/Challenge

This interesting nonfiction reader enriches and extends chapter concepts. **Reading Level 4.0-5.5**

Summary The water cycle describes the movement of water through Earth's oceans, land, and air. Learning about Earth's water helps you understand the water cycle more fully.

Preview/Set a Purpose Refer students to the diagram of Earth's water cycle on page 3. Have students familiarize themselves with the figure prior to reading this book.

Key Vocabulary
evaporation   precipitation
condensation   transpiration

Read for Fluency As students read each page, have them find the process or part of the water cycle being discussed on the diagram on page 3. Associating a word with the figure will reinforce the concept being presented.

Respond Have students respond to the Think and Write questions in the back of the reader. A Hands-on Activity and School-Home Connection are also provided.
Answers to Think and Write Questions
1. Sample answer: During condensation gas changes to a liquid.
2. Sample answer: Glaciers are large masses of solid water. They store fresh water until it melts.
3. Sample answer: Plants have an important role in the water cycle. Their roots take up water from the ground. This water travels through the plant. It is released through openings in the plant's leaves. It evaporates from the plant's leaves into the atmosphere. This process is called transpiration.

Chapter 10 Earth's Place in the Solar System

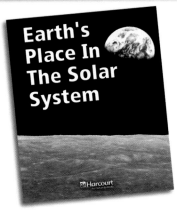

Earth's Place In The Solar System

 Below-Level/Intervention   Reading Level 1.5-2.0

The Intervention Reader presents identical chapter content and vocabulary at a below grade reading level. The reader uses a visual glossary, simplified language, and comprehension aids especially designed for struggling readers. The Intervention Reader Teacher Guide provides scaffolded strategies for using the reader and student worksheets for vocabulary, fluency, and comprehension.

 On-Level/Enrichment

This reader promotes success on state science tests by reinforcing tested content objectives, chapter vocabulary, and reading skills. **Reading Level 2.5-3.5**

Summary The characteristics and components of the solar system are explained. Other galaxies and characteristics of the universe are discussed.

Preview/Set a Purpose Have students preview the book by looking at illustrations and headings. Have students predict what they think they will learn.

Key Vocabulary
planet
solar system
star

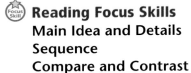 **Reading Focus Skills**
Main Idea and Details
Sequence
Compare and Contrast

Read for Fluency Have students work in pairs. Ask them to choose and read aloud favorite parts of the book to one another, paying attention to vocabulary words.

Respond —Answers to Think and Write Questions
1. Inner planets: Mercury, Venus, Earth and Mars; outer planets: Jupiter, Saturn, Uranus, Neptune and Pluto.
2. The Earth rotates on its axis. One side faces the sun, and it is day. The other side faces away from the sun, and it is night. As Earth continues rotating, the cycle repeats itself.
3. It is colder because of the angle of the sun.
4. Students' answers should reference the different features mentioned on each planet. Encourage students to do additional research on planets that interest them.

 **Advanced/Challenge**

This interesting nonfiction reader enriches and extends chapter concepts. **Reading Level 4.0-5.5**

Summary The student learns about the affect of the moon and sun on tides. How tides are measured and who uses this information is also discussed.

Preview/Set a Purpose Have students read the title and look at the illustrations. Ask them to predict what the book is about. Help students set a purpose for reading.

Key Vocabulary
gravity   semi-diurnal tide
inertia   diurnal tide

Read for Fluency Have students work in pairs. Ask them to choose and read aloud favorite parts of the book to each other.

Respond Have students respond to the Think and Write questions in the back of the reader. A Hands-on Activity and School-Home Connection are also provided.
Answers to Think and Write Questions

1. Sample answer: Tidal range is the height difference between the water levels of high tide and low tide.
2. Sample answer: Gravity and inertia cause tidal bulges.
3. Sample answer: The sun, Earth, and moon form a right angle during a neap tide.
4. Sample answer: Knowing the tides is important for an engineer building a dock in the ocean. The engineer must build the dock high enough so it isn't under water part of the time! Also, the engineer might be designing a dock for ships to use.

Chapter 11 Properties of Matter

Below-Level/Intervention

Reading Level 1.5-2.0

The Intervention Reader presents identical chapter content and vocabulary at a below grade reading level. The reader uses a visual glossary, simplified language, and comprehension aids especially designed for struggling readers. The *Intervention Reader Teacher Guide* provides scaffolded strategies for using the reader and student worksheets for vocabulary, fluency, and comprehension.

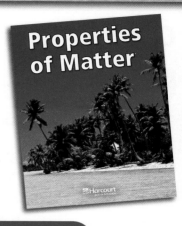

On-Level/Enrichment

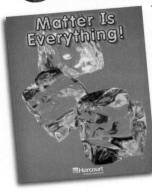

This reader promotes success on state science tests by reinforcing tested content objectives, chapter vocabulary, and reading skills. **Reading Level 2.5-3.5**

Summary The states and properties of matter are explained, with attention given to density, evaporation, and condensation. Mixtures and solutions are discussed.

Preview/Set a Purpose Help students preview the book. Point out and discuss the title, headings, and illustrations.

Key Vocabulary
- solid
- liquid
- gas
- matter

 Reading Focus Skills
- **Main Idea and Details**
- **Compare and Contrast**
- **Sequence**

Read for Fluency Have students work in pairs. Ask them to choose and read aloud favorite parts of the book to one another.

Respond —Answers to Think and Write Questions
1. Matter is anything that takes up space. Possible answers: solid: a rock; liquid: juice; gas: air.
2. Floating and sinking depends on density. Matter that is less dense than water floats. Matter that is denser than water does not float. It sinks.
3. Both liquids and solids are matter. They both have mass and volume. Liquids have a volume that stays the same and a shape that changes. Gases do not have a definite volume or shape.
4. Students' answers will vary, but should show an understanding of the changes in state water undergoes when heated and cooled.

Advanced/Challenge

This interesting nonfiction reader enriches and extends chapter concepts. **Reading Level 4.0-5.5**

Summary Many examples are given to demonstrate the concept of weight, mass, and volume. The story of Archimedes is also presented.

Preview/Set a Purpose Have students preview the book and predict what they think they will learn. Ask them before they read what they know about weight, mass, and volume. Have each student write a definition of those terms before reading.

Key Vocabulary
- weight
- mass
- volume

Read for Fluency Have each student choose a favorite section of the book and reread it aloud to you.

Respond Have students respond to the Think and Write questions in the back of the reader. A Hands-on Activity and School-Home Connection are also provided.
Answers to Think and Write Questions
1. Each object has a different amount of mass occupying the same amount of space.
2. The ship's shape makes its overall density less than that of water.
3. Mass is the amount of matter an object contains. Weight is a measure of the force of gravity on that object.
4. The story should include a description of feeling heavy and perhaps the difficulty of moving around. Stories will vary.

Chapter 12 Energy

Below-Level/Intervention

Reading Level 1.5-2.0

The Intervention Reader presents identical chapter content and vocabulary at a below grade reading level. The reader uses a visual glossary, simplified language, and comprehension aids especially designed for struggling readers. The Intervention Reader Teacher Guide provides scaffolded strategies for using the reader and student worksheets for vocabulary, fluency, and comprehension.

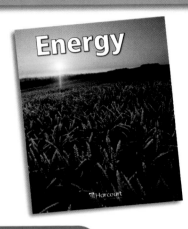

On-Level/Enrichment

Summary Heat, light, and sound energy and their importance for individuals and communities are discussed. The difference between kinetic and potential energy, ways energy is involved in common events, the concept of energy resources, including the difference between renewable and nonrenewable resources, are explained. **Reading Level 2.5-3.5**

Preview/Set a Purpose Have students preview the book by reading the title and the headings. Ask them to predict what the book is about and what they think they will learn by reading it.

Key Vocabulary
energy resource
potential energy
kinetic energy

 Reading Focus Skills
Main Idea and Details
Compare and Contrast

Read for Fluency Have students find the sections in which vocabulary words are defined. Ask them to read those sections aloud.

Respond —Answers to Think and Write Questions
1. Plants get energy from food they make. People and animals get energy from plants or animals that they eat.
2. Plants get energy directly from the sun. People get energy by eating the plants that got energy from the sun. People can also use the sun to make electricity.
3. Renewable resources can be replaced. Nonrenewable resources cannot be replaced.
4. Letters will vary, but should have a salutation, body, and closing. Letters should contain at least two specific examples of how a school could save energy.

Advanced/Challenge

Summary Solar energy is an alternative energy source that we are using right now. Space vehicles use it and so do solar homes and cars. In the future, more of our energy needs will be met through advances in solar technology. **Reading Level 4.0-5.5**

Preview/Set a Purpose Have students read the title and look at the illustrations. Ask them to predict what the book is about. Help students set a purpose for reading.

Have students read the names of the animals shown in the illustrations. Ask them to tell what they know about any of the animals.

Key Vocabulary
rover   pollution
solar panel   solar array

Read for Fluency Have each student choose a section of the reader and read it aloud.

Respond Have students respond to the Think and Write questions in the back of the reader. A Hands-on Activity and School-Home Connection are also provided.
Answers to Think and Write Questions
1. I will use energy stored in our batteries or I will use another energy source.
2. They both orbit Earth and they both use solar energy for their power.
3. Sample answer: Yes. It would be a challenge to see if my car would go faster than the others.
4. Paragraph should explain that solar power is cheaper and cleaner than power generated by ordinary means at a power plant.

Chapter 13 Electricity and Magnets

Below-Level/Intervention

Reading Level 1.5-2.0

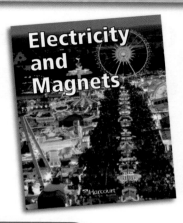

The Intervention Reader presents identical chapter content and vocabulary at a below grade reading level. The reader uses a visual glossary, simplified language, and comprehension aids especially designed for struggling readers. The *Intervention Reader Teacher Guide* provides scaffolded strategies for using the reader and student worksheets for vocabulary, fluency, and comprehension.

On-Level/Enrichment

This reader promotes success on state science tests by reinforcing tested content objectives, chapter vocabulary, and reading skills. **Reading Level 2.5-3.5**

Summary Electricity and its uses are described. Current and static electricity are explained. Magnetism and its relation to electricity are covered.

Preview/Set a Purpose Help students preview the book. Point out and discuss the title, headings, and illustrations.

Key Vocabulary
circuit
electricity
magnet

 Reading Focus Skills
Main Idea and Details
Compare and Contrast

Read for Fluency Have each student choose a section of the reader and read it aloud.

Respond Have students respond to the Think and Write questions in the back of the reader. A Hands-On Activity and a School-Home Connection are also provided.
Answers to Think and Write Questions

1. Possible answers: electromagnets can be turned on and off with electricity; generators use magnets to make electricity; motors use electricity and magnets to move wires.

2. Static electricity is built up in one place, it stays in one object. Current electricity moves through wires.

3. No. A magnet can only attract items with iron in them. Plastic tacks do not have iron in them.

4. Students should be encouraged to be creative. Check for an accurate understanding of motors, generators, or electromagnets.

Advanced/Challenge

This interesting nonfiction reader enriches and extends chapter concepts. **Reading Level 4.0-5.5**

Summary The student learns about the history of electricity. How electricity is made and used in the United States today is also discussed.

Preview/Set a Purpose Help students preview the book. Point out and discuss the title, headings, and illustrations.

Key Vocabulary
magnetism   electromagnet
current   step-up transformer

Read for Fluency Have each student choose a section of the reader and read it aloud.

Respond Have students respond to the Think and Write questions in the back of the reader. A Hands-on Activity and School-Home Connection are also provided.
Answers to Think and Write Questions

1. During a classroom demonstration, Hans Oersted discovered that the needle of a compass deflected when a current flowed through a nearby wire.

2. Induction is the process in which a current is generated in a wire by moving a magnet through a coil of this wire.

3. For the first time in history, the telegraph allowed instant communication over long distances.

4. Both step-up transformers and step-down transformers are used to change voltage. Both types of transformers are used to deliver power from a power plant to your home. Step-up transformers increase voltage. Step-down transformers decrease the voltage.

Chapter 14 Heat, Light, and Sound

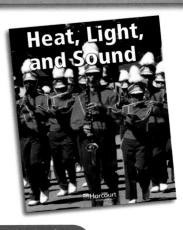

 Below-Level/Intervention

Reading Level 1.5-2.0

The Intervention Reader presents identical chapter content and vocabulary at a below grade reading level. The reader uses a visual glossary, simplified language, and comprehension aids especially designed for struggling readers. The *Intervention Reader Teacher Guide* provides scaffolded strategies for using the reader and student worksheets for vocabulary, fluency, and comprehension.

 On-Level/Enrichment

This reader promotes success on state science tests by reinforcing tested content objectives, chapter vocabulary, and reading skills. **Reading Level 2.5-3.5**

Summary Heat, light, and are described as types of energy. The way in which they move is explained.

Preview/Set a Purpose Have students read the title and look at the illustrations. Ask them to predict what the book is about. Help students set a purpose for reading.

Key Vocabulary
conduction
pitch
refraction

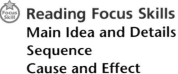 **Reading Focus Skills**
Main Idea and Details
Sequence
Cause and Effect

Read for Fluency Have each student choose a section of the book that he or she likes and reread it aloud to you.

Respond Have students respond to the Think and Write questions in the back of the reader. A Hands-On Activity and a School-Home Connection are also provided.
Answers to Think and Write Questions

1. They are all forms of energy that move.
2. Thermal energy moves from the fire to the person.
3. The string vibrates, making the air around it vibrate. These vibrations are sound waves.
4. Check students' answers for accuracy and for an understanding of reflection.

 Advanced/Challenge

This interesting nonfiction reader enriches and extends chapter concepts. **Reading Level 4.0-5.5**

Summary White light is actually composed of all of the colors of the rainbow. Our eyes add together the three primary colors of light to make all the colors we see. Televisions use that same principle to produce a color image.

Preview/Set a Purpose Help students preview the book. Point out and discuss the title, headings, and photographs.

Key Vocabulary
ray   cones
rods   pixels

Read for Fluency Have students reread the section about how the brain's interpretation of signals from the eye allows us to perceive color. Then have them explain the process in their own words.

Respond Have students respond to the Think and Write questions in the back of the reader. A Hands-on Activity and School-Home Connection are also provided.
Answers to Think and Write Questions

1. During a classroom demonstration, Hans Oersted discovered that the needle of a compass deflected when a current flowed through a nearby wire.
2. A magnet and a coil (conductor) must move past each other.
3. For the first time in history, the telegraph allowed instant communication over vast distances.
4. The narrative will vary, but should be a fairly comprehensive listing of the electrical devices one might use in a day.

Chapter 15 Forces and Motion

 Below-Level/Intervention

Reading Level 1.5–2.0

The Intervention Reader presents identical chapter content and vocabulary at a below grade reading level. The reader uses a visual glossary, simplified language, and comprehension aids especially designed for struggling readers. The Intervention Reader Teacher Guide provides scaffolded strategies for using the reader and student worksheets for vocabulary, fluency, and comprehension.

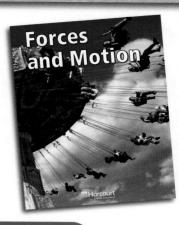

 On-Level/Enrichment

Summary Motion of objects is described in terms of force, net force, speed, distance, mass, and weight. The effects of gravity and friction on motion are also explained.

Preview/Set a Purpose Have students preview the book by reading the title and headings. Have them choose a term in a heading and tell what they know about it and what they think they will learn from reading the book.

Key Vocabulary
gravity
force
motion

Reading Focus Skills
Compare and Contrast
Main Idea and Details
Reading Level 2.5–3.5

Read for Fluency Have students work in pairs. Ask them to choose sections that taught them a new word or idea and to read those sections aloud to one another.

Respond —Answers to Think and Write Questions
1. Motion is caused by a push or a pull on an object.
2. Magnetic force and gravity do not need to touch an object to affect it. Magnetic force attracts only some metals. Gravity attracts all objects.
3. If the force is increased, the object will move farther or faster. If the force is decreased, the object will slow down. If the direction of the object is changed, the direction the object is moving will change.
4. Narratives will vary, but should indicate that bikers would have to use more force to go faster. Students might also mention that the mass of bicycles would affect the amount of force needed to move them.

 Advanced/Challenge

Reading Level 4.0–5.5

Summary Throughout history people have pondered the mechanics behind motion. This reader explores some of the thought processes and experiments from Aristotle to Galileo to Newton.

Preview/Set a Purpose Have students preview the book by reading the headings and captions. Ask them to tell what they think they might learn from this book.

Key Vocabulary
astronomy   friction
physics   linear

Read for Fluency Have each student choose a section of the reader and read it aloud.

Respond Have students respond to the Think and Write questions in the back of the reader. A Hands-on Activity and School-Home Connection are also provided.

Answers to Questions

1. Aristotle's ideas were difficult to disprove because science as we know it today did not exist. For hundreds of years after Aristotle, it was not possible to make accurate and precise measurements or conduct experiments that would have shown his ideas to be in error.
2. Galileo experimented by dropping weights and observing their motion.
3. The resulting acceleration of the wagon would be less.
4. Answers will vary but should discuss how more aerodynamic shapes produce less friction, and with less friction the vehicles would require less force and energy to be propelled.

Chapter 16 Work and Machines

Reading Level 1.5-2.0

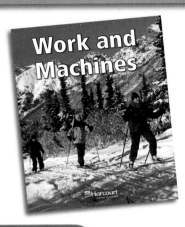

The Intervention Reader presents identical chapter content and vocabulary at a below grade reading level. The reader uses a visual glossary, simplified language, and comprehension aids especially designed for struggling readers. The Intervention Reader Teacher Guide provides scaffolded strategies for using the reader and student worksheets for vocabulary, fluency, and comprehension.

On-Level/Enrichment

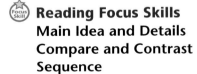

Summary The scientific definition of work is given, and the concept of simple machines is introduced. The six simple machines—lever, wheel-and-axle, pulley, wedge, inclined plane, and screw—are defined, and examples of each are given. **Reading Level 2.5-3.5**

Preview/Set a Purpose Have students preview the book by reading the title and headings. Ask them to tell what they think they will learn from reading the book.

Key Vocabulary
work
simple machine
lever
wedge

 Reading Focus Skills
Main Idea and Details
Compare and Contrast
Sequence

Read for Fluency Have students work in pairs. Ask students to choose the simple machine they thought was most useful and to read the sections about those machines aloud to one another.

Respond —Answers to Think and Write Questions
1. Possible answers: Levers help move heavy objects. Screws hold things together. We use knives (wedges) to cut things apart. We use inclined planes to move heavy objects up and down. We use pulleys to lift things into the air.
2. Nails have smooth sides. They could fall out of a hole easily. This would make the building less stable.
3. Both inclined planes and pulleys can be used to lift items to greater heights. An inclined plane has no moving parts. A pulley has a string that moves.
4. Answers will vary, but should show an understanding of the tool discussed and how it makes work easier.

Advanced/Challenge

Summary Three girls have a delightful time cooking breakfast using simple machines.

Preview/Set a Purpose Have students read the title and look at the illustrations. Ask them what kinds of machines they think the reader is about. **Reading Level 4.0-4.5**

Key Vocabulary
machine leverage
wedge

Read for Fluency Have students work in groups of three and take turns reading aloud to one another. Suggest that each student choose a character from the story and read that character's part.

Respond —Answers to Think and Write Questions
1. Simple pulleys change the direction of the force applied. Simple pulleys have a cord that sits in the groove of a wheel. When one end of the cord is pulled downward, objects attached to the other end move upward. It is easier to raise an object by pulling down than by pushing up because when you pull down, gravity is working with you. When you push up, you have to work against gravity.
2. A force applied to the thick edge is directed outward by the tapering edge of a wedge, which allows it to cut through a material more easily.
3. Student's drawings should show an understanding of the mechanics of an inclined plane (screw)—for example, a jar with a screw-top lid.
4. Students' descriptions should indicate an understanding of how the machine they chose to write about would make their work easier.

Grade-Level Materials List

The following chart provides a list of materials needed for all Experiments and Investigates in this grade level. Quantities are indicated for a class of 30 students working individually or in groups of 5, depending on the nature of the activity. Where shared equipment is suggested, a smaller number of items are specified.

Nonconsumable Materials

Materials	Class Quantity	Kit Quantity	Activity Page
apron, lab	30		247
balance, student (with masses)	1	1	239, 369A
beaker, plastic	6	6	383
block, wooden	6		337
block, wood (3" x 1.5" x 1.5")	6	pkg/6	149, 505
board, wood	6		545
book	several		493A
book, large	6		337
bottle, spray with trigger	6	6	149, 313
bowl (20 oz)	6	6	447
brush, small	6		369A
button, metal	6	pkg/6	461
calculator	6		287
car, toy (pull-back action)	6	6	545
chair	6		545
checker	6	pkg/24	527
checkerboard	6		527
clock	1		407
coin	6		505
comb, plastic	6	6	435
cookie sheet	6		505
cup, measuring	6	6	247
cup, measuring (metric)	6	6	369A, 373, 383, 391

Consumable Materials

Materials	Class Quantity	Kit Quantity	Activity Page
aluminum can (one week's use)	6		287
bag, trash (large)	6		287
bag, zip-top (3" x 4")	36	36	39, 63, 95
baking soda (454 g)	1	1	247
battery, D-cell	12	12	337, 345, 467
bead, plastic	bag	pkg/144	447
bowl, plastic (large)	6	6	95
bowl, plastic (small)	6		215
brick, clay (pieces)	24	24	239
cap, ballpoint pen	1		321
cardboard	6 sheets		193A
cardboard strip	6		321
cardboard, thin	6 sheets		493A
chenille stick, white (12")	24	pkg/100	141
clay, modeling (4 colors)	1 set	1 set	215, 497
cloth, wool (12" x 24")	1	1	435, 461
clothes hanger, wire	6		125
container, clear plastic (large)	1		373
container, deli-type	6	6	313
container, plastic (8 oz)	6		373
cotton ball	1 bag		27A
crayons	6 boxes		31, 141, 179, 473
cup, clear, plastic (16 oz)	18	pkg/25	279
cup, clear plastic (300 ml)	18	pkg/50	373, 415
cup, paper (200 ml)	36	50	55, 73, 321
cup, plastic (300 ml)	18	pkg/50	205, 231
cup, plastic foam	18		461

Grade-Level Materials List

Nonconsumable Materials

Materials	Class Quantity	Kit Quantity	Activity Page
dropper	6	pkg/6	263, 321
encyclopedia	1 set		87
flashlight, D-cell battery	6	6	337, 345, 467
forceps	6	pkg/6	535
globe, plastic/inflatable	1		305
gloves, garden	6 pairs		301A
goggles, safety	6		125, 193A, 197, 247, 461, 527, 545
graduated cylinder (10 ml)	6	6	279
hair dryer	1		193A
hand lens	6	pkg/6	63, 133, 205, 271, 391
hooked weight (200 g)	2	2	239
jar, plastic wide-mouth specimen (237 ml)	6	6	239, 247
jump rope	6	6	513
magnet, bar	6	6	441, 447
magnet, horseshoe	6	6	441
marble	6		493A
meterstick	6		193A, 337
microscope, monoscope, boreal	1		271
mineral collection (10 spec/6 each)	1 set	1 set	197
mirror	6	pkg/6	163
nut and bolt (large)	6 pairs	6 pairs	301A
penny	6		461

Consumable Materials

Materials	Class Activity	Kit Activity	Activity Page
earthworm	24 worms	coupon for 24 worms	105
eraser, flat	6	5	505
felt, square (dark)	1	1	105
flour	1 lb	1 lb	247
food coloring (4 colors)	1	1	247
gloves, plastic	6 pair	6 pair	95, 301A, 493A
glue, white	6 bottles		141, 179, 205, 215
gravel, aquarium (1 kg)	1 bag	1 bag	55
gravel (2.5 kg)	1 bag	1 bag	205
index card (3" x 5")	30	pkg/100	87, 171, 179
jar, plastic (12 oz)	12	12	373
jar, plastic, wide-mouth (16 oz)	6	6	391
jar with lid, (canning, 1-L)	6	6	105
label	6		369A
leaf & twig set	6 sets		149
lid	6	6	535
lid, screw-type specimen	6	6	239
marker, black	6		337
marker, permanent	6		171
marker, red	6		337
marker set	6 sets		87, 141, 179
milk carton, empty	18		369A
newspaper	6		205
oatmeal	2		105
oatmeal-raisin cookie	6		263
pan, aluminum	6	6	247
paper	6 sheets		31, 305, 353, 421

Nonconsumable Materials

Materials	Class Quantity	Kit Quantity	Activity Page
petri dish, plastic (100 mm)	6	pkg/6	271
picture cards, animal set	6 sets		31, 87, 163
picture cards, planet set	6 sets		353
prism	6	6	473
refrigerator	1		27A
ruler, metric	6	6	39, 121A, 133, 141, 421, 505
scale, bathroom	1		287
scissors	6		141, 193A, 321, 369A, 421, 493A
slinky, plastic	6	6	513
spoon, measuring	6	6	247, 321, 391, 535
spoon, mixing	6		95
spring scale	6	6	545
stapler	1		321, 481
stopwatch	6	6	27A, 447, 493A
storage box, large plastic	12		121A
tape measure	6	pkg/6	545
thermometer (plastic, dual scale)	6	6	27A, 383, 407, 415
tray, plastic (large)	6		247
truck, toy (matchbox-type)	6	6	467
watch	6		141, 321
watering can	6	6	121A, 149
volleyball	1		345

Consumable Materials

Materials	Class Quantity	Kit Quantity	Activity Page
paper, construction	1		141
paper, graph	6 sheets		337
paper, red	6 sheets		473
paper, tissue	6		435
paper, wax (75 sq ft)	1 roll	1 roll	205, 247
paper, white	24 sheets		133, 421, 435, 461, 473
paper and pencil	6		133, 163
paper clip, steel	1 box	1 box	441, 447
paper towel	36		39, 63, 231, 271
pencil	6		305, 353
pencil, colored	6 sets		305
pencil with eraser	6		421
petroleum jelly	1	1	215
plant, grass	12		133
plant, small	18		55, 73
plate, paper (9")	18	pkg/50	215, 263, 271
poster board	6		179, 467
pushpin	1 box	1 box	421
rice (1 lb)	1 bag	1 bag	481
rice, brown	1 bag	1 bag	535
rice, white	1 bag	1 bag	535
salt, non-iodized (737 g)	1	1	279
sand, fine (2.5 kg)	2 bags	2 bags	55, 105, 149, 193A, 205, 391, 369A, 391
seashell	6	pkg/30	215
seeds, lima bean	6 seeds	1 packet	39, 63
seeds, mixed plant	1 bag	1 bag	121A
seeds, pea	6 seeds	1 packet	39

Grade-Level Materials List

Consumable Materials

Materials	Class Quantity	Kit Quantity	Activity Page
seeds, pinto	1 bag	1 bag	481
seeds, radish	6 seeds	1 packet	39, 279, 313
shoe box	6		149, 193A
shoe box lid	6		493A
soil, loam (2.5 kg)	3 bag	3 bag	271
soil, potting	2 bags	2 bags	55, 73, 105, 121A, 247, 271, 279, 313
spoon, plastic	6	pkg/24	205, 383, 391, 461
straw, plastic	12	pkg/50	497, 527
string (200')	1 ball	1 ball	497, 545
tape	6 rolls		39
tape, masking	1 roll		373, 481
tape, transparent	6		141, 171, 179, 337, 493A
toothpick, round	1 box	1 box	263, 271
tube, cardboard (large)	6	6	481
vegetable oil	1 bottle	1 bottle	279
vegetable shortening	6 sticks	6 sticks	95
vinegar, white (500 ml)	1 bottle	1 bottle	247
wire, copper	1 spool	1 spool	321
yarn, red	1 skein	1 skein	171
yarn, wool	6 skeins	6 skeins	27A

Index

Index

Index

on water, 305
on weather, 325
Gazelles, 183
Generalizations, **506**
General Motors, **552**
General Theory of Relativity, **364**
Generators, 450, 453
Van de Graaff, 434, **434**
wind, 262
Geodes, 224
Geothermal energy, **420**, 424
Giant ground sloth, 214
Gills, 102
Giraffes, 91, **91**
Glaciers, 244, 308
Glucose (in photosynthesis), **38**
Gold, 198, 199
Goldfish, 117
Grams (g), 378
Grand Canyon, 234, **234**, 236
Grand Tetons, **233**
Granite, 212
Graphics, **74, 106, 134, 322, 338**
Graphite, **196**, 198, 199
imports of, **281**
Graphs, **415**, R29–31
bar, **41**
Grasses, 64–65, 172
energy for, **172**
in food chain, 175
Grasshoppers, **172**, 175, 181
life cycle of, 43
Grasslands, 135
Gravity, 510
orbits and, **355**
sled movement and, **504**
Gray whales, 145
Great Plains, 235
Great Red Spot (Jupiter), **358**
Green Belt Movement, 46–47
Green chemistry, **78**
Greenhouse effect, 283
Groundbreakers, 364
Groundwater, 308
Growth, **396**
Gulf of Mexico, 310

Habitats, 129, 130, 152
Halite, 199, **199**
Hand lenses, 4, **4**
Harps, **482**
Hawks, 176
Hayden Planetarium (New York City), 352
Headings, using, **536**
Health, foods for, **168**
Hearing, **480**, 484, **484**, R11
Heart replacement, 426–427

Heart replacements, 426–427
Heat
change of state and, **385**
conductors of, 463
definition of, 462
insulators, 464
lost energy as, **460**
production of, 462
temperature vs., **458**
See also Thermal energy
Hells Canyon (Oregon and Washington), **234**
Hematite, 199, 201
Herbivores, 166, **168**, 174, 175, 184
Heredity, 44
Herons, 180
Hibernation, **140**, 144
Hillman, Stacey, 116
Hockey sticks, **539**
Homes, animal, **86**
Honeybees, 112
Hooke, Robert, **512**
Hoover Dam, 148
Horseshoe crabs, 107, 166
Hubble Space Telescope, **362**, 362–363
Humanoid robots, 552–553
Humans
energy in, **414**
food for, **91**
Hummingbirds, **160**, 161, **165**, 166, 502
Humus, 272–273
Hurricanes, **324, 330**
Hypothesis, 21
Hypothesizing (static electricity), 435

Identifying variables, 15
Igneous rocks, 206, 208, 210–211, 218
formation of, **204**
Iguanas, 100
Illness, R12–13
Imprints, 216
Inches, **13**
Inclined planes, **544**, 546–547
wedges vs., **549**
Inference, 13
animal homes, 31
condensation in terrariums, 313
electromagnets, 447
environments, 125
how insects hide, 141
observing temperature, 407
path of light, 467
roots, 133
seed growth, 39
solar heating, 415
speed ramps, 505
Inherited traits, 44
Inner planets, **352**, 356–357

Inquiries, 4–5
definition of, 4–5
skills for, 12–16
tools for, 5–7
Insects, 107
classification of, **104**
metamorphosis of, **43**
as prey, 183
Insets, **531**
Instincts, 142, **143**
in animals, **140**
Insulators, 438, 464
Interpreting data, 13
inclined planes, 545
making objects move, 497
water at work, 239
Inventions, **428**
Invertebrates, 106–107
clams, 110
diversity of, **104**
earthworms, **270**
importance of, 112
insects, 108
snails, 110
spiders, 109
squids, 110
ticks, 109
Investigation, 20–22
Iron, 199
Irrigation, **307**

Jarvik-7 artificial heart, **426**
Jellyfish, 106, **111**
Jobbers, speed of, **496**
Jupiter, 352, 355, 358

Kangaroos, **97**, 98
Kaplan, David, 115
Kenya, planting trees in, 46–47
Kilauea, **248**
Kilocalories, **174**
Kilograms (kg), 378
Kilometers, **13**
Kinetic energy, 410–412
Kloma, **324**
Knives, 548
Koalas, 127, **127**

Index

Index

Time/space relationships, 15
Titles, using, **536**
Tools, 2, 8
    for inquiries, 4–7
    for observing matter, **377**
    for scientific testing, x
Topsoil, 273
Torricelli, Evangelista, 400
Total lunar eclipses, **348, 349**
Total solar eclipses, **350**
Toucans, 96
Touch, 376
Traits, 44
Translucent objects, 475
Transparent objects, 475
Transverse sand dunes, **243**
Trash in oceans, **328**
Tree frogs, 97
Trees, 64–65
    planting, 46–47
Triceratops, 219
Tropical rain forests, 138
Tropical storms, **324**
Trough (of waves), 516
Tubers, 41
Tulips, 54
Tundra, **60,** 132
Turbines, 254
    wind, 295
Turtles, 128, 180
Ty-fung, **324**
Typhoons, **324,** 330
Typographic clues, **216, 392**

Units of time, 501
Uranus, 358, 359
Using numbers, 13
    ordering planets, 353

Vacuoles, 34, 35
VAD (ventricular assist device), **426**
Valleys, 234
Van de Graaff, Robert J., **434**
Van de Graaff generators, 434
Variables, 15
Ventricular assist device (VAD), **426**
Venus, 356

Verdi (Janell Cannon), **100**
Vertebrates, **94,** 96–97
    amphibians, 101
    birds, 99
    fish, 102
    mammals, 98
    reptiles, 100
Vibrations, sound, 472–474
Vision, human, R10
Volcanoes, 208, 246, 250–251
    eruptions of, **246**
    land changes from, **251**
    observing, **250**
    rock from, **208**
Volcanologists, 256
Volume (quantity), **378,** 379
    of liquids, **386**
    measurement of, **2,** 401

Walking stick, 146
Water
    animals' need for, 90
    changes in state of, 316–317
    different states of, 314–315
    erosion and, 242
    floods, 252
    fresh, 307–309
    importance of, **306,** 306–307
    on maps, **310**
    for plants, 75
    pollution of, 284
    salt, 310
    sounds of, **308**
    sound transmission in, **483**
    states of, **314**
    usage of, **312**
    water cycle, 318
    water treatment plant, 297
    weathering by, **240**
Water animals, oxygen for, 89
Water cycle, 318
Watering holes, **90**
Water lilies, 60, 129
Water vapor, 314, **317**
    in atmosphere, 322
Wavelength, 516
Waves
    definition of, 514, **514**
    measuring, 516
    types of, 514–515
    of water, 512

Weather
    atmosphere and, 322–323
    clouds and, **323**
    definition of, 324
    gathering data on, 325
    patterns of, 324
    predicting, 326
    sky indicators of, **320**
    tropical storms, **324**
Weathering, 240–241
Weather maps, 326, **326**
Weather satellites, **326**
Weather station, 331
Weather vanes, 320
Wedges, **544,** 548–549
    inclined planes vs., **549**
Weight, 510
Wheel-and-axle, 540–541
Wheelbarrows, **539**
Wildebeests, 183
Williams, Deshanique, 188
Williams, Reva Kay, 364
Wind, erosion by, 243
Wind energy, **262, 420,** 424
Wind farms, **294,** 294–295
Wind generators, 262
Witloof, **72**
Wolves, 167
Wool, **393**
Woolly mammoths, **214**
Word structure, **288, 354, 448**
Work, 526
    components of, **534**
    different types of, 528–529
    measuring, 532
    muscular, 530–531
Worms, **110,** 111, 112
    earthworms, **270**
Wright, Wilbur and Orville, 520

Yards, **13**
Year, 339
Young Eagles program, 520

Zollars, Michael, 520

Teaching Notes

Teaching Notes

Teaching Notes

Correlations

National Science Education Standards

Correlation—Grades K-4

The Science Content Standards, which are within The National Science Education Standards, outline what students should know, understand, and be able to do in the natural sciences. The Standards are targeted for grades K through 8, with the standards organized into two sets—grades K-4, and grades 5-8. The following chart shows where the Standards for grades K-4 are met in *Science*, grades K-4. A correlation to the Standards for grades 5-6 is provided in those levels of *Science*.

Standards for Grades K through 4	Teacher Edition Page Numbers
PHYSICAL SCIENCE	
PROPERTIES OF OBJECTS AND MATERIALS	
•Objects have many observable properties, including size, weight, shape, color, temperature, and the ability to react with other substances. Those properties can be measured using tools, such as rulers, balances, and thermometers.	**Grade K:** 12–13, 30–39, 148–153 **Grade 1:** 312–317, 318–325, 326–333 **Grade 2:** 228–235, 288–295, 296–303, 304–309 **Grade 3:** 4–11, 12, 20, 24, 30, 36, 38, 44, 54, 57, 62, 67, 72, 76, 86, 89, 94, 101, 104, 108, 124, 129, 132, 137, 140, 143, 148, 151, 162, 167, 170, 196–203, 207, 214, 220, 224, 230, 236, 238, 243, 246, 249, 262, 267, 270, 275, 278, 283, 286, 304, 309, 312, 317, 320, 325, 336, 339, 344, 348, 352, 372–381, 382–389, 390, 396, 401, 406, 410, 414, 417, 420, 434–439, 440, 443, 446, 450, 460, 464, 466, 469, 472, 475, 480, 484, 496, 502, 504–511, 512, 515, 526, 533, 534, 539, 544, 549 **Grade 4:** 2–9, 10, 18, 30, 35, 40, 45, 48, 53, 64, 69, 72, 76, 80, 85, 96, 101, 104, 110, 112, 117, 130, 135, 138, 142, 148, 153,164, 169, 172, 177, 192, 197, 200, 204, 206, 211, 214, 219, 224, 225, 230, 238, 241, 248, 253, 266, 271, 274, 279, 282, 286, 288, 291, 306, 311, 314, 319, 322, 327, 340–347, 348, 356, 361, 367, 372–381, 382, 385, 387, 390–397, 401, 406, 411, 414, 419, 422, 427, 438, 443, 446–453, 454, 459, 465, 472, 475, 484, 489, 496, 502, 504, 509, 515, 520, 525, 528, 533, 536–543, 552, 557, 560,565, 568, 573
•Objects are made of one or more materials, such as paper, wood, and metal. Objects can be described by the properties of the materials from which they are made, and those properties can be used to separate or sort a group of objects or materials.	**Grade K:** 40–49 **Grade 1:** 312–317 **Grade 2:** 324–331 **Grade 3:** 390–397 **Grade 4:** 340–347, 351, 356–363, 372, 388, 390–397, 398–399
•Materials can exist in different states—solid, liquid, and gas. Some common materials, such as water, can be changed from one state to another by heating or cooling.	**Grade K:** 24–29 **Grade 1:** 318–325, 326–333, 334–341, 345 **Grade 2:** 48–49, 50–51, 80–81, 152–159, 236–243, 288–295, 296–303, 304–309, 310–315, 332–339, 340–345 **Grade 3:** 312–319, 328–329, 382–389, 390–397, 489 **Grade 4:** 225, 266–273, 282–287, 340–347, 348–355, 364–365, 382–389, 390, 401

Standards for Grades K through 4	Teacher Edition Page Numbers
POSITION AND MOTION OF OBJECTS	
•The position of an object can be described by locating it relative to another object or the background.	**Grade 3:** 512–517 **Grade 4:** 520–527, 547
•An object's motion can be described by tracing and measuring its position over time.	**Grade 1:** 358, 359, 380–385 **Grade 3:** 496–503, 504–511, 512–517 **Grade 4:** 520–527, 528–535, 544–545, 547
•The position and motion of objects can be changed by pushing or pulling. The size of the change is related to the strength of the push or pull.	**Grade K:** 104–109 **Grade 1:** 380–385, 386–393 **Grade 2:** 178, 418–423, 424–431, 432–439 **Grade 3:** 420–425, 496–503, 504–511, 518–519, 521, 526–533, 534–543, 544, 551, 555 **Grade 4:** 528–535, 536–543, 544–545, 552–559, 560–567, 568–575, 601
•Sound is produced by vibrating objects. The pitch of the sound can be varied by changing the rate of vibration.	**Grade K:** 118–123 **Grade 1:** 364–371, 372, 375 **Grade 2:** 210–212, 212, 213, 390–395, 396–403, 404–409 **Grade 3:** 480–485 **Grade 4:** 406–413, 414–421, 422–429, 430–431, 433
LIGHT, HEAT, ELECTRICITY, AND MAGNETISM	
•Light travels in a straight line until it strikes an object.	**Grade 1:** 362 **Grade 2:** 366–371 **Grade 3:** 466–467, 472–479 **Grade 4:** 438–445
•Light can be reflected by a mirror, refracted by a lens, or absorbed by the object.	**Grade 1:** 361, 362 **Grade 2:** 336–371 **Grade 3:** 20, 466–467, 472–479, 489 **Grade 4:** 438–445, 465
•Heat can be produced in many ways, such as burning, rubbing, or mixing one substance with another.	**Grade K:** 82–87 **Grade 1:** 352–357 **Grade 2:** 372–381 **Grade 4:** 454–461, 541
•Heat can move from one object to another by conduction.	**Grade 2:** 372–381 **Grade 3:** 434–439, 460–465 **Grade 4:** 348, 446–453, 454–461, 462–463, 465, 515
•Electricity in circuits can produce light, heat, sound, and magnetic effects.	**Grade 3:** 406–413, 414–419, 434–439 **Grade 4:** 464, 472–483, 484–495, 496–503, 504–511
•Electrical circuits require a complete loop through which an electrical current can pass.	**Grade 3:** 429, 434–439, 446–451 **Grade 4:** 472–483, 515
•Magnets attract and repel each other and certain kinds of other materials.	**Grade K:** 110–117 **Grade 1:** 400–407 **Grade 2:** 432–439 **Grade 3:** 440–445, 446–451, 455 **Grade 4:** 484–495

Standards for Grades K through 4	Teacher Edition Page Numbers
LIFE SCIENCE	

THE CHARACTERISTICS OF ORGANISMS	
•Organisms have basic needs. For example, animals need air, water, and food; plants require air, water, nutrients, and light.	**Grade K:** 240–247, 270–275 **Grade 1:** 30–35, 36–41, 60, 61, 66–71, 99, 120–127, 131, 136–141, 142–147, 148–153, 156, 157, 164–171, 250–257 **Grade 2:** 30–35, 36–41, 88–93, 142–143, 145, 382–383 **Grade 3:** 72–77, 86–93, 117 **Grade 4:** 96–103, 164
•Organisms can survive only in environments in which their needs can be met.	**Grade K:** 292–301 **Grade 1:** 112–119 **Grade 2:** 36–41, 42–47 **Grade 3:** 30–37, 86–93, 117 **Grade 4:** 158, 182–183
•The world has many different environments, and distinct environments support the life of different types of organisms.	**Grade K:** 292–301 **Grade 1:** 106–111, 136–141, 142–147, 148–153, 157 **Grade 2:** 42–47 **Grade 3:** 60, 117, 124–131, 132–139 **Grade 4:** 123, 130–137, 156–157, 172
•Each plant or animal has different structures that serve different functions in growth, survival, and reproduction. For example, humans have distinct body structures for walking, holding, seeing, and talking.	**Grade K:** 232–239 **Grade 1:** 42–49, 72–79, 96, 99, 106–111, 112–119, 130, 131, 136–141, 142–147, 148–153, 154, 156 **Grade 2:** 56–63, 64–71, 88–93, 94–99 **Grade 3:** 30–37, 48, 49, 54–61, 62–71, 72–77, 81, 94–103, 104–113, 114–115, 117, 140–147, 162–169, 480–485 **Grade 4:** 30–39, 40–47, 48–55, 56–57, 59, 72–79, 96–103, 120–121, 164, 422–429, 438–443
•The behavior of individual organisms is influenced by internal cues (such as hunger) and by external cues (such as a change in the environment).	**Grade K:** 8–9 **Grade 3:** 67, 140–147 **Grade 4:** 88–89, 101, 104–111, 120–121
•Humans and other organisms have senses that help them detect internal and external cues.	**Grade K:** 8–9, 15 **Grade 1:** 2–7, 312–317, 328 **Grade 3:** 67, 140–147 **Grade 4:** 104–111

LIFE CYCLES OF ORGANISMS	
•Plants and animals have life cycles that include being born, developing into adults, reproducing, and eventually dying. The details of this life cycle are different for different organisms.	**Grade K:** 248–255, 276–283 **Grade 1:** 50–57, 61, 80–87 **Grade 2:** 30–35, 72–79, 100–107 **Grade 3:** 38–45, 49, 62–71, 81 **Grade 4:** 58, 59, 72–79, 80–87, 88–89, 91, 104

Standards for Grades K through 4	Teacher Edition Page Numbers
•Plants and animals closely resemble their parents.	**Grade K:** 248–255 **Grade 1:** 50–57 **Grade 2:** 30–35, 72–79, 100–107 **Grade 4:** 64–71
•Many characteristics of an organism are inherited from the parents of the organism, but other characteristics result from an individual's interactions with the environment.	**Grade K:** 248–255 **Grade 2:** 30–35, 56–63, 64–71, 72–79, 100–107, 126–135 **Grade 3:** 80 **Grade 4:** 64–71, 72, 104–111
•Inherited characteristics include the color of flowers and the number of limbs of an animal.	**Grade K:** 248–255 **Grade 1:** **Grade 2:** 56–63, 64–71, 72–79, 100–107
•Other features, such as the ability to ride a bicycle, are learned through interactions with the environment and cannot be passed on to the next generation.	**Grade 4:** 110
ORGANISMS AND THEIR ENVIRONMENTS	
•All animals depend on plants. Some animals eat plants for food. Other animals eat animals that eat the plants.	**Grade K:** 302–307 **Grade 1:** 36, 37, 38, 39, 93, 120–127, 140, 156 **Grade 2:** 118–125, 136–141, 144, 190 **Grade 3:** 162–169, 170–177, 178–185, 188, 189 **Grade 4:** 130–137, 138–147, 164–171, 172–181, 182–183, 185
•An organism's patterns of behavior are related to the nature of that organism's environment, including the kinds and numbers of other organisms present, the availability of food and resources, and the physical characteristics of the environment.	**Grade 1:** 156 **Grade 2:** 118–125, 126–135, 136–141 **Grade 3:** 178–185 **Grade 4:** 88–89, 104, 130–137, 164–171, 172, 182–183
•When the environment changes, some plants and animals survive and reproduce, and others die or move to new locations.	**Grade 1:** 38, 106–111 **Grade 2:** 118–125, 126–135, 136–141, 443 **Grade 3:** 217 **Grade 4:** 72, 112–119, 138–147, 184
•All organisms cause changes in the environment where they live. Some of these changes are detrimental to the organism or other organisms, whereas others are beneficial.	**Grade K:** 302–307 **Grade 1:** 110, 140 **Grade 2:** 136–141 **Grade 3:** 86 **Grade 4:** 123, 138–147
•Humans depend on their natural and constructed environments.	**Grade 1:** 192–197, 200 **Grade 2:** 184–193 **Grade 3:** 130 **Grade 4:** 148–155, 156–157
•Humans change environments in ways that can be either beneficial or detrimental for themselves and other organisms.	**Grade K:** 302–307 **Grade 1:** 140, 206–213, 214–215 **Grade 2:** 194–201 **Grade 3:** 148–153 **Grade 4:** 148–155, 156–157, 182–183, 184

EARTH AND SPACE SCIENCE

PROPERTIES OF EARTH MATERIALS

Standards for Grades K through 4	Teacher Edition Page Numbers
•Earth materials are solid rocks and soils, water, and the gases of the atmosphere.	**Grade K:** 140–147 **Grade 1:** 198–205 **Grade 2:** 152–159, 160–167 **Grade 3:** 196–203, 204–213, 304–311 **Grade 4:** 159, 192–199, 200–205, 214–221
•The varied Earth materials have different physical and chemical properties, which make them useful in different ways, for example, as building materials, as sources of fuel, or for growing the plants we use as food.	**Grade 1:** 324 **Grade 2:** 160–167 **Grade 3:** 196–203, 204–213, 224, 225, 270–277 **Grade 4:** 253, 390–397, 509
•Earth materials provide many of the resources that humans use.	**Grade 1:** 192–197 **Grade 2:** 160–167, 184–193 **Grade 3:** 204–213 **Grade 4:** 148–155
•Soils have properties of color and texture, capacity to retain water, and ability to support the growth of many kinds of plants, including those in our food supply.	**Grade K:** 140–147 **Grade 1:** 202, 203, 204, 205 **Grade 2:** 152–159, 160–167 **Grade 3:** 157, 225, 270–277 **Grade 4:** 142, 143, 214–221, 224
•Fossils provide evidence about the plants and animals that lived long ago and the nature of the environment at that time.	**Grade K:** 136 **Grade 2:** 168–175 **Grade 3:** 214–221, 222–223, 225 **Grade 4:** 112–119, 248–255

OBJECTS IN THE SKY

Standards for Grades K through 4	Teacher Edition Page Numbers
•The sun, moon, stars, clouds, birds, and airplanes all have properties, locations, and movements that can be observed and described.	**Grade K:** 204–209 **Grade 1:** 284–289, 290–295 **Grade 2:** 252–257, 258–263, 264–269 **Grade 3:** 336–337, 334–351, 352–361, 362–363, 364 **Grade 4:** 306–313, 314–321, 322–329, 330–331
•The sun provides the light and heat necessary to maintain the temperature of the Earth.	**Grade K:** 62–69 **Grade 1:** 305, 352–357, 358–363 **Grade 2:** 372–381 **Grade 3:** 414–419, 429 **Grade 4:** 306–454

Standards for Grades K through 4	Teacher Edition Page Numbers
CHANGES IN THE EARTH AND SKY	
•The surface of the Earth changes. Some changes are due to slow processes, such as erosion and weathering, and some changes are due to rapid processes, such as landslides, volcanic eruptions, and earthquakes.	**Grade 1:** 178–183, 184–185, 186, 187 **Grade 2:** 154, 220–227 **Grade 3:** 148–153, 204–213, 230–237, 238–245, 246–253, 256, 257 **Grade 4:** 148, 200–205, 206–213, 222–223, 230–237, 238–247, 256–257, 258, 259, 274–281
•Weather changes from day to day and over the seasons.	**Grade K:** 168–175, 182–195 **Grade 1:** 230–235, 248–249, 250–257, 258–263, 264–269, 270–275 **Grade 2:** 220–227, 270–277, 316–317, 384 **Grade 3:** 320–327, 330, 331 **Grade 4:** 274–281, 282, 292, 301
•Weather can be described by measurable quantities, such as temperature, wind direction and speed, and precipitation.	**Grade K:** 176–181 **Grade 1:** 224–229, 230–235 **Grade 2:** 220–227, 228–235 **Grade 3:** 312–319, 320–327, 330, 331, 400 **Grade 4:** 144, 274–281, 282, 285, 288–297, 301
•Objects in the sky have patterns of movement. The sun, for example, appears to move across the sky in the same way every day, but its path changes slowly over the seasons.	**Grade K:** 204–209 **Grade 1:** 290–295 **Grade 2:** 258–263, 264–269, 270–277 **Grade 3:** 336–337, 344–351, 365 **Grade 4:** 306–313
•The moon moves across the sky on a daily basis much like the sun.	**Grade K:** 210–217 **Grade 1:** 296–301 **Grade 2:** 264–269 **Grade 3:** 344–351 **Grade 4:** 311, 332, 333

Standards for Grades K through 4	Teacher Edition Page Numbers
SCIENCE IN PERSONAL AND SOCIAL PERSPECTIVES	

PERSONAL HEALTH

•Safety and security are basic needs of humans. Safety involves freedom from danger, risk, or injury. Security involves feelings of confidence and lack of anxiety and fear. Student understandings include following safety rules for home and school, preventing abuse and neglect, avoiding injury, knowing whom to ask for help, and when and how to say no.	**Grade K:** 12–13 **Grade 1:** 260, 368 **Grade 3:** 4–11 **Grade 4:** 2–9, 464

CHARACTERISTICS AND CHANGES IN POPULATIONS

•Human populations include groups of individuals living in a particular location. One important characteristic of a human population is the population density—the number of individuals of a particular population that lives in a given amount of space.	
•The size of a human population can increase or decrease. Populations will increase unless other factors such as disease or famine decrease the population.	

TYPES OF RESOURCES

•Resources are things that we get from the living and nonliving environment to meet the needs and wants of a population.	**Grade 1:** 192–197 **Grade 2:** 184–193, 281 **Grade 3:** 262–269 **Grade 4:** 496, 504–511
•Some resources are basic materials, such as air, water, and soil; some are produced from basic resource, such as food, fuel, and building materials; and some resources are nonmaterial, such as quiet places, beauty, security, and safety.	**Grade 1:** 94, 192–197 **Grade 2:** 184–193, 281 **Grade 3:** 262–269, 278–285, 304–311, 420–425 **Grade 4:** 496, 504–511
•The supply of many resources is limited. If used, resources can be extended through recycling and decreased use.	**Grade K:** 154–161 **Grade 1:** 206–213, 214–215, 216 **Grade 2:** 184–193, 281 **Grade 3:** 262–269, 286–293, 294–295, 296, 297, 420–425 **Grade 4:** 300

CHANGES IN ENVIRONMENTS

•Environments are the space, conditions, and factors that affect an individual's and a population's ability to survive and their quality of life.	**Grade 1:** 106–111 **Grade 2:** 194–201 **Grade 4:** 148–155
•Changes in environments can be natural or influenced by humans. Some changes are good, some are bad, and some are neither good nor bad. Pollution is a change in the environment that can influence the health, survival, or activities of organisms, including humans.	**Grade 1:** 110, 206–213, 214–215, 216, 342–343 **Grade 2:** 194–201, 202–209, 278–279, 280, 440–441 **Grade 3:** 156, 170, 186–187, 278–285, 328–329 **Grade 4:** 182–183, 184, 401, 512–513
•Some environmental changes occur slowly, and others occur rapidly. Students should understand the different consequences of changing environments in small increments over long periods as compared with changing environments in large increments over short periods.	**Grade 1:** 178–183, 184–185, 216 **Grade 2:** 194–201, 202–209 **Grade 3:** 230–237, 246–253, 257 **Grade 4:** 206–213, 230–237, 238–247, 258, 259

Standards for Grades K through 4	Teacher Edition Page Numbers
SCIENCE AND TECHNOLOGY IN LOCAL CHALLENGES	
•People continue inventing new ways of doing things, solving problems, and getting work done. New ideas and inventions often affect other people; sometimes the effects are good and sometimes they are bad. It is helpful to try to determine in advance how ideas and inventions will affect other people.	**Grade K:** 9 **Grade 1:** 60–61, 96–97, 128–129, 154–155, 184–185, 214–215, 242–243, 276–277, 278, 302–303, 304, 342–343, 372–373, 408–409 **Grade 2:** 176–177, 202–209, 442 **Grade 3:** 80, 114–115, 116, 156, 188, 294–295, 398–399, 428, 454, 486–487, 488, 534–543, 552–553, 554, 555 **Grade 4:** 56–57, 156–157, 256–257, 330–331, 364–365, 432, 464, 512, 552–559, 560–567, 568–575, 578–579, 600
•Science and technology have greatly improved food quality and quantity, transportation, health, sanitation, and communication. These benefits of science and technology are not available to all the people in the world.	**Grade K:** 9, 69 **Grade 1:** 60–61, 96–97, 154–155, 302–303, 342–343, 372–373, 408–409 **Grade 2:** 442 **Grade 3:** 297, 426–427, 428, 552–553 **Grade 4:** 159, 300, 420, 459, 491, 494, 600

Standards for Grades K through 4	Teacher Edition Page Numbers
HISTORY AND NATURE OF SCIENCE	
SCIENCE AS A HUMAN ENDEAVOR	
•Science and technology have been practiced by people for a long time.	**Grade 1:** 18, 98, 216, 276–277, 374 **Grade 2:** 48–49 **Grade 3:** 520 **Grade 4:** 7, 322, 326, 366, 459, 462–463, 488, 514, 573, 600
•Men and women have made a variety of contributions throughout the history of science and technology.	**Grade 1:** 98, 216, 278, 374 **Grade 2:** 442 **Grade 3:** 364, 400, 426–427, 454, 488, 520 **Grade 4:** 90, 322, 366, 459, 514, 573
•Although men and women using scientific inquiry have learned much about the objects, events, and phenomena in nature, much more remains to be understood. Science will never be finished.	**Grade 1:** 302–303, 304 **Grade 2:** 2–9, 18–23, 50, 80–81, 82, 176–177, 202, 278–279, 316–317, 318, 382–383, 412 **Grade 3:** 12–19 **Grade 4:** 10–17, 18–23, 512–513
•Many people choose science as a career and devote their entire lives to studying it. Many people derive great pleasure from doing science.	**Grade K:** 15, 116, 136 **Grade 1:** 60–61, 96–97, 130, 156, 186, 216, 278, 304, 344, 410 **Grade 2:** 144, 178 **Grade 3:** 48, 80, 156, 256, 330, 364, 400, 454 **Grade 4:** 58, 90, 120–121, 158, 258, 332, 366, 401, 430–431, 432, 488, 514, 600

Using Science with Collections and Trophies
Harcourt Reading/Language Arts Programs
Grade 3

Reading Skill	Science Chapter and Lesson Number or Page	Collections Teacher Edition Page Number	Trophies Teacher Edition Page Number
Identify Main Idea and Details	Intro Chapter 1, 2, 3 Chapter 2 Lesson 1, 2 Chapter 3 Lesson 1, 2 Chapter 4 Lesson 1, 2, 3 Chapter 5 Lesson 3 Chapter 6 Lesson 1, 3 Chapter 9 Lesson 1 Chapter 8 Lesson 1, 4 Chapter 10 Lesson 1 Chapter 11 Lesson 1, 3 Chapter 12 Lesson 2, 3 Chapter 13 Lesson 1, 3 Chapter 14 Lesson 1 Chapter 15 Lesson 2, 3 Chapter 16 Lesson 1, 2	**3–1:** *Rosie, A Visiting Dog's Story:* T612–T613, T616, T618, T636–T637, *Centerfield Ballhawk:* T665, *Ramona Forever:* T707 **3–2:** *A Bookworm Who Hatched:* T101	**3–2:** *Yippee-Yay!:* 168I, 172, 176, 180, 188, 192–193, *Boom Town:* 206, 216, 221B, *If You Made a Million:* 262I, 266, 272, 276, 296–297
Compare and Contrast	Chapter 1 Lesson 1 Chapter 3 Lesson 3 Chapter 5 Lesson 1 Chapter 6 Lesson 2 Chapter 7 Lesson 1 Chapter 9 Lesson 3 Chapter 8 Lesson 2 Chapter 10 Lesson 3 Chapter 11 Lesson 2 Chapter 12 Lesson 1 Chapter 13 Lesson 2 Chapter 15 Lesson 1 Chapter 16 Lesson 3	**3–2:** *The Three Little Javelinas,* T304–T305, T314, T326–T327, T337	**3–2:** *Coyote Places the Stars:* 36I, 40, 42, 44, 52, 54, 58–59, *Why Mosquitoes Buzz in People's Ears:* 93B, *Lon Po Po:* 94I, 100, 104, 110, 116–117, *Cocoa Ice:* 221I, 230, 242, 248, 260–261
Identify Cause and Effect	Chapter 2 Lesson 3 Chapter 4 Lesson 4 Chapter 7 Lesson 3 Chapter 8 Lesson 3 Chapter 14 Lesson 3, 4	**3–2:** *Rocking and Rolling:* T624–T625, T646–T647, *The Armadillo from Amarillo:* T683, *Visitors from Space:* T727	**3–2:** *Alejandro's Gift:* 324I, 328, 330, 336, 342, 346–347, *Rocking and Rolling:* 369D, *The Armadillo from Amarillo:* 370I, 376, 382, 384, 386, 388, 398–399

Reading Skill	*Science* Chapter and Lesson Number or Page	*Collections* Teacher Edition Page Number	*Trophies* Teacher Edition Page Number
Sequence	Chapter 1 Lesson 2 Chapter 5 Lesson 2 Chapter 7 Lesson 2 Chapter 9 Lesson 2 Chapter 10 Lesson 2 Chapter 14 Lesson 2	**3–2:** *Coyote Places the Stars:* T20–T21, T40–T41, *Why Mosquitoes Buzz in People's Ears:* T75, *A Bookworm Who Hatched:* T119, *Leah's Pony:* T269	**3-1:** *The Stories Julian Tells:* 282I, 288, 292, 294, 302–303, *The Talent Show:* 329D, *Centerfield Ballhawk:* 330I, 334, 336, 342, 244, 354–355 **3–2:** *Coyote Places the Stars:* 59D
Draw Conclusions	9, 17, 23, 37, 45, 61, 71, 77, 93, 103, 113, 131, 139, 147, 153, 169, 177, 185, 203, 213, 221, 237, 245, 253, 269, 277, 285, 293, 311, 319, 327, 343, 351, 361, 381, 389, 397, 413, 419, 425, 439, 445, 451, 466, 471, 479, 485, 503, 511, 517, 533, 543, 551	**3–1:** *Turtle Bay,* T322–T323, T339, T350–T351, *Balto,* T417, *The Talent Show,* T579 **3–2:** *Why Mosquitoes Buzz in People's Ears,* T64, T74, T78, *A Bookworm Who Hatched,* T118, T122, *Cocoa Ice,* T350, T370, T372, *Yippee-Yay!,* T410, T412, T414, *If You Made a Million,* T458, T462, T470, T474, *Alejandro's Gift,* T584, T594	**3–1:** *The Talent Show:* 329A–329B, *Centerfield Ballhawk:* 355C, *Ramona Forever,* 387C **3–2:** *Boom Town:* 221D
Summarize	9, 17, 23, 37, 45, 61, 71, 77, 93, 103, 113, 131, 139, 147, 153, 169, 177, 185, 203, 213, 221, 237, 245, 253, 269, 277, 285, 293, 311, 319, 327, 343, 351, 361, 381, 389, 397, 413, 419, 425, 439, 445, 451, 466, 471, 479, 485, 503, 511, 517, 533, 543, 551	**3–1:** *Allie's Basketball Dream,* T170, T174, *Officer Buckle and Gloria,* T286, *Little Grunt and the Big Egg,* T466, *The Talent Show,* T572, *Centerfield Ballhawk,* T664 **3–2:** *Why Mosquitoes Buzz in People's Ears,* T68, *A Bookworm Who Hatched,* T120, *Cocoa Ice,* T366	**3–1:** *Allie's Basketball Dream:* 100J, 111, 115, *Centerfield Ballhawk:* 330J, 339, 341 **3–2:** *Papa Tells Chita a Story:* 14I, 20, 24, 34–35, *Coyote Places the Stars:* 36J, 43, 49, 53, 59B, *Why Mosquitoes Buzz in People's Ears:* 60I, 68, 78, 88, 92–93, *Lon Po Po:* 94J, 103, 111, *I'm in Charge of Celebrations:* 300I, 306, 308, 310, 312, 322–323

Teaching Notes